ß

COVID-19:
The Science
vs.
The Lockdowns

Michael G. Betrus

Headline Books, Inc.
Terra Alta, WV

COVID-19: The Science vs. The Lockdowns

by Michael G. Betrus

To order additional copies of this book or for book publishing information, or to contact the author:

Headline Books, Inc.
P.O. Box 52
Terra Alta, WV 26764
www.HeadlineBooks.com

Tel: 304-789-3001
Email: mybook@headlinebooks.com

ISBN 13: 9781951556709

Library of Congress Control Number: 2021949063

PRINTED IN THE UNITED STATES OF AMERICA

To my son Michael, for your help in tirelessly reviewing and editing this book, and for bringing a purity into this world

Also, to the hundreds of thousands that lost their lives to COVID-19, and the tens of millions of kids that have suffered absent the science throughout the lockdowns.

Table of Contents

Forewords

by Dr. Shveta Raju and Dr. Kristen Walsh

Dr. Shveta Raju:

In February 2020, I had a cold that seemed to linger for a week or two longer than usual (no, it wasn't COVID-19); this was followed by a very unusual skin infection above my left eyelid that required me to take antibiotics. As someone blessed with good health most of my life, I was definitely not feeling myself, and the various duties of maintaining my private practice, administrative responsibilities, and my young kids' routines consumed me. I stopped watching the news most days since early 2017 because the political tone of the news was too exhausting. However, that first week of March, I did happen to have NPR on the radio while driving to work and I heard in the local news segment that a man who had returned from Italy tested positive for COVID-19 and was home quarantining with his family in Atlanta.

That same day, an Italian physician with whom I was familiar started posting messages online about COVID-19 – that it was filling up hospitals in Italy and even making his colleagues sick. I read a sense of alarm in his writing and then heard in the news that Italy was taking steps to control the outbreak. At that time, despite completing thirteen years of K-12 school, four years of college, one year of business school, four years of medical school, three years of residency, and one year of fellowship, I had never heard of a "lockdown" to control the spread of an illness.

My mother is also a medical doctor, and over the weekend I suggested she continue to let her nurse practitioners see the sick patients (we were in the throes of a busy flu season). At the same time, I suggested to my mother-in-law that she take a week or two off from going to the preschool where she volunteered to teach reading.

I remember the call I got on Monday, March 9, 2020, as if it were yesterday. I was in the office seeing patients when my children's chess program director frantically called to tell me they were stopping the chess class because two teachers in our school district had tested positive for COVID-19. We then got a message the school would be closed for two days and would reopen after a risk assessment was made. The children returned on Wednesday and Thursday and came home Thursday evening to the message that school would be closed for two weeks.

By this time, social media posts about "slowing the spread" and "flattening the curve" were circulating widely. Two weeks seemed reasonable enough. I continued going to work with some precautions (we screened sick patients for travel history), but what unfolded over the next two weeks and then in the subsequent almost eighteen months was beyond my worst nightmares. My children were kept home from school; my patients were afraid to come into the office; and most of society shut down, only to reopen to widespread protocols including masks, physical distancing, and mass testing, irrespective of clinical symptoms.

Normally, our practice operated at full capacity with one-to-two-hour wait times and suddenly, we were seeing only a handful of patients a day and worrying about untreated high blood pressure, uncontrolled diabetes, and delays in diagnosis for preventable illness. In a busy flu season, hospitals routinely boarded patients in the hallways or transferred patients because beds were full. In April 2020, hospital census occupancy was hovering around 54%, where it is 83% at the time of this writing. How many people were avoiding care for serious conditions such as heart attacks? We later learned, far too many.

I took it upon myself to learn everything I could about this new illness and how to diagnose it, manage my patients who contracted it, and understand the epidemiology and transmission of the virus. I was confident in some basic facts by early April 2020: kids were at very little risk; the virus did not spread that easily from people without symptoms (though it could spread in a short pre-symptomatic period); and it was important to keep up with one's metabolic health to reduce risk of complications. Clinically, our practice volunteered to help with testing and ultimately the vaccination of our community. But as more and more time passed, I saw the problem of the COVID-19 response less through the lens of a physician and more as a mother and as a citizen of what I thought was a free nation.

Every reasonable precaution was turned into a political matter. Governors used their new COVID-19 emergency powers to keep businesses closed and schools shuttered. Like many of you, I found myself living in a medical dystopia. I connected with a few parents in our school district who were also concerned about the direction of the COVID-19 response, and one of these connections led me to connect with Michael Betrus. The work Michael and others have done, much of which is summarized in the forthcoming pages, is critical to accounting for all the mistakes that have been made and are still being made with respect to COVID-19 and what Dr. Stefan Baral [from Johns Hopkins] has coined "The Worst Public Health Response Ever."

I remain hopeful we will emerge from the trauma, tyranny, and hysteria we have all just experienced and return to a compassionate, rational, and facts-based approach to the problems we face. The work herein is an incredible and well-researched contribution to that collective effort.

Dr. Shveta Raju, MD, MBA
September 5, 2021

(Dr. Raju's opinions are her own and are not necessarily representative of her employer)

Dr. Kristen Walsh:

Since 2012, I have served as the Early Childhood Champion for the New Jersey Chapter of the American Academy of Pediatrics. In this role, I work with Head Start, Early Head Start, the Child Care Association, and several other organizations concerned with early childhood advocacy. I have also been a community pediatrician since 2003. When the pandemic hit the United States in March 2020, I was very concerned to see public schools and childcare facilities ignoring specific pre-COVID-19 CDC guidance recommending time-limited and targeted closures. Instead, doors to schools and childcare facilities were immediately closed and locked across the United States, with some not to open for more than a year.

As this was occurring, I wrote a letter to the *New York Times* (never published) about my concerns, in which the opening sentence was "children are paying—and will continue to pay—too high a price for our fears about COVID-19 in this country." Sadly, eighteen months later, much of what I feared became a reality. During the pandemic lockdowns, low-income children had devastating learning loss, child abuse increased almost everywhere, pediatric mental health took a nosedive ("the prevalence of clinical depression and anxiety have already doubled for children globally since the beginning of the COVID-19 pandemic and will likely worsen with continued restrictions," and childhood obesity is skyrocketing. I have been horrified to see draconian restrictions (school closures, mask mandates, etc.) being imposed on children with little to no evidence of efficacy yet seemingly obvious harms. Harms to children from pandemic restrictions were easy to predict from established tenets of child development, as well as the indisputable fact that school is a lifeline for many urban lower socioeconomic children.

Incredibly, eighteen months in, we seemed to have learned very little, and school closures seem to be again on the table this fall. Many schools are already halting in-person learning when a COVID-19 "case" is identified. As much of Europe gets rid of most pandemic restrictions on children and schools, the

United States is doubling down on masking two-year-olds for ten hours a day in childcare. Much of this is due to our country's never-ending drumbeat of media fear and hysteria around COVID-19 and kids. This particular narrative appears to be a uniquely American eccentricity. As a longtime child advocate, it has been exhausting to attempt to push back—even in small ways—against the U.S. media's love affair with draconian COVID restrictions. I am, therefore, filled with admiration for the journalists and writers like Michael Betrus who have taken on this very daunting task. I can only hope that we listen to them and learn from our mistakes, so that next time, we will keep the school doors open and prioritize the needs of children over the baseless fears of adults.

Kristen Walsh MD, Early Childhood Champion, NJ Chapter

August 30, 2021

(Dr. Walsh's opinions are her own and are not necessarily representative of the American Academy of Pediatrics or her employer)

Introduction

The COVID-19 period from 2020 to 2021 will be the most historic pandemic era in history. Other pandemics were more lethal, much more lethal. Around 1350, the Black Death is said to have wiped out half of Europe and Asia. The Spanish Flu in 1918 may have infected 500 million people and killed 50 million. It was also much more dangerous than COVID-19 for three reasons: all ages and healthy people were at serious risk; it killed five to ten times the number of people COVID-19 did, adjusted for population; treatments for COVID-19 were more advanced than a hundred years earlier. Antibiotics and other treatments helped with infections both pandemics caused. Still, COVID-19 was the most prolific pandemic in a hundred years.

Long after COVID-19 recedes into the background of a small number of seasonal deaths, the era should be remembered more for the lockdowns and government interventions than the death toll. Unlike previous pandemics, COVID-19 mostly accelerated deaths in those that were very elderly and had several underlying conditions. It tore through long-term care facilities. It caused a surge in hospitalizations for four-to-six weeks in each community, if they were hit at all. Excess deaths for the year between March 2020 and 2021 went up over 500,000. Not all of those were from COVID-19; many were from the lockdowns. Later, excess deaths decreased sharply, showing COVID-19 mostly pulled forward deaths that would've occurred within a year or two.

Before COVID-19, both the Centers for Disease Control and the World Health Organization published playbooks for different levels of pandemics. COVID-19 was a category two pandemic. Both the CDC and WHO had each recommended closed schools for up to four weeks, social distancing, isolation, and possibly wearing face masks for those that were sick and in public. Government leaders threw those playbooks out as though no prior work had been done, and by April 2020, nearly three billion people were locked down. Schools closed, businesses closed, and people worked remotely if they could. Hundreds of millions of people lost their jobs. Depression seeped in and health conditions unrelated to COVID-19 went undiagnosed or untreated.

Face masks were mandated for billions of people worldwide. It didn't matter that nearly all science before COVID-19 showed anything less than an N95 respirator mask was ineffective at blocking viral particles. Mandating face masks even if alone outdoors, closing schools, closing indoor dining, and preventing non-COVID-19 illnesses from treatment were all trigger-happy mitigations that U.S. state leaders and leaders of countries all over the world employed for a year and a half. Those mitigations did not work and caused historical collateral damage.

Before the United States went into lockdown in March 2020, there were two key indicators that this would not be a Spanish Flu-level pandemic: the cruise ships and the early outbreak in Italy. Both showed, beyond any doubt, the virus was only a material risk to the elderly and those frail or with multiple underlying conditions. There were outliers, but this did represent over 98% of all COVID-19 deaths.

Early COVID-19 models projected millions of deaths, and those were quickly proven wrong. Countries went into lockdown not to stop the virus, but to streamline the infections so hospitals would not be overwhelmed. While the New York City area was stressed in April 2020, hundreds of thousands of hospitals beds and ICUs were left empty around the country. Hundreds of millions of people were locked down to their homes, seventy million students were out of class, and for most of America, nothing was happening. In fact, other than a four to six-week surge in each community, only once, if at all in most cases, you would not know COVID-19 existed. Still, the lockdowns continued for a year and a half. It was the greatest overreach and disaster of public policy in America since slavery.

The media drove COVID-19 fear for over a year, inciting so much public fear there were few protests to reopen. Most people of any political affiliation were resistant to get back to normal. Less than five percent of Americans could have passed a test on COVID-19 risk or the fallout from the lockdowns. Very few ever understood the age stratification of COVID-19 illnesses. Very few understood exactly how many people got sick, how full (or not) hospitals were, and how much damage the lockdowns caused. The information was hard to find because the media, the National Institute for Health, and the CDC did not talk about it.

Inside you will see the case against governments ever employing sweeping lockdowns ever again. This isn't a study in politics. It is a study of COVID-19 risk and the consequence of the lockdowns. The argument is not based on civil liberties or freedom. It's based on math and qualitative occurrences. The lockdowns were the most disproportionate government response to a crisis in history.

This book is dedicated to the thousands that lost their lives to COVID-19. It is dedicated to the couple hundred thousand that died alone in a nursing home, sitting ducks dying with COVID-19, including a cousin of mine. It is also dedicated to the hundreds of millions that felt great anxiety because the risk and consequence were never explained and to the tens of millions that lost their jobs without cause.

Finally, this is dedicated to the tens of millions of kids that lost over a year of school, to the two-year-olds forced to wear face masks on airplanes, to the kids demonized for playdates, and for the sadness and isolation. You were the most preventable casualties of the pandemic. You are owed an apology. It wasn't following the science. You will be leading the country one day. Never forget this.

Please reach out with any comments you have about this work at michaelgbetrus@gmail.com. I would like to hear about your experiences and your thoughts about the pandemic, the lockdowns, and the case made here.

Michael

CHAPTER ONE
Science BC (before COVID-19)

Follow the science. That's what we were told. When Governor Whitmer of Michigan issued restriction after restriction on Michiganders in 2020, her comment was always, "We need to follow the science." When Governor Cuomo closed down indoor dining while COVID-19 hospitals in New York were less than 1% occupied with COVID-19 patients, he told us to "follow the science." When those in the media told us to wear face coverings and masks, then two masks, and up to four (!), their rationale was to follow the science. But what is science? Apoorva Mandavilli wrote about COVID-19 for the *New York Times*. She tweeted out a great definition about science on February 16, 2021:

> *Making conclusive statements based on little and mixed evidence = ideology. Looking for clear, solid trends before rushing to conclusion = science.*

Let's go with this one. We will see later how much Mandavilli and most in the media reported and influenced Americans based on ideology versus science, but she gets a high mark for this definition. What are some differences then between science and ideology?

Soda pop is not a nutritious drink. That is science. It's high in sugar, rich in high fructose corn syrup, and has no real nutritional value. Science. Soda pop causes obesity. That is ideology. Soda pop does not cause obesity. It's the difference between causation and correlation. Obesity is caused by a medical condition like slow metabolism, or by consuming too many calories relative to what you burn. That is science. In 2012 then-New York Mayor Michael Bloomberg tried to ban sugary drinks over sixteen ounces, the Big Gulp Ban. In 2017 Philadelphia instituted an aggressive soda tax, and Chicago made a run at a soda tax as well. These are government policies disguised as science but really enacted to drive revenue under a noble vail. They are based on a sin tax ideology and unfairly burden select consumers.

There are two kinds of science when we look at NPIs (non-pharmaceutical interventions) and the COVID-19 pandemic. There is science BC (before

COVID-19) and science AC (after COVID-19). The two rarely intersected in 2020 and 2021. The lines intersected in Sweden. They got close in a few states like Florida and South Dakota, and even in those states they never really intersected. Science before COVID-19 had a bit to say on the efficacy of lockdown measures such as closing restaurants, schools, other businesses and wearing personal protective equipment (PPE) like face masks.

What is a Lockdown?

We have understood lockdowns to encompass many things in 2020 and 2021. They include stay-at-home orders, where you are not supposed to leave your home except for essential errands like going to the grocery or a doctor's office. Wait, those were largely closed for weeks or months in some places, so it included going to the hospital—no going to school, no going to visit friends or family. In Michigan, it included not going to a second home you owned.[1] Other things that are casually included in the lockdown bucket are social distancing, quarantining if you're sick or around someone sick, or not attending large events.

Before COVID-19, nearly all measures recommended were voluntary measures. Quarantining was a voluntary suggestion, and a good one if you were sick. That is always the case. Often in the workplace, if you were sick and called in to stay away from work, there was some part of soft shaming that took place. It never made sense. I always encouraged my teams to stay home if they were sick. Getting others sick or working a partial speed doesn't make anyone a hero.

The reason you lockdown is to stop the R_0, the reproduction. If one person gets infected and they are isolated, they recover in a week or so and aren't contagious. If you lockdown for even a couple of weeks, the virus spread dies out and it's over. Academically that's how it works.

A reader of *COVID-19: Lockdowns on Trial*, a man named Phil, who was a self-identified Democrat, emailed me in January 2021 and asked, "Do you believe that if we locked down properly, we would have eliminated the pandemic in America?" It's a thoughtful question. Here was my reply:

> *A perfect lockdown would keep kids from all schooling and activities. No one would work. No one would travel. Food and essential goods would be delivered via drones, or select people tested and wearing hazmat suits. Only emergency medical procedures would be done. The military would be instituting martial law and the entire country or world would be managed like that small town in the movie Outbreak. No one would leave their property. That would pretty much do it. And when you open things up to the world, it would resume as if the lockdowns never happened with no immunity acquired. The virus would still be out there, and at some point,*

we'd be back where we were. A partial lockdown like the governors have ordered could never stop the virus spread; just slow it down to where we would end up where we would without one and end up with more total excess deaths and incredible economic, educational, and psychological harm.

What would be gained? It's all about risk and consequence. The consequence of such a lockdown would cause massive deaths of despair, well beyond the spikes we're seeing. Non-COVID-19 ailments would go untreated. Cancer deaths would soar over time, both in missed diagnosis and treatments. Domestic violence would soar (more than it is). Vaccinations would be missed. Organ transplants would be missed. Overall deaths would be faaaar greater in that scenario than what we're doing, within a 2-3 year period. That list of lockdown casualties is endless. All the things I mentioned above are happening now. It's amazing to me how many people are blind to the harms of the lockdowns. In my personal experience, people that think like that have jobs, no economic hardship, no relatives in care facilities, and no kids in school, or if they do, not underperforming kids.

Antarctica in 1969

In 1969 a fascinating virus-learning was observed.[2] It's a terrific thirty-minute read. Twelve men ages 21-35 (and several husky dogs) spent weeks isolated at Adelaide Island Base in Antarctica. None were sick when they began their isolation trip. In past experiences, men had not experienced respiratory infections until perhaps when supplies were flown in and they interacted with newcomers to a base. After seventeen weeks of isolation, one man became ill with an upper respiratory symptoms and within a week nine became symptomatic with upper respiratory compromises. No virus was artificially introduced during these weeks from the outside.

The four men that did not become infected were notably more isolated from the other eight. Subsequent studies voided a possible infection from the husky dogs. Past epidemiological studies showed that adults don't usually carry viruses like this for long, where children tend to for long periods. No children were at the base. A final hypothesis was that at least one adult carried the virus that was "dormant" and was perhaps triggered to active by stressful activity, or respiratory stress associated with working in extreme cold. The point is that from this study, a rhinovirus acted dormant and was suddenly activated and contagious well after an effective "lockdown."

Science Before The Lockdown

Laura Glass was a fifteen-year-old in Albuquerque, NM, in 2006 when she came up with an idea. How could you stop a bird flu outbreak in a community before it becomes an epidemic? She created a model[3] that showed that with normal human interactions, half of her modeled 10,000 population community became infected. She showed that the most mobile segment of the population were middle and high school-age kids. By closing schools and minimizing their touchpoints, infections were reduced to 500. Her conclusion:

> *High-school students may form the local transmission backbone of the next pandemic. Closing schools and keeping students at home during a pandemic would remove the transmission potential within these ages and could be effective at thwarting its spread within a community. Social contact networks characterized as groups and public activities with the time, level of contact, and primary links within each, yield a comprehensive view, which, if extended to all ages, would allow design of effective community containment for pandemic influenza.*

What a respectable analysis to come from a fifteen-year-old. Laura's father, Robert Glass, was a scientist at Sandia National Laboratories, a government contractor. He reviewed her work, tuned it up, and sent it on to two federal government doctors, Richard Hatchett and Carter Mecher. Hatchett and Mecher were working on a project around that time for then-President George W. Bush.[4] Bush apparently read *The Great Influenza* by John Barry. I cited Barry's work on the Spanish Flu in *COVID-19: Lockdowns on Trial*, a very comprehensive work on the worst pandemic in U.S. history.

Bush was concerned about a future pandemic or bio-terror incident following 9-11 and commissioned work to be done on potential remedies. Mecher had little experience in this type of work and was moved by the work of Glass. The modern idea of social distancing and closing schools to contain the spread of a virus was born.

Dr. Howard Markel leads the efforts of University of Michigan's History of Medicine. Markel was part of Bush's Pentagon research team. The scope at the time was protecting American troops from a viral threat. When Asia was hit with a bird flu in 2005, Markel coined the phrase "protective sequestration," essentially quarantining them on a ship to stop a spread.

In 2007 Markel wrote a paper published in the *Jama Network* called "Non-pharmaceutical Interventions Implemented by U.S. Cities during the 1918-1919 Influenza Pandemic."[5] Mecher, Hatchett, and Mark Lipsitch wrote a piece in the *Proceedings of the National Academy of Sciences* called "Public health interventions and epidemic intensity during the 1918 influenza pandemic,"[6] also in 2007.

The Spanish Flu

Where the Spanish Flu originated is questionable. Some suggest it emerged from soldiers returning from France in WWI and arriving in Kansas in early 1918. Hundreds of soldiers at Fort Riley, KS fell ill from flu-like symptoms.[7] It seemed to pass and some of those soldiers went on to Europe, where the virus mutated and became deadly. From those soldiers, the disease spread in Europe and ravaged populations across the world. Ill soldiers returned to America, and in the fall of 1918, it spread like wildfire. Some speculate the disease originated in China and was brought to North America by Chinese laborers in cramped trains traveling across Canada or supporting Chinese in WWI front lines in France.[8]

The Spanish Flu, the H1N1 virus, swept across the world from 1918-1919, claiming up to fifty million lives.[9] No vaccine existed, nor antibiotics, which made treating secondary bacterial infections, unlike today, an ultimate game-changer. It was most deadly for a sixteen-week period in the last quarter of 1918. According to the Centers for Disease Control (CDC), up to 500 million people were infected, about a third of the world's population at the time. In the United States, it claimed approximately 675,000 lives. Unique vulnerable age clusters varied from typical flu victim demographics. It's worth calling out that twice the number of Americans died from the Spanish Flu than from the battlefields of World War I.

The Spanish Flu claimed a high proportion of infected very young children and then spiked up dramatically for those aged 20-40. Unique to flu viruses was that the older you got, the less vulnerable to H1N1 you were, until you were over 80 and then the mortality rates skyrocketed.[10] It does not appear any source is certain why, other than as one aged, they developed a kind of natural or antibody immunity based on previous mild inflictions of variant strains of this virus. Most deaths attributed to the Spanish Flu were in people under age 65. John Barry cited in *The Great Influenza* that the single most vulnerable group of victims were pregnant women.

When the Spanish Flu reached Boston, it began with soldiers in nearby Camp Devins. One soldier was misdiagnosed with it and then spread it to a dozen soldiers within a day or two. Soon after a soldier contracted it, "he began to turn blue from a loss of oxygen and it is only a matter of a few hours then until death comes."[11] It took decades for the cause-virus to be isolated and a vaccine developed to combat future outbreaks.[12]

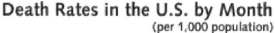

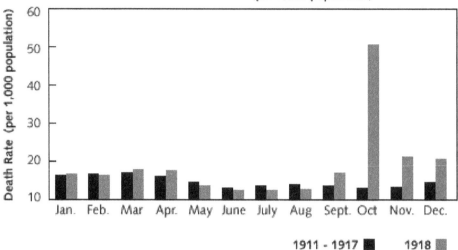

Above is a chart of the death rates in America during the Spanish Flu. Below is a visual stratification of the ages most vulnerable. It's shocking looking back at how the Spanish Flu ravaged through the country without a vaccine or pharmaceutical treatments, antibiotics key among them. Not long after, herd immunity was developed for survivors and it disappeared.

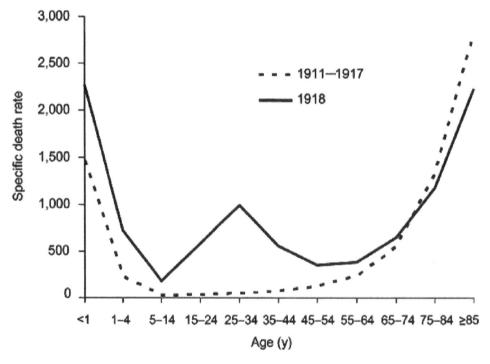

Figure above: Life expectancy in the United States, 1900–60, showing the impact of the 1918 influenza pandemic (Grove and Hetzel 1968; Linder and Grove 1943; United States Department of Commerce 1976).

United States Actions

There's an interesting and tragic story about when the Spanish Flu broke out in Philadelphia.[13] Public Health Director Wilmer Krusen was allegedly aware of an outbreak of a serious flu with soldiers returning from the war to Philadelphia. A large parade was planned for September 28, 1918, and Krusen declined to have it canceled. Within three days of the parade, each of Philadelphia's hospitals were full, and days later, 2,800 people had died. The Spanish Flu spread like wildfire in Philadelphia. On a single day, over 700 people died from that outbreak.

In contrast, according to Dave Roos of the History Channel, St. Louis and San Francisco made more aggressive efforts to stave off the contagion. Schools were shut down, public gatherings were stunted, many people wore gauze masks (later proved to not be much help), and these two cities had a much lower death rate than Philadelphia. San Francisco was hit later, in early 1919, with a third wave and it proved very lethal. According to Roos, many people protested against the masks and ban of public gatherings when not much happened, and the third time around they were hit hard. It reads as if San Francisco and St. Louis early on practiced what nearly all cities and states were doing in the spring of 2020 to stave off COVID-19.

By 1919 the Spanish Flu was winding down and nearly disappeared. The death rates vary from source to source, but by any measure, it was the most merciless pandemic anyone alive had seen. Some distinguishing qualifiers of the Spanish Flu pandemic:

- Highly contagious, likely airborne, and certainly transmitted by contact
- Prompted pneumonia as a frequent cause of death
- Impacted the world in a fairly short time (months) largely facilitated by multi-national soldier interaction through World War I
- Caused death in otherwise healthy people, did not rely on underlying conditions
- Impacted multiple age brackets (very young, 20-40, over 80)

One thing that is different between the Spanish Flu and COVID-19 is that COVID-19 preyed almost exclusively on the elderly and those with multiple pre-existing conditions. The Spanish Flu killed the very young, men and women at their strongest (20-40), and then the very elderly. While the at-risk population is vastly different between the two pandemics, we saw interventions applied to Americans (and billions worldwide) in 2020-2021 that were barely fitting of the Spanish Flu.

Homeland Security Strategy in 2006

In May 2006, Homeland Security released the National Strategy for Pandemic Influenza[14] with an introduction from President Bush. The 233-page report addressed potential federal responses, international concerns, domestic transportation, borders, animal health, law enforcement, and protection within various institutions.

The report opens with a planning assumption list in chapter two. Number one on that list? "Susceptibility to the pandemic influenza virus will be universal." What this means, or should mean, is that like the Spanish Flu, or even HIV, all ages, races, and genders would be equally at risk of the pandemic. You will see later it was not accurate in describing those at measurable risk to COVID-19.

Number three on the Homeland Security list? "Illnesses will be highest among school-aged children and decline with age." Later it goes on to state that an epidemic will typically last six to eight weeks. Six to eight weeks, while kids at no measurable risk to COVID-19 missed at least 75 weeks of traditional learning. As you'll see, lockdown measures were applied to a pandemic model that never fit the COVID-19 data well before the first lockdown in California, going back to the cruise ships and what we saw in Italy in early 2020.

Other interesting positions from Homeland Security in 2006:

- In the event of a pandemic, a border closure would likely delay but not stop the spread of influenza to the United States and would have significant negative social, economic, and foreign policy consequences.
- The United States could deny entry of travelers, or place conditions on the return of travelers from countries with outbreaks and other countries that have not instituted acceptable pre-departure screening, prohibit entry of travelers from the affected area, or continue to accept travelers with appropriate conditions from countries with outbreaks.
- Contact tracing could be useful very early on in a pandemic and with very few infected.
- The clinical attack rates for seasonal and pandemic influenza would be highest among children. Intervention is maximized if school closure occurs early in the course of a community outbreak.
- The benefit of wearing disposable surgical or procedure masks at school or in the workplace has not been established. Mask use by the public should be based on risk, including the frequency of exposure and closeness of contact with potentially infectious persons.

The 2007 Papers

Mecher, Hatchett, and Lipsitch's paper connected observations of the Spanish Flu to a flu pandemic. Below are some quoted highlights. The paper is lengthy and worth a read. Links to the base report include media clippings from the moment, interesting to review. Their takeaways include:

- Using non-pharmaceutical interventions (NPIs; i.e., voluntary quarantine of infected households, closure of schools, bans on public gatherings, and other measures) to decrease disease. transmission is supported by mathematical models, which suggest that multiple simultaneous NPIs applied early in an epidemic may significantly reduce disease transmission.
- The evidence base for recommending such interventions is limited, consisting primarily of historical and contemporary observations rather than controlled studies, demonstrating low confidence in the point above.
- Spanish Flu comparisons across 17 U.S. cities showed that compared to the first wave, excess pneumonia and influenza death rates during the second wave were ~50% lower in cities that implemented multiple NPIs to control disease spread early in their epidemics than in cities that made such interventions late or not at all.
- No city in their Spanish Flu analysis experienced a second wave while its main battery of NPIs was in place. Second waves occurred only after the relaxation of interventions.
- In the absence of an effective vaccine, cities that use NPIs to mitigate the impact of a pandemic remain vulnerable. In practice, and until emergency vaccine production capacity increases, this means that in the event of a severe pandemic, cities will likely need to maintain NPIs for longer than the 2–8 weeks that was the norm in 1918 [do you wonder if they imagined NPIs in place for a year or two as acceptable?].

The cornerstone of the analysis compared hard, first-hit Philadelphia to later-hit and mitigated St. Louis. Of 17 cities studied, the most frequently used NPIs (14 or more cities) were closed schools, churches, public gatherings, and public funerals. The average duration for these interventions was five weeks. Their analysis showed a correlation between policy interventions and fewer cases and deaths. They also called out many variables that could cause fluctuations in the results.

This was the beginning of zero-COVID-19 thinking. The paper does enumerate casualties of the NPIs – loss of education, untreated medical needs, and economic destruction. However, implementing NPIs for such a short duration probably seemed inconsequential. Side note: comparing the first hard-hit area of a pandemic to a geographically separate later hit area is rarely an equivalent matchup. It's like comparing New York City in April 2020 to Denver in May 2020 or even the upcoming winter. Even without Denver's lockdown, they would never have reached what New York did in COVID-19 deaths, in part because the treatments in New York City at that time were often barbaric and not repeated later in 2020.

- Harvey B. Lipman, J. Alexander Navarro, Alexandra Sloan, Joseph R. Michalsen, Alexandra Minna Stern, and Martin S. Cetron contributed to Markel's white paper. They analyzed the results of 43 U.S. cities, significantly broader than the previously discussed paper. Below are some highlights from their analysis:
- 34 of the 43 cities implemented school closures for an average of four weeks and public gathering bans. "School closure and public gathering bans activated concurrently represented the most common combination and was significantly associated with reductions in weekly [excess deaths]." Only 22 of the 43 cities in the study closed schools.
- They found a strong association between early, sustained, and layered application of non-pharmaceutical interventions mitigating the consequences of the Spanish Flu in the United States. "In planning for future severe influenza pandemics, non-pharmaceutical interventions should be considered for inclusion as companion measures to developing effective vaccines and medications for prophylaxis and treatment."
- Some cities had better-than-average outcomes with few NPIs: Grand Rapids, Michigan, and St. Paul, Minnesota.
- Public support and trust in these NPIs would likely be lower than they were a hundred years ago.

These are two of the major foundational studies for implementing NPIs like school closures, banning public gatherings and funerals, closing churches and theaters. No mention was made about restaurants and dining out. Around the time these two analyses were done and there was some talk about NPIs that included what we experienced as "lockdowns" in 2020-2021, there were dissenting papers regarding the effectiveness of the measures.

Donald Ainslie Henderson was a leader of the international effort to eradicate smallpox and a former dean of what is now the Johns Hopkins Bloomberg School of Public Health. He was on President Bush's team to develop strategies for U.S. bio-defense efforts following 9-11. Henderson, along with Thomas Inglesby, Tara O'Toole, and Jennifer Nuzzo, wrote a paper called "Disease Mitigation Measures in the Control of Pandemic Influenza."[15] Henderson essentially argued a position similar to the authors of 2020's Great Barrington Declaration: let the pandemic ease its way through the population while treating those that get sick and isolate the vulnerable.

Some key findings from this analysis regarding policy interventions include:

- "Closing schools for eight weeks to eight months would also require school-age kid congregation spots like fast-food restaurants [not to mention that high school kids spent far more time. working at fast-food restaurants than in class in 2020 and 2021], daycare, malls, etc."
- "Hospitals must establish strategies for coping with what will presumably be a large and relatively sustained surge in demand for medical care."
- "There are no historical observations or scientific studies that support the confinement by quarantine of groups of possibly infected people for extended periods in order to slow the spread of influenza. A World Health Organization (WHO) Writing Group, after reviewing the literature and considering contemporary international experience, concluded that 'forced isolation and quarantine are ineffective and impractical.'"
- "Travel restrictions, such as closing airports and screening travelers at borders, have historically been ineffective. The World Health Organization Writing Group concluded that screening and quarantining entering travelers at international borders did not substantially delay virus introduction in past pandemics . . . and will likely be even less effective in the modern era."
- "Studies have shown that the ordinary surgical mask does little to prevent inhalation of small droplets bearing influenza virus. The pores in the mask become blocked by moisture from breathing, and the air stream simply diverts around the mask. There are few data available to support the efficacy of N95 or surgical masks outside a healthcare setting. N95 masks need to be fit-tested to be efficacious and are uncomfortable to wear for more than an hour or two."

Beyond these opinion recommendations, not a lot happened with hypothetical pandemic responses for the following ten years. The one commonality from opinions on both sides was what to do with schools. Schools remaining open or closed during pandemic waves, as well as large gatherings, remained open for debates.

Why were schools so prominent in Laura Glass's model, as well as in the studies led by Markel and Mecher, Hatchett, and Mark Lipsitch? Because kids were known to be the number one vectors of transmission of the flu. Ask any parent or teacher and they will tell you as much. What went wrong in applying these concepts to COVID-19? Kids were the least transmittable segment of the population.

The CDC View in 2007

The CDC published "Interim Pre-pandemic Planning Guidance: Community Strategy for Pandemic Influenza Mitigation in the United States— Early, Targeted, Layered Use of Non-pharmaceutical Interventions."[16] The guide provides "planning guidance that might be useful during an influenza pandemic to reduce its harm." They identified three overarching reasons to use non-pharmaceutical interventions (NPIs):

1. Delay the exponential growth in incident cases and shift the epidemic curve in order to "buy time" for production and distribution of a well-matched pandemic strain vaccine
2. Decrease the epidemic peak
3. Reduce the total number of incident cases, thus reducing community morbidity and mortality.

The CDC then classified pandemic severities as seen below:

Figure 1. Pandemic Severity Index

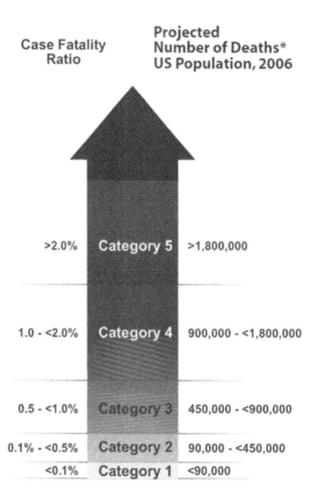

Case Fatality Ratio		Projected Number of Deaths* US Population, 2006
>2.0%	Category 5	>1,800,000
1.0 - <2.0%	Category 4	900,000 - <1,800,000
0.5 - <1.0%	Category 3	450,000 - <900,000
0.1% - <0.5%	Category 2	90,000 - <450,000
<0.1%	Category 1	<90,000

Based on this, COVID-19 certainly fell into the high end of Category 2. While official COVID-19 deaths will officially exceed a million deaths when it "ends," we will see later the actual death impact of the virus itself was below that threshold. For each category of severity, see the NPI considerations below:

Table 1. Summary of the Community Mitigation Strategy by Pandemic Severity

	Pandemic Severity Index		
Interventions* by Setting	1	2 and 3	4 and 5
Home Voluntary isolation of ill at home (adults and children); combine with use of antiviral treatment as available and indicated	Recommend†§	Recommend†§	Recommend†§
Voluntary quarantine of household members in homes with ill persons¶ (adults and children); consider combining with antiviral prophylaxis if effective, feasible, and quantities sufficient	Generally not recommended	Consider**	Recommend**
School Child social distancing -dismissal of students from schools and school based activities, and closure of child care programs	Generally not recommended	Consider: ≤4 weeks††	Recommend: ≤12 weeks§§
-reduce out-of-school social contacts and community mixing	Generally not recommended	Consider: ≤4 weeks††	Recommend: ≤12 weeks§§
Workplace / Community Adult social distancing -decrease number of social contacts (e.g., encourage teleconferences, alternatives to face-to-face meetings)	Generally not recommended	Consider	Recommend
-increase distance between persons (e.g., reduce density in public transit, workplace)	Generally not recommended	Consider	Recommend
-modify postpone, or cancel selected public gatherings to promote social distance (e.g., postpone indoor stadium events, theatre performances)	Generally not recommended	Consider	Recommend
-modify work place schedules and practices (e.g., telework, staggered shifts)	Generally not recommended	Consider	Recommend

It's interesting that for a category one pandemic, really nothing was recommended beyond voluntarily staying home if you're sick. For our category two COVID-19 pandemic, all other interventions are considerations. Interestingly, even in a worst-case pandemic, schools would be closed for twelve weeks. For a category two pandemic, they recommended up to four weeks of closed schools, this as we ended up at over seventy weeks. In no place is there a hint that we should be engaged in the strict lockdowns we saw all over the world for over a year. The CDC modeled out a pandemic chart with a model of what may happen with and without interventions. The case curves mirror those in nearly all states and countries in 2020, those with strict interventions, and those with little to none.

Figure 1.

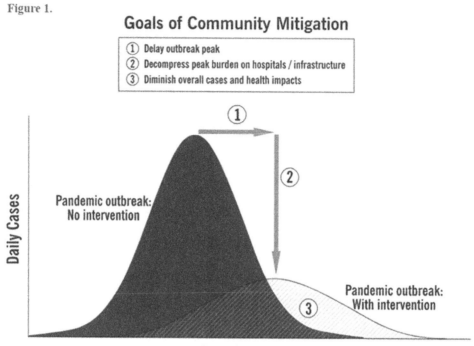

Goals of Community Mitigation

① Delay outbreak peak
② Decompress peak burden on hospitals / infrastructure
③ Diminish overall cases and health impacts

This model curve was identical to the COVID-19 models created by the Imperial College and the IHME, two models that were used by governments to justify what we came to know as lockdown mitigations. Nowhere in the planning guide did they recommend closing schools for prolonged periods. Nowhere is closing retail stores, restaurants, gyms, or places of worship mentioned. The CDC explicitly stated that a worst-case scenario could result in twelve weeks of "lockdowns." When the COVID-19 dust settles, the CDC and WHO must perform peer-reviewed (and by peer we mean include scientists like the Great Barrington Declaration doctors) after-action analysis of the COVID-19 lockdown interventions.

Here is one final point that is representative of the problem with "public health experts" analyzing school closings. The CDC called out these casualties from school and childcare closings:

1. The economic impact to families
2. The potential disruption to all employers, including businesses and governmental agencies
3. Access to essential goods and services
4. The disruption of school-related services (e.g., school meal programs)

It's clear here and in what we saw from the year-plus school closings and so pointedly by the California school board members in February 2021 (detailed later) that school was viewed as more childcare than education. Public health does not prioritize our kids' education.

The CDC in 2017

The Centers for Disease Control and Prevention released "Community Mitigation Guidelines to Prevent Pandemic Influenza — United States, 2017"[17] as the most recent pre-COVID-19 guideline for an influenza pandemic, very similar in nature to the COVID-19 pandemic. The focus is on non-pharmaceutical interventions (NPIs) as a means to slow a spread in the absence of a vaccine. Below is their chart identifying pandemic transmission severity:

TABLE 6. Refined assessment: scaled measures of influenza virus transmissibility and clinical severity							
Measures of transmissibility and clinical severity	Scale						
	1	2	3	4	5	6	7
Transmissibility (scale of 1–5)							
Symptomatic attack rate, community	≤10%	11% –15%	16% –20%	21% –24%	≥25%	-	-
Symptomatic attack rate, school	≤20%	21% –25%	26% –30%	31% –35%	≥36%	-	-
Symptomatic attack rate, workplace	≤10%	11% –15%	16% –20%	21% –24%	≥25%	-	-
Household secondary attack rate, symptomatic	≤5%	6% –10%	11% –15%	16% –20%	≥21%	-	-
R^0: basic reproductive number	≤1.1	1.2 –1.3	1.4–1.5	1.6–1.7	≥1.8	-	-
Peak percentage of outpatient visits for influenza-like illness	1%–3%	4% –6%	7%–9%	10% –12%	≥13%	-	-
Clinical severity (scale of 1–7)							
Case-fatality ratio	<0.02%	0.02% –0.05%	0.05% –0.1%	0.1% –0.25%	0.25% –0.5%	0.5% –1%	>1%
Case-hospitalization ratio	<0.5%	0.5% –0.8%	0.8% –1.5%	1.5% –3%	3% – 5%	5% – 7%	>7%
Deaths-hospitalizations ratio	≤3%	4% – 6%	7% – 9%	10% –12%	13% –15%	16% –18%	>18%

Source: Reed C, Biggerstaff M, Finelli L, et al. Novel framework for assessing epidemiologic effects of influenza epidemics and pandemics. Emerg Infect Dis 2013;19:85–91.

COVID-19 was an interesting pandemic as applied to this CDC chart. COVID-19's community attack rate is clearly at the high end of the chart, as the majority of Americans became infected. However, within schools, it would rank at the lowest end, number one on the scale. While the data is not clear on workplace attack rate, it was likely low to mid-range except for manufacturing environments. Household secondary attack rate was high, as most COVID-19 spread was nosocomial (someone caught it in a hospital) and then from within the household. The reproductive number is of some debate. At times it seemed to hover near two and other times was clearly below one.

The case fatality rate is also a loose number. As the pandemic wound down in the spring of 2021, nearly all estimations gauged the number of Americans infected to be close to 200 million. Then, if you take the 600,000 COVID-19 deaths, samplings tell us that a third to half of those did not die from COVID-19, but with the virus at some point prior to death. We will get into those details later. If you work off 400,000 real COVID-19 deaths compared to 200 million infected, we get a fatality rate of about .2%. That puts us in level four above. Over a year since the first COVID-19 death in America, about one million different people were hospitalized with or from COVID-19. That puts the fatality rate at about 4%, level two on the scale above. There is some estimating this, but there is no way the case and hospitalization fatality rate was at the high end of that chart, it had to be low to medium on the scale.

The takeaway from this comparison is that in some ways, COVID-19 was definitely high on the severity scale, and in other ways, it was low. This matters when applying the NPIs to the pandemic and what was appropriate. Below is a second chart from the CDC guide on transmissibility and severity:

TABLE 5. Initial assessment: scaled measures of influenza virus transmissibility and clinical severity		
Measures of transmissibility and clinical severity	Scale	
	Low to moderate	Moderate to high
Transmissibility		
Secondary attack rate, household	≤20%	>20%
Attack rate, school or university	≤30%	>30%
Attack rate, workplace, or community	≤20%	>20%
R^0: basic reproductive number	1–1.7	≥1.8
Underlying population immunity	Some underlying population immunity	Little to no underlying population immunity
Emergency department or other outpatient visits for influenza-like illness	<10%	≥10%
Virologic characterization	Genetic markers for transmissibility absent	Genetic markers for transmissibility present

Animal models, transmission studies	Less efficient or similar to seasonal influenza	More efficient than seasonal influenza
Clinical severity		
Upper bound of case-fatality ratio	<1%	≥1%
Upper bound of case-hospitalization ratio	<10%	≥10%
Deaths-hospitalizations ratio	<10%	≥10%
Virologic characterization	Genetic markers for virulence absent	Genetic markers for virulence present
Animal models, evaluation of morbidity and mortality	Less virulent or similar to seasonal influenza	More virulent than seasonal influenza

Source: Reed C, Biggerstaff M, Finelli L, et al. Novel framework for assessing epidemiologic effects of influenza epidemics and pandemics. Emerg Infect Dis 2013;19:85–91.

On this chart, COVID-19 fell into the moderate to high classification of transmission within the household - little doubt about that. However, within schools, it was low to moderate. In fact, it was barely measurable, very low. This is critical when we later examine why schools were closed in the 2019-2020 school year and remained remote for the entire 2020-2021 school year. Case fatality rates were low, as well as deaths to hospitalizations. Finally, the pandemic severity chart from the CDC is shown on the following page.

TABLE 9. Prepandemic influenza planning scenarios to guide implementation of non-pharmaceutical interventions by severity of pandemic and the Pandemic Severity Assessment Framework quadrant

Severity of pandemic and PSAF quadrant	Implications of clinical severity and transmissibility in this scenario*	Possible no. of hospitalizations and deaths if unmitigated by age group			Historical experience
		Age groups (yrs)	No. of hospitalizations	No. of deaths	
Low to moderate severity (mild to moderate pandemic) PSAF quadrant: A	Clinical severity and transmissibility similar to the range seen during annual influenza seasons. Estimated overall attack and case-fatality rates: 18% and 0.03%, respectively. Rates of severe outcomes are greater among younger persons than during influenza seasons.	All ages	340,000	17,000	**2009 pandemic** First detected in North America, the 2009 H1N1 pandemic quickly spread to all continents. In the United States, persons at high risk for severe complications included pregnant women and those with neuromuscular disease, lung disease, morbid obesity, and other chronic conditions. An estimated 43–89 million people in the United States became ill with H1N1 from April 2009 through April 2010, and approximately 12,000 people died. A total of 87% of deaths were among persons aged ≤65 yrs, with a mean age of 43 yrs. During typical influenza seasons, 80%–90% of deaths are among persons aged ≥65 yrs, and the mean age of influenza-related deaths is approximately 76 yrs.
		0–18	50,000	1,000	
		18–64	135,000	6,000	
		≥65	155,000	10,000	

Moderate to high severity (moderate to severe pandemic) PSAF quadrant: B	Clinical severity is similar to the range seen during annual influenza seasons. Transmissibility greater than during influenza seasons. Estimated overall attack and case-fatality rates: 22% and 0.05%, respectively. Rates of severe outcomes are greater than during influenza seasons, especially among younger persons.	All ages	550,000	35,000	**1968 pandemic** First detected in Hong Kong in July 1968, a new influenza virus (H3N2) spread worldwide. The first cases in the United States were detected in September 1968. The 1968 influenza pandemic resulted in approximately 30,000 deaths in the United States, with approximately half among those aged ≥65 yrs.
		0–18	80,000	2,500	
		18–64	220,000	12,000	
		≥65	250,000	20,000	
Very high severity (very severe to extreme pandemic) PSAF quadrant: B	Clinical severity similar to the range seen during annual influenza seasons. Transmissibility greater than during influenza seasons. Estimated overall attack and case-fatality rates: 28% and 0.1%, respectively. Rates of severe outcomes are greater than during influenza seasons.	All ages	1,100,000	86,000	**1957 pandemic** A new influenza virus, H2N2 (the Asian strain), emerged in China in February 1957 and spread to approximately 20 countries, including the United States, by June 1957. An estimated 25% of the U.S. population became ill with the new pandemic virus strain. U.S. infection rates were highest among school-aged children and adults aged ≤40 yrs, with most (64%) of the approximately 70,000 deaths occurring among older adults.
		0–18	150,000	6,000	
		18–64	450,000	30,000	
		≥65	500,000	50,000	

Very high severity (very severe to extreme pandemic) PSAF quadrant: D	Both clinical severity and transmissibility are greater than during annual influenza seasons. Estimated overall attack and case-fatality rates: 30% and 1.5%, respectively. Rates of severe outcomes are greater than during influenza seasons, especially among young adults.	All ages	7,500,000	1,400,000	**1918 pandemic** The 1918 pandemic resulted in death for 2%–3% of those infected, a case-fatality rate that was much greater than the rate during an average influenza season. The pandemic virus was easily transmitted. Approximately one-fourth of the U.S. population became ill, and approximately 500,000 died; 99% of deaths occurred in persons aged ≤65 yrs.
		0–18	1,000,000	100,000	
		18–64	3,000,000	500,000	
		≥65	3,400,000	800,000	

Some other key parts of the 2017 CDC report on pandemic mitigations (emphasis added):

- The guidance considered the results of a 2006 opinion poll that stated that 85% of the respondents said that they and all *members of their household would stay home for 7–10 days if another household member were ill with pandemic influenza.*
- CDC might recommend *voluntary home quarantine* of exposed household members as a personal protective measure during severe, very severe, or extreme influenza pandemics.
- Face masks (disposable surgical, medical, or dental procedure masks) might be worn by ill persons during severe, very severe, or extreme pandemics to prevent the spread of influenza to household members and others in the community. However, *little evidence supports the use of face masks by well persons in community settings.*
- CDC might recommend the use of preemptive, coordinated school closures and dismissals during severe, very severe, or extreme influenza pandemics. *Children have higher influenza attack rates than adults and are infectious for a longer period than adults.* Influenza transmission is common in schools and contributes to school absenteeism and parental absenteeism from work. The presence of school-aged children in a household is a risk factor for influenza virus infection in families.
- Influenza outbreaks on college and university campuses typically have high attack rates (44%–73%) and cause substantial morbidity.
- *The task force found insufficient evidence to recommend for or against preemptive, coordinated school dismissals during a mild or moderate influenza pandemic.* In these instances, jurisdictions should make decisions that balance local benefits and potential harms.

The WHO in 2019

In 2019 the World Health Organization released "Non-pharmaceutical public health measures for mitigating the risk and impact of epidemic and pandemic influenza."[18] It was their 91-page playbook for an influenza pandemic. The study opens with, "The evidence base on the effectiveness of NPIs in community settings is limited, and the overall quality of evidence was very low for most interventions." It's just like the opening of the book *Moneyball*, where Michael Lewis writes, "The evidence of statistical analysis in baseball is limited, but here's a book on it anyway." Just kidding. Lewis did not qualify his analysis as largely unfounded before he chronicled the biggest overhaul in roster management in sports history.

A foundational understanding of what mitigation tactics to employ began with understanding the level of severity. The WHO lists levels as Any, Moderate, Extreme, and Extraordinary. Finally, it lists things not to do in any circumstance. Below is the WHO's severity pandemic chart published in 2019:

Table 1. Recommendations on the use of NPIs by severity level

SEVERITY	PANDEMIC*	EPIDEMIC
Any	Hand hygiene Respiratory etiquette Face masks for symptomatic individuals Surface and object cleaning Increased ventilation Isolation of sick individuals Travel advice	Hand hygiene Respiratory etiquette Face masks for symptomatic individuals Surface and object cleaning Increased ventilation Isolation of sick individuals Travel advice
Moderate	*As above, plus* Avoiding crowding	*As above, plus* Avoiding crowding
High	*As above, plus* Face masks for public School measures and closures	*As above, plus* Face masks for public School measures and closures
Extraordinary	*As above, plus* Workplace measures and closures Internal travel restrictions	*As above, plus* Workplace measures and closures
Not recommended in any circumstances	UV light Modifying humidity Contact tracing Quarantine of exposed individuals Entry and exit screening Border closure	UV light Modifying humidity Contact tracing Quarantine of exposed individuals Entry and exit screening Internal travel restrictions Border closure

NPI: non-pharmaceutical intervention; UV: ultraviolet.

First, note the things not recommended include contact tracing and quarantining of exposed individuals. Then think about how much we heard from politicians and health care professionals about the need to trace and quarantine. Think about kids in college locked in their dorms because they were around someone that *may have* COVID-19 or did test positive for SARS-CoV-2, though they weren't symptomatic or sick.

The WHO stated that "although there is no evidence that [wearing face masks] is effective in reducing [influenza] transmission, there is mechanistic plausibility for the potential effectiveness of this measure." What this means is it *seems* like face masks should work, but there's no evidence to support it. Home quarantining of exposed people that are not symptomatic was discouraged from quarantining because "there is no obvious rationale to it." School measures were rated as having "very low" evidence of doing anything productive, but they did mention school closures, desk spacing, staggering recesses, and lunch breaks. Why? Because this was written under the guise that a pandemic's primary spreaders are kids.

Not one recommendation the WHO listed was associated with a high quality of evidence to support it. This is to their credit to list possible measure and recommendations, the rationale behind it, and how much "science" supported it. In this case, there is a list of best-guess efforts without science to back it up. In 2020 all these recommendations and more were met with "follow the science." The CDC and WHO circulated NPIs as tactics to slow the spread of a pandemic. If you read them, it's clear the view is that all these are all temporary interventions. Not temporary for a year and half, but in days to less than a month.

The crazy part of reading their playbooks is that they never suggested the lockdowns we came to know. In fact, they rejected them for anything other than a short period, meaning days, a month at the most for schools, assuming kids were primary vectors. Both had low confidence that any of the NPIs were effective. It's surprising they did not conduct some intentional studies on face masks limiting transmission for influenza viruses.

Key Takeaways

- Pandemic models referenced in the Glass model, the papers that followed, and the planning guides from the CDC and WHO all assumed children and young adults were the primary spreaders of the virus. The opposite was true with COVID-19. Children and young adults were barely even measurable spreaders, a gift COVID-19 gave us that was always ignored by policymakers.
- The stay-at-home order concept was to be voluntary and for those exposed to symptomatic people. In extreme situations, there were suggestions for something like a stay-at-home order.

- Face mask-wearing had no data behind it for the general population and was recommended for symptomatic individuals in some situations—however, both the CDC and WHO thought it seemed like a good idea.

CHAPTER 2
Mask Science BC
(before COVID-19)

Nothing became the face of non-pharmaceutical interventions, the lockdowns, like face masks. Nothing stirred up more emotion in Americans than mask mandates. Millions refused to wear them or wore them as sparingly as possible. For others, it became their faith. Nearly all the early COVID-19 book covers illustrated a face mask as the sign of the times. Wearing masks or not, supporting them or not, was the most prominent virtue signal throughout the pandemic.

"Follow the science." "Wear two masks." "Wear four masks." The mask business boomed in 2020 and 2021. Over fifty billion were sold in 2020. Celebrities sported designer masks. La Sportiva sold branded masks representing one of my hobbies, but I couldn't bring myself to buy one. Who climbs mountains in a face mask? It was hard to demonstrate that kind of support for face masks. Why? Because I studied the science.

It would have been great if masks worked. Almost magical. A pandemic rolls in, everyone masks up, and then the spread is suppressed, the R_0 drops below one, and in a few weeks it's over. I wish that had been the case. I would have written books dedicated to masking up if it worked; this was no anti-mask crusade. I wanted us out of this as much as anyone. Unfortunately, that isn't how it worked. It's not how it worked anywhere in the world. Is that a surprise? Not if you studied the science before COVID-19.

There were many studies about the effectiveness of all kinds of face masks preventing viral spread before COVID-19. Some of that science is still out there; some of it has been redacted. Actual scientific studies were redacted for fear of being cast as a COVID-19, or mask, denier.

The *Lancet*

The *Lancet* is one of the best known and relied upon medical journal repositories, founded in 1823 by Thomas Wakley. They have published over 10,000 articles since inception and provide detailed insight and analysis on seemingly everything medical. They have locations in New York, London, and

Beijing, three key geographies to this pandemic. They wrote several pieces on the efficacy of face masks to stunt viral spread.

In 2017 the *Lancet* published "Clearing the air: do facemasks protect health?"[19] Below are excerpts from their reporting:

- Traditional facemasks can be made of paper or cloth (originally cotton gauze), and they provide a physical barrier between the mouth and nose and the outside environment. These include the traditional surgical masks associated with doctors and dentists, which are made of paper or other non-woven materials. They can protect the wearer from potentially harmful substances (e.g., blood spray); however, they do not provide protection from airborne particles or pathogens.
- Cloth masks may be worse than not wearing a mask at all. "We did a big trial comparing cloth masks with surgical masks in Vietnam," said Dr. Raina MacIntyre, Prof of Infectious Disease Epidemiology at the University of New South Wales, Sydney, Australia. "In countries like Vietnam and China, healthcare workers often have to pay for their own PPE, and they use cloth masks because it's a lot cheaper for them than even the disposable surgical masks. That study showed that your risk of infection actually increases if you use a cloth mask, which is quite concerning. We don't know the reason exactly. It could be because people aren't washing them enough, because of the properties of the cloth, pathogens may accumulate in the cloth."
- Surgical masks and cloth masks do not offer protection from inhaling particles or pathogens in the air—for that, you need to turn to respirators.

Another study was published by The *Lancet* in 2019 called "Facemask versus No Facemask in Preventing Viral Respiratory Infections During Hajj: A Cluster Randomised Open Label Trial."[20] It's not clear what type of face mask is used in this study, though a probable assumption is a surgical mask. Below are the conclusions of this study:

- "7,687 adult participants were randomized to facemasks or no facemasks; 3,864 participants were assigned to the Facemask group and 3,823 participants to the Control group. In the Facemask arm, respectively 27% and 51% of participants used facemasks daily and intermittently, 22% did not; in the Control arm, respectively 15% and 38% of participants used facemasks daily and intermittently, 47% did not."
- "Respiratory viruses were detected in 277 of 650 (43%) nasal/pharyngeal swabs from symptomatic pilgrims. In intention-to-treat analysis, facemask use was neither effective against laboratory-confirmed VRTIs (viral respiratory tract infections) nor against CRI (clinical respiratory infection)."

- Interpretation: facemask use does not prevent clinical or laboratory-confirmed viral respiratory infections among Hajj pilgrims.

The Infectious Disease Society of America

The *IDSA* published the following findings in 2017:[21]

- "With one exception, case-control studies consistently reported a protective effect of medical masks against SARS. Compared to "no PPE" controls, N95 respirators conferred protection against confirmed SARS-CoV infection in 2 of 3 case-control studies."
- "No protective effect against SARS was reported for disposable, cotton, or paper masks."
- Another study reported a reduced risk of SARS-CoV infection among healthcare workers wearing a medical mask. Two studies found no protective effect of either medical masks or N95 respirators against SARS, although lower attack rates were reported among nurses consistently wearing either type of PPE.
- "We found evidence to support universal medical mask use in hospital settings as part of infection control measures to reduce the risk of CRI and ILI among healthcare workers. Overall, the evidence to inform policies on mask use in healthcare workers is poor, with a small number of studies that are prone to reporting biases and lack of statistical power."

In 2011, Faisal bin-Reza, Angus Nicoll, and Mary E. Chamberland published a study called "The use of masks and respirators to prevent transmission of influenza: a systematic review of the scientific evidence" while working at the Health Protection Agency in the U.K. They reported on the efficacy of mask use and specific to SARS (severe acute respiratory syndrome), with a couple of interesting findings:

Anticipating the paucity of studies that focused solely on influenza, we included the effect of masks/respirators on respiratory viruses other than influenza. SARS is an unusual acute viral respiratory infection with a very different epidemiology to almost all other respiratory viral infections. It is fundamentally different from human influenza: it rarely infects children, has a long incubation period, transmits little early on, mostly transmits in healthcare settings, is not prone to extensive global spread, and has only appeared once.

They identified the low SARS infection rate in children, though SARS-CoV-2 did have a short incubation period, transmitted early on and by any definition was prone to global spread. Below is the study wrap-up:

In conclusion, there is a limited evidence base to support the use of masks and/or respirators in healthcare or community settings. Mask use is best undertaken as part of a package of personal protection, especially including hand hygiene in both home and healthcare settings. Early initiation and correct and consistent wearing of masks/respirators may improve their effectiveness.

In 2014 the *BMJ* (British Medical Journal) published research on the difference between cloth masks and medical masks (not N95s) for ILIs, influenza-like illnesses, in "A cluster randomized trial of cloth masks compared with medical masks in healthcare workers."[22] Their consensus was that cloth masks are ineffective at blocking viral particles. Their findings:

- The rates of all infection outcomes were highest in the cloth mask arm, with the rate of ILI statistically significantly higher in the cloth mask arm compared with the medical mask arm.
- Cloth masks also had significantly higher rates of ILI compared with the control arm. An analysis by mask use showed ILI and laboratory confirmed virus were significantly higher in the cloth masks group compared with the medical masks group.
- Penetration of cloth masks by particles was almost 97% and medical masks 44%.
- This study is the first RCT of cloth masks, and the results caution against the use of cloth.
- Masks. This is an important finding to inform occupational health and safety. Moisture retention, reuse of cloth masks, and poor filtration may result in increased risk of infection.
- As a precautionary measure, cloth masks should not be recommended for HCWs.

Cambridge University Press

Cambridge published a study in 2010 called "Face masks to prevent transmission of influenza virus: a systematic review."[23] In contrast to other study conclusions drawn on face masks, it's fair to show a study in support of their efficacy. Here are a couple of their observations:

- There is some evidence to support the wearing of masks or respirators during illness to protect others, and public health emphasis on mask-wearing during illness may help to reduce influenza virus transmission.
- There are fewer data to support the use of masks or respirators to prevent becoming infected.

It's not exactly proven science to them that masks or even respirators are sure things, but they are leaning toward masks helping to not infect others.

This is consistent with early recommendations from the WHO and CDC that *symptomatic* people wear masks.

UT Southwestern Medical Center did an interesting study in 2019 called "Surgical masks as good as respirators for flu and respiratory virus protection."[24] There they compared the efficacy of surgical masks to N95s for healthcare workers relative to the prevention of influenza or other viral respiratory illness. The study was performed at several cities across the country and researchers from the CDC, Johns Hopkins, University of Texas, and others. Almost 2,400 healthcare workers participated in the study spanning four years. Their findings:

- 207 laboratory-confirmed influenza infections occurred in the N95 groups versus 193 among medical mask wearers.
- In addition, there were 2,734 cases of influenza-like symptoms, laboratory-confirmed respiratory illnesses, and acute or laboratory-detected respiratory infections (where the worker may not have felt ill) in the N95 groups, compared with 3,039 such events among medical mask wearers.
- "This study showed there is no difference in the incidence of viral respiratory transmission among health care workers wearing the two types of protection," said Dr. Trish Perl, Chief of UT Southwestern's Division of Infectious Diseases and Geographic Medicine and the report's senior author.

In nearly all studies, the paper surgical masks were deemed ineffective at blocking viral particles. In this study, the two groups were statistically similar. Could it be the variability lies not in the mask-wearing at the healthcare setting but in catching ILI (influenza-like illness) away from that setting?

In 2016, Dr. John Hardie wrote for the Oral Health Group a published analysis called "Why Face Masks Don't Work: A Revealing Review."[25] Hardie made several compelling points illustrating why face masks do not work to blunt airborne transmissions. What happened to his findings as COVID-19 entered the scientific world? His piece was redacted. You can find it in an archive, but the initial study on the Oral Health Group website looked like this in 2020:

Update: Why Face Masks Don't Work: A Revealing Review

October 18, 2016
by Oral Health

If you are looking for "Why Face Masks Don't Work: A Revealing Review" by John Hardie, BDS, MSc, PhD, FRCDC, it has been removed. The content was published in 2016 and is no longer relevant in our current climate.

The science that was good enough in 2016 is "no longer relevant in our current climate?" Why was the science good enough in 2016? Below are Hardie's original findings, and within the study are many citations to support each:

Through the use of highly sensitive instruments, it is now appreciated that the aerosols transmitted from the respiratory tract due to coughing, sneezing, talking, and exhalation produce respiratory particles that range from the very small (less than 5 microns) to the very large (greater than a 100 microns) and that all of these particles are capable of being inhaled by persons close to the source.

Disposable face masks usually consist of three to four layers of flat non-woven mats of fine fibers separated by one or two polypropylene barrier layers which act as filters capable of trapping material greater than 1 micron in diameter. No matter how well a mask conforms to the shape of a person's face, it is not designed to create an airtight seal around the face. These gaps do not provide adequate protection as they permit the passage of air and aerosols when the wearer inhales. It is important to appreciate that if masks contained filters capable of trapping viruses, the peripheral gaps around the masks would continue to permit the inhalation of unfiltered air and aerosols.

The filters in masks do not act as sieves by trapping particles greater than a specific size while allowing smaller particles to pass through. Accordingly, it should be no surprise that a study of eight brands of face masks found that they did not filter out 20-100% of particles varying in size from 0.1 to 4.0 microns. Another investigation showed penetration ranged from 5-100% when masks were challenged with relatively large 1.0 micron particles. A further study found that masks were incapable of filtering out 80-85% of particles varying in size from 0.3 to 2.0 microns.

Hardie makes the argument based on the size of an airborne particle compared to the pore size of a mask. We will get into that in more detail later in this chapter. Some final scientific commentary on face masks from various sources are below:

Surgical masks offer some protection for the mucous membranes of the nose and mouth of the wearer from large droplets and splashes but will not protect against the inhalation of aerosols. The filtering efficiency of available masks varies widely; most do not effectively filter small particles from the air, and many studies have demonstrated the poor filter performance of single (or even multiple) surgical masks. Surgical masks should never be used to protect healthcare workers from inhalation of airborne infectious aerosols because their filters are not designed to prevent the passage of small particles. Moreover, even if a surgical mask has a "better" filter, the lack of a close seal to the face will negate filter performance because particles will follow the path of least resistance and travel through the gaps between the surgical mask and the face.[26]

Surgical masks can also be used as a fluid barrier to help keep blood splatter from reaching the wearer's mouth and nose. However, surgical/procedure masks cannot provide certified respiratory protection unless they are also designed, tested, and government-certified as a respirator. If a wearer wants to reduce inhalation of smaller, inhalable particles (those smaller than 100 microns), they need to obtain and properly use a government-certified respirator, such as a NIOSH-approved N95 filtering facepiece particulate respirator.[27]

Surgical mask filters are very inefficient, and the mask itself allows leakage around the facepiece. Even with "good" filters, 30% to 50% of particles will leak into the facepiece of a "well-fitting" surgical mask. This performance is far below that of even the least protective type of respirator, which (if fit tested) will allow less than 10% particle leakage. In the case of SARS or MERS—and similar potentially severe infectious respiratory diseases with no vaccines and few or no treatment options—HCWs deserve better protection than a surgical mask.[28]

Masks do not filter all particulates from the air inhaled and exhaled by the wearer. Much of the air is drawn in and escapes where there is least resistance to flow, usually around the sides of the mask (venting). The masks do not form a complete seal against the face. A mask wet with exhaled moisture has increased resistance to airflow, is less efficient at filtering bacteria, and has increased venting. Surgical masks alone do not provide sufficient protection against SARS.[29]

From the Canadian Centre for Occupational Health and Safety: Surgical masks are a barrier to splashes, droplets, and spit; surgical masks are not designed to seal tight against the face; surgical masks do not effectively filter small particles from the air.[30] [reminder: typical cloth face masks are inferior to surgical masks]

Types of Face Masks

N95 masks are named such because they are rated to filter out 95% of the particles we breathe in. They are often called respirators. Some N95s have valves that make the exhale easier; the exhale is unfiltered. My primary care physician wore one of these when I went in for a check-up in late 2020. I joked with him that his mask protects him but not me. He smiled and said, that's why you're wearing a mask. But wait, my mask doesn't filter out aerosol particles. We went into an entertaining circular conversation. Respirators with one-way valves were banned on some airlines for this reason.

A fitted N95 is closer to gap-free around the face than other masks and can filter out most particles that are .3 μm (micron sizes described later in this chapter) and larger. This is why they work for the most part. With 87% of particles exhaled under 1 μm (but many larger than .3 μm), they likely do an efficient job filtering.

Surgical Masks

Surgical masks are most commonly seen as the pleated blue masks retailers and restaurants provided to patrons in order to comply with state or local ordinances. They allow particles to pass that are ten times larger than what N95s allow. Surgical masks are generally worn to prevent larger sprays or splatters from reaching the wearer and may keep a patient from catching germs from the doctor or nurse. They are generally loose-fitting worn with loops around the ears.

Cloth Face Masks

Cloth face masks varied wildly in quality and design. We saw people wearing bandanas, designer cloth masks, and gaiters (while climbing in Jackson Hole, there were hikers pulling up gaiters when someone came near them at over 10,000 feet).

Cloth face coverings vary tremendously by material, design, and content (with or without additional filter layers), so not surprisingly, studies show they block anywhere from 10-50% of these same airborne particles. The pore size is quite large compared to an aerosol particle, and that is why they don't work to block viral particles like that from COVID-19. They are probably better than nothing at blocking particles, but then you add in moisture, decreased oxygen, and contamination from being thrown around in a car, purse, bag, reused… you get the idea. They didn't work and the data showed that throughout the pandemic. So many health "experts" said they did. Challenge them to refute the evidence provided throughout this book.

McDonald's Cup

The CDC did not recommend a fast-food drink cup as effective protection. However, in July, when Texas began its mask mandate, I went into a Subway to get lunch. While in line, two young men walked in with McDonald's cups over their faces. "Those are some great masks you guys have!" One replied, "We forgot our masks and are on our work break and we're starved." They got served and it remains the most inventive face-covering seen to date.

Why Didn't Face Masks Work?

Viral particles that spread in the air vary in size. A micron or micrometer symbol is μm. A micron is defined as one-millionth of a meter, a little more than one twenty-five thousandth of an inch. A large droplet is defined as 5 μm or larger.[31] You can't see these. Many people visualize a droplet housing a virus as something you can see, like something you'd sneeze out. Certainly, they can, but that's not where real transmission resides. You can easily block those, and if they become airborne, they drop in seconds. The coronavirus that turned life upside down in 2020 spread through particles as small as .1 μm. Below is a visualization of particle sizes:

Source: *https://www.visualcapitalist.com/visualizing-relative-size-of-particles/*

One additional comparison: wildfire smoke particles are over 4 microns. Recall that the CDC said during the California wildfires that face masks were ineffective at blocking smoke particles,[32] which you can visually see and smell aggregated near a fire, and that a SARS-CoV-2 particle is smaller than that. If the masks couldn't block the larger smoke particles, they would not block smaller viral particles.

Dr. Kevin Fennelly wrote "Particle sizes of infectious aerosols: implications for infection control," published in The *Lancet*[33] in 2020:

- "Airborne transmission has often been attributed to infectious droplet nuclei produced by the desiccation of suspended droplets and defined as 5 μm or smaller in size."
- "Infectious aerosols are suspensions of pathogens in particles in the air, subject to both physical and biological laws. Particle size is the most

important determinant of aerosol behavior. Particles that are 5 μm or smaller in size can remain airborne indefinitely under most indoor conditions unless there is removal due to air currents or dilution ventilation. Particles sized 6–12 μm deposit in the upper airways of the head and neck."

- "The studies reviewed in this paper consistently show that humans produce infectious aerosols in a wide range of particle sizes, but pathogens predominate in small particles <5 μm that are immediately respirable by exposed individuals."

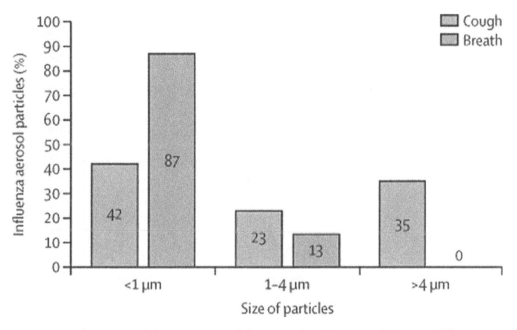

Source: https://www.thelancet.com/journals/lanres/article/PIIS2213-2600(20)30323-4/fulltext

The figure above shows that 87% of exhaled particles are under 1 μm, and this is why face masks did not work. A peer-reviewed study called "Optical microscopic study of surface morphology and filtering efficiency of face masks" was published in June 2020 in the National Center for Biotechnology Information and filed in the National Institute of Health library.[34] In this study, they found the pore size of face masks to hover about 80-500 times larger than a SARS-CoV-2 aerosol particle:

The pore size of cloth masks ranged from 80 to 500 μm. Interestingly, we found that efficiency dropped by 20% after the 4th washing and drying cycle. We observed a change in pore size and shape and a decrease in microfibers within the pores after washing. Stretching of cloth mask surface also altered the pore size and potentially decreased the filtering efficiency. As compared to cloth masks, the less frequently used surgical/ paper masks had complicated networks of fibers and much smaller pores in multiple layers in comparison to CMs, and therefore had better filtering efficiency. This study showed that the filtering efficiency of cloth face masks were relatively lower, and washing and drying practices deteriorated the efficiency.

Below is an image of two cloth face masks, before and after stretching on someone's face:

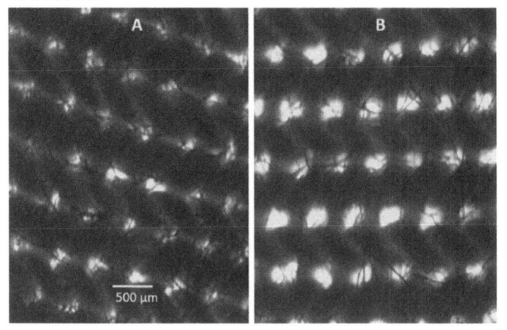

Source: NCBI study "Optical microscopic study of surface morphology and filtering efficiency of face masks"

What you see is that in cloth mask A (before stretching or washing), the pore size is about 250 μm. After stretching (which happens when we put it on our face stretched ear to ear), the pore size is maybe 400 μm. This is why the average face mask Americans wore didn't work. The face mask pores are up to a thousand times larger than an aerosol particle that can spread a SARS-CoV-2 virus. It's all in the math.

Two other comments on this have to do with fit and filter size. First, there are some studies we can find that show nearly all face masks are 75% effective at filtering out particles over 2 μm. Other show much smaller rates. The second point is most important: fit. Do you wear a face mask and glasses? Have you seen the glasses fog up? These filtration rates do not account for huge seepages through the gaps between the mask and your face. An insightful video circulated on Twitter in 2020. A man was vaping and wearing masks. He would inhale a vape, then put on several different masks. A vape exhale is larger than a viral particle. The exhale you can visually see through the mask was enlightening. If you know a vaper, try it out.

Health Care Leaders on Masks Before COVID-19

It's hard not to go back to comments or tweets that several leaders in healthcare made about masks before the lockdowns. We heard from our Surgeon General, Dr. Fauci, CDC Director Redfield, and others in the first quarter of 2020, based on the science.

Dr. Anthony Fauci

USA Today reported this from Dr. Fauci on February 17, 2020: "The only people who need masks are those who are already infected to keep from exposing others. The masks sold at drugstores aren't even good enough to truly protect anyone. If you look at the masks that you buy in a drug store, the leakage around that doesn't really do much to protect you. People start saying, 'Should I start wearing a mask?' Now, in the United States, there is absolutely no reason whatsoever to wear a mask."[35]

In March 2020, Dr. Fauci was interviewed for "*60 Minutes.*" He then said, "There's no reason to be walking around with a mask. While masks may block some droplets, they do not provide the level of protection people think they do. Wearing a mask may also have unintended consequences: People who wear masks tend to touch their face more often to adjust them, which can spread germs from their hands."[36]

US Surgeon General Dr. Jerome Adams

On March 2, 2020, Dr. Adams said this: "You can increase your risk of getting it by wearing a mask if you are not a health care provider. Folks who don't know how to wear them properly tend to touch their faces a lot and actually can increase the spread of coronavirus. There are things people can do to stay safe. There are things they shouldn't be doing and one of the things they shouldn't be doing in the general public is going out and buying masks."[37]

Adams tweeted this on February 29, 2020: "Seriously people - STOP BUYING MASKS! They are NOT effective in preventing general public from catching #Coronavirus, but if healthcare providers can't get them to care for sick patients, it puts them and our communities at risk!"

CNN ran this headline and piece in March 2020[38]:

Americans Don't Need Masks. They Buy Them Because They're Scared

To be clear once again, Americans don't need masks. The CDC says that healthy people in the U.S. shouldn't wear them because they won't protect them from the novel coronavirus. In fact, warns U.S. Surgeon General Dr. Jerome Adams, face masks might actually increase your risk of infection if they aren't worn properly.

The CDC

CBS News reported this on March 3, 2020: The Centers for Disease Control and Prevention said it "does not recommend that people who are well wear a facemask to protect themselves from respiratory diseases, including COVID-19."[39] Rather, experts cautioned that putting on a face mask without proper fitting and training could actually increase your risk.

Dr. Sanjay Gupta

On February 26, 2020, just a couple of weeks before the lockdowns began, Dr. Sanjay Gupta said this on *CNN*:[40]

- "80% of the people infected will have minimal or no symptoms" (this proved to be true a year later)
- "People more likely to be affected by COVID-19 are those with preexisting conditions" (true a year later)
- "People don't need to wear masks if they're not sick" (also true a year later)

Health and Human Services Secretary Alex Azar

HHS Secretary Alex Azar said on March 2, 2020: "If it's not fitted right, you're going to fumble with it. You're going to be touching your face, which is the number one way you're going to get disease, is unclean hands touching your face."[41] Actually, the number one way one was going to get COVID-19 was through airborne particles.

University of Minnesota CIDRAP

University of Minnesota's Center for Infectious Disease Research and Policy (home to Michael Osterholm, whom we will discuss later) published "COMMENTARY: Masks-for-all for COVID-19 not based on sound data."[42] early in the pandemic on April 4, 2020. The article opens with "The authors and CIDRAP have received requests in recent weeks to remove this article from the CIDRAP website. Reasons have included: (1) we don't truly know that cloth masks (face coverings) are not effective, since the data are so limited, (2) wearing a cloth mask or face covering is better than doing nothing, (3) the article is being used by individuals and groups to support non-mask wearing where mandated and (4) there are now many modeling studies suggesting that cloth masks or face coverings could be effective at flattening the curve and preventing many cases of infection."

The study cites ten other studies as the basis for their claim. They also reviewed other studies purporting that cloth masks and face coverings could flatten the curve or significantly reduce cases. They found holes in these arguments based on:

- Fit is an inhibitor to efficacy. If a mask fits poorly, it will have gaps and not work.
- These coverings have no standards and so believing "cloth masks or coverings" would work uniformly is unlikely.
- The particle size compared to mask pore size is too incongruent.

The authors close, stating they support wearing masks, but that masks are unlikely to have much impact on lowering COVID-19 transmission. Science. Further, they worry that people wearing masks will reduce social distancing, a genuine mitigation tactic that does work (that statement is accurate).

Emily Oster, a professor at Brown University, economist, and reopen-school advocate told *Time* in April 2019, "One of my least favorite phrases is 'studies say' because you can always find a study that says whatever is the thing that you think already. And one of the things I try to do here is not what does a study say but what do all the studies say."[43] She's right. We can find studies before COVID-19 that advocated face masks to stop the spread of a virus, or wearing them when you are not sick. It's just not what nearly all the studies said.

We can go on and on quoting prominent healthcare leaders in the first quarter of 2020 and their dismissal of masks as effective blockers of SARS-CoV-2. In their defense, then no one saw COVID-19 sweeping through America the way it did. However, they did know a whole lot about viral transmission and the efficacy of masks. SARS-CoV-2 did transmit similar to influenza. Very similar, with one exception: kids are the primary vectors of influenza and were barely transmitters of SARS-CoV-2. Healthcare "experts" knew face masks did not work. They propped them up to get Americans to do something to stop the spread, and they ignored science on the way. They should have been straight with Americans from the beginning:

- Face masks other than N95s won't do much to help
- If you are severely overweight, you are at high risk, so be responsible and isolate
- If you suffer from diabetes, hypertension, or respiratory disease, you are at high risk and should isolate
- If you are over 65 years old, you are at high risk and should isolate

Key Takeaways on Face Masks BC (before COVID-19):

- The CDC and WHO reported in concert before COVID-19 that face masks could help if worn by symptomatic people during a pandemic.
- The science supported the effectiveness of N95s in blocking aerosol particles.
- The science did not support surgical masks or lesser face coverings in blocking aerosol particles due to pore size within the fabric and loose fit around the face.
- Not one health expert in the United States promoted wearing masks to stunt the spread of COVID-19 in early 2020. The CDC was the first to make that proclamation in March, and even then, other experts did not back it up.
- Not one major medical journal study showed data proof that anything less than an N95 was effective at blocking a virus spread like we saw with COVID-19.

CHAPTER 3
Mask Science AC
(after COVID-19)

One mask, two mask, red mask, blue mask,
Etsy mask, Gucci mask,
Some are old and some are new.
Some are thick, and some are thin,
And we're told they all will win.
Do they work if they breathe with ease?
I do not know, go ask the CDC.
Fauci says wear one, wear two,
Wear three, wear four.
No one can catch the virus
If they can't breathe anymore.
From here to there,
Masks are everywhere.
There are masks for those who like to run.
Who cares if they're not needed in the hot, hot sun?
Some have one layer and some have four.
The virus still slips through their pores.
They're better than any vaccine.
They're the coolest thing you've ever seen.
Little kids wear them on a plane,
They all get shamed if they dare complain.
We wear the mask to protect each other,
That the virus spreads still makes you wonder.

It's a little tongue-in-cheek and not meant to offend. When Texas had a state order, I wore a mask when required. I wore them when I traveled when required. I'd have delivered them door to door if they worked. And mostly, I'd have written a book about how important they are to stunt COVID-19 if they worked.

Mask wearing became the most controversial and consistent talking point of the lockdown era. It should have been schools closed, businesses closed, nursing homes continuously hammered by COVID-19. For some reason, major media outlets spent a hundred times more airtime and print space reporting on mask-deniers than our poor kids that lost over a year of schooling. That story didn't break until the fall of 2020 and didn't reach any critical mass until January 2021. Nursing homes? Zero pressure from nearly all media outlets. Mask wearing? Daily.

Politicians issued state, county, or city mask mandates in most places in the United States. Below is what each state did and the date they issued mandates, if they did:

State	Statewide Mask Order	Requirements
Alabama	May 21, 2020	Indoors at places of business and schools
Alaska	None. Some cities adopted indoor mask mandates	
Arizona	None. Some counties/cities adopted indoor mask mandates	
Arkansas	July 15, 2020	Indoors for those over the age of 10 when in public and in the presence of non-household members, if social distancing is not possible.
California	June 18, 2020. Some cities and counties issued mandates prior to this	Indoors; outdoors in a public space where non-household members are present and social distancing is not possible. Children included in the order.
Colorado	July 16, 2020	Indoors for those over the age of 10.
Connecticut	April 17, 2020	In any public space for those over the age of 2.
Delaware	April 25, 2020	Indoors; public transportation; outdoors: in public spaces where non-household members are present, if social distancing is not possible; applies to those over the age of 12, with exceptions.
District of Columbia	July 22, 2020	In any public space for those over the age of 2.
Florida	None. Some counties/cities adopted indoor mask mandates	

Georgia	None. Some counties/ cities adopted indoor mask mandates	
Hawaii	April 16, 2020	Everyone at or waiting at a business age 5 and over. No more than two people in a boat and no group hiking.
Idaho	None. Some counties/ cities adopted indoor mask mandates	
Illinois	May 1, 2020	Indoors if over the age of two.
Indiana	July 27, 2020	Indoors if over the age of eight.
Iowa	November 17, 2020	Between Nov. 17 and Feb. 6, a mask mandate was in place for individuals when in indoor public spaces and when within 6 feet of non-household members for 15 minutes or longer.
Kansas	July 3, 2020	Indoors; public transportation; outdoors: in public spaces where non-household members are present, if social distancing is not possible.
Kentucky	July 10, 2020	Indoors; public transportation; outdoors: in public spaces where non-household members are present, if social distancing is not possible to those 6 and older.
Louisiana	July 13, 2020	Required in public settings for those 9 and older.
Maine	April 29, 2020	Required for those over age 2 with no exemptions allowed.
Maryland	April 15, 2020	Required in public settings for those 6 and older.
Massachusetts	May 6, 2020	Required in public settings for those 6 and older.
Michigan	July 10, 2020	Required in public settings for those 6 and older.
Minnesota	July 25, 2020	Required in public settings for those 6 and older.
Mississippi	None. Some counties/ cities adopted indoor mask mandates	
Missouri	None. Some counties/ cities adopted indoor mask mandates	

Montana	None. Some counties/ cities adopted indoor mask mandates	
Nebraska	None. Some counties/ cities adopted indoor mask mandates	
Nevada	June 25, 2020	Required in public settings for those 9 and older.
New Hampshire	November 20, 2020	Required in public settings, notably not required for K-12 staff and students.
New Jersey	April 10, then enhanced July 8, 2020	Required in public settings for those over 2 years old.
New Mexico	May 16, 2020	Required in public settings.
New York	April 15, 2020	Required in public settings for those over 2 years old.
North Carolina	June 26, 2020	Required in public settings.
North Dakota	November 14 to January 18	Required in public settings.
Ohio	July 23, 2020	Required in public settings for those 11 and older.
Oklahoma	None. Some counties/ cities adopted indoor mask mandates.	
Oregon	July 1, 2020	Initially required in public settings and expanded to all times outside the residence or while eating/ drinking for those 6 and older.
Pennsylvania	July 1, enhanced on November 17, 2020	Initially required in public settings and expanded to all times gathering with non-household members, for those 2 and older.
Rhode Island	May 8, 2020, enhanced in November	Initially required in public settings and expanded to all times gathering with non-household members including outdoors, for those 2 and older.
South Carolina	None. Some counties/ cities adopted indoor mask mandates	
South Dakota	None. Some counties/ cities adopted indoor mask mandates	

Tennessee	None. Some counties/ cities adopted indoor mask mandates	
Texas	July 3, 2020	Required indoors and in public settings outdoors when social distancing is not possible.
Utah	November 9, 2020	Required indoors and in public settings outdoors when social distancing is not possible.
Vermont	August 1, 2020	Required indoors and in public settings outdoors when social distancing is not possible for those over 2 years old.
Virginia	May 29, enhanced on December 14, 2020	Required indoors and in public settings outdoors when social distancing is not possible for those over 6 years old.
Washington	June 26, 2020	Required indoors and in public settings outdoors when social distancing is not possible for those over 2 years old.
West Virginia	November 14, 2020	Required indoors for those over 9 years old.
Wyoming	December 9; Some counties/cities adopted indoor mask mandates earlier.	Note: we visited Teton County in July 2020 and they required masks. A few climbers wore them at 10,000 feet. We did practice social distancing when a bear occupied our trail on a descent for thirty minutes.

Source: U.S. News and World Report: https://www.usnews.com/news/best-states/articles/these-are-the-states-with-mask-mandates#ind

Mask mandates were in every state, if not through a state order, then through a county or city mandate. Face masks were required in grocery stores, in airplanes, in the malls if they were open, in schools, and in churches. If a community was lucky enough to allow indoor dining, masks were usually required to enter. Then you sit down and take them off. You could walk to the bar to get something, go to the restroom, and usually even leave with them off. Entering a restaurant must have been a lot riskier than leaving one.

Some states and municipalities were far more stringent about wearing them than others. In northern Florida, you could walk around anywhere and not be called out if you weren't wearing one. In San Francisco? One would quickly be publicly shamed if they weren't masked completely walking in the breezy cool air off the bay. I visited Jackson Hole in July 2020, and Wyoming had no mask mandate. We popped in a grocery store, and wearing glasses, I dropped my mask below my nose so my glasses would stop fogging up. A younger man stopped me and lectured me about proper mask-wearing, with a bit of a tone. Never mind, I'd just written *COVID-19: Lockdowns on Trial* and knew a fair amount face mask science. I just nodded and pulled my mask up. There's no worthy crusade to make people feel uncomfortable when nearly all the media was pounding coverage about how face masks would put this pandemic at bay.

The most apparent observation through the pandemic in America was the lack of critical thinking. If masks work, then why did cases, hospitalizations, and deaths continue weeks after mask mandates? With so many counties and even states relaxed about them or not wearing them, the logical comparisons were never asked. Why weren't there far worse results in Georgia and Florida than Alabama and Louisiana? Why did Oklahoma, once the least stringent state in the country for COVID-19 restrictions,[44] fare better than every state it borders? Why did the case/hospitalization curves of California and Arizona and Nevada look identical, though California had by far the tightest restrictions of the three states? Why did very tightly locked down and masked Rhode Island climb to third in the country in COVID-19 deaths per capita long after the first wave in the northeast in the spring of 2020?

The answer lies in a simple phrase journalist Alex Berenson coined early on in the pandemic: virus gonna virus. You simply cannot achieve a zero-COVID-19 environment with anything less than a solitary confinement quarantine. And at whatever point you open, it will then show up, and you'll pick up where you would have been before the lockdown. There is one way out of a pandemic: population immunity. You get that artificially through a vaccine, or through natural infection and subsequent immunity.

The amount of impact a state or community was at risk to COVID-19 relied on two things: the number of elderly and vulnerable people combined with how good a job those individuals isolated. All the other mitigations were mathematically meaningless. Still, governors and other leaders became trigger-happy with mandating masks, and it went from wearing masks in crowded indoor settings to something we would not have believed had it been in a fictional movie.

Wearing Masks At Home

Sometimes wearing a mask in a crowded place wasn't enough. Sometimes we needed to wear them at home. The Wisconsin Department of Natural Resources required its employees to wear masks when having meetings.[45] At home. On Zoom calls. On August 3, 2021, Dr. Francis Collins, the head of the National Institutes of Health, encouraged parents to wear masks at home, even if vaccinated, around their children.[46] If you can't see this was going off the rails fast, sit back and enjoy the data supporting all the mask-wearing.

On November 12, 2020, the *"Today* Show" did a segment on when we should wear a mask at home.[47] Their piece begins with a CDC assertion that COVID-19 was spiking in November due to small gatherings. There was zero evidence to support this; rather, we saw cool weather seasonality combined with a likely push indoors (because of colder weather) driving COVID-19 activity. This happens at that time of the year, every year, with the flu. Their reporting instructed us to wear a mask whenever someone came over that was not in our household and when someone in our household was sick.

WebMd reported in May 2020 that wearing a mask at home can reduce CO-VID-19 transmission by over 75%.[48] No, *WebMd* isn't a real science authority. However, it is widely read and could have influenced readers. It's true that most infections occurred in healthcare settings and at home. It's also true that if you are contagious, that peaks a couple of days before and after symptoms appear. Maybe everyone should wear masks all the time at home. Maybe forever, since the flu comes and is just as dangerous if you're under 50 and healthy. Maybe more.

In the middle of 2020, a new recommendation rose for when we should wear masks. When having sex. Multiple media outlets reported on this, from the UK to Canada to America. *CNN* ran this headline on September 3, 2020: "Wear a mask while having sex and avoid kissing new people, Canada's top doctor advises."[49] Dr. Theresa Tam is Canada's Chief Public Health Officer. She issued a public statement on staying safe from the virus when engaging in sexual activities.

She said sex should be avoided if either partner has COVID-19 symptoms, a fair point, and good advice. Then this: "The lowest risk sexual activity during COVID-19 involves yourself alone." But for Canadians choosing to "engage in an in-person sexual encounter" outside their bubble, she suggests wearing a mask. You can't get COVID-19 (they think) by exchanging bodily fluids, so if you have sex, wear a mask. That did not come with a qualifier that one of the partners be at least feeling a little off, in which case….you get the idea. There are so many ridiculous and illogical assertions to this that you can figure out for yourselves. After a while, you get the idea that some in the media, politics, and healthcare are trying to one-up the next with a new mask requirement.

Jumping The Shark

Then it happened. We reached our peak. But like the COVID-19 waves, there were three peaks. The CDC gets credit for all three of these distinctions. It's disheartening to pick on the CDC because there are some brilliant doctors and scientists that do incredible work. Still, it's clear after COVID-19, the leadership needed an overhaul. They jumped off the mountain of public healthcare three times and flew off in a wingsuit of Zero-COVID-19. If you follow extreme sports, you know how dangerous that can be. Just look up climbing great Dean Potter.

I watched *Happy Days* as a little kid. Before the expression of jumping the shark became a commonplace term, seeing Fonzie jumping a shark on water skis wearing a leather jacket in real-time was just too much. Businesses created products that jumped the shark. Many television shows have done it. You've probably had a dinner party when someone made a comment so over the top you had to look down to see if they were wearing water skis. The CDC did it with two different directors.

Dr. Robert Redfield seems like a nice enough man. He achieved his undergraduate and doctorate degrees at Georgetown. He served as a doctor in the U.S. Army and was distinguished through his work in immunology and virology. No tone in this, Redfield must be very bright. Fast forward to 2018, when he was appointed director of the CDC. He came into this role with the healthcare crisis of generations in front of him. The CDC was the first to proclaim wearing masks was necessary to curb COVID-19 transmission in the spring of 2020.

On September 16, 2020, Dr. Redfield spoke to a Senate committee. While holding up a disposable surgical mask (below), he said this:[50]

"We have clear scientific evidence they work. I might even go so far as to say that this face mask is more guaranteed to protect me against COVID than when I take a COVID vaccine because the immunogenicity may be 70 percent, and if I don't get an immune response, the vaccine's not going to protect me, this face mask will. Masks are the most important, powerful public health tool we have."

He said that the pandemic would be brought under control if Americans embraced mask-wearing for six to twelve weeks (just two more weeks!). He specifically called out 18- to 25-year-olds whom he said are responsible for continuing the outbreak in America. Mask-wearing was up to 90% in the United States, and months later, the seasonal wave hit, breaking through mask-wearing like a tornado through a hut. The picture doesn't show it, but Redfield must have been wearing water skis under that table.

There's a lot to unpack here. First, some percent of the population has natural immunity, what they call T-cell immunity. We don't know how much, but with so many people infected and asymptomatic (most of the infections), it could be 20-50% of the population.[51] Second, the only way out of any pandemic is population, or herd, immunity. When a high percentage of the population acquires recovered infection or vaccinated immunity, there just aren't enough people able to pass it on, and it fizzles out.

If masks work, then why would individuals wearing masks need to quarantine if they were exposed to someone also wearing a mask? If masks offer better protection than a vaccine, then why were there capacity restrictions or closings of indoor dining when masks were required? Or, why were schools ever closed or allowed remote if teachers and students wore masks? Why did Sweden have a curve similar to other hard-hit countries without mask mandates, or any mask-wearing?

The world had very high mask-wearing compliance. If masks are better than a vaccine, why didn't they work? Anywhere? Dr. Redfield went on to say that vaccines were months away. President Donald Trump said that week that vaccines were three to four weeks away, and the media pounced on him for saying that. The first vaccine was announced as complete and ready to go one week after the election, seven weeks after Dr. Redfield's statement.

In January 2021, some inventive middle-schoolers took some leftover mannequins from one of the retailers that went out of business because of the lockdowns. For their science project, they placed a surgical mask on a dummy head and a cloth mask over it. Double masking. They declared it more effective than single masking (it probably was). Oh, one thing. It wasn't some middle-schoolers. It was the CDC:

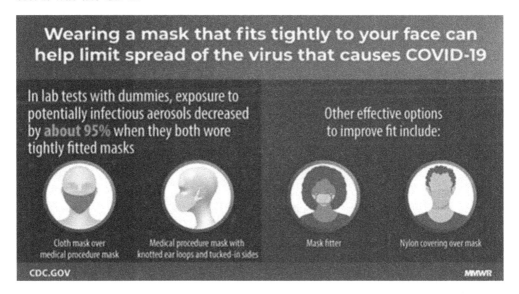

Wearing a mask that fits tightly to your face can help limit spread of the virus that causes COVID-19

In lab tests with dummies, exposure to potentially infectious aerosols decreased by about 95% when they both wore tightly fitted masks

Other effective options to improve fit include:

Cloth mask over medical procedure mask

Medical procedure mask with knotted ear loops and tucked-in sides

Mask fitter

Nylon covering over mask

CDC.GOV

MMWR

The second shark jump. We need to wear two masks. On February 11, 2021, Dr. Fauci told Savannah Guthrie on the *"Today* Show" that "two masks are better than one, it's common sense."[52] First, this recommendation by the CDC came nearly one year after the initial face mask recommendation. We went from mask science-BC that symptomatic individuals should maybe wear masks to the CDC recommending everyone wear masks in March 2020 to them now recommending two face masks for everyone, at a point when the hospitalizations were plummeting. How could a finding or recommendation like this take a full year?

There was no actual data that wearing two masks actually improved mask efficacy. In the mask-wearing universe, there were three segments of wearers: those that believed masks worked and wore them with great discipline; those that wore them whenever they were required, the rule-followers; and those that rebelled and either refused to wear them or wore them as little as possible, curbing their behaviors for a year to avoid wearing them.

The middle group lost confidence in the CDC and the effectiveness of masks to protect against COVID-19. The CDC should have identified by late summer 2020 on, that mask-wearing wasn't stunting the spread, that cases and hospitalizations in places with high mask usage weren't doing better than the places without mandates.

CDC Study on Mask Efficacy

On November 27, 2020, the CDC released a mask study called "Trends in County-Level COVID-19 Incidence in Counties With and Without a Mask Mandate — Kansas, June 1–August 23, 2020."[53] The governor of Kansas issued an executive order requiring wearing masks in public spaces, effective July 3, 2020, which was subject to county authority to opt out. The study reported that "after July 3, COVID-19 incidence decreased in 24 counties with mask mandates but continued to increase in 81 counties without mask mandates."

The study was released in late November but had a cutoff of late August. During the test period, COVID-19 hospitalizations in Kansas hovered around 300 a day against a capacity of 6,400, so about 5% of capacity. In October, hospitalizations rose, like every state in their part of the country. By December, COVID-19 hospitalizations hovered around 1,000 a day for several weeks and then dropped sharply in January.

Below is what happened with absolute numbers of cases during the CDC study period:

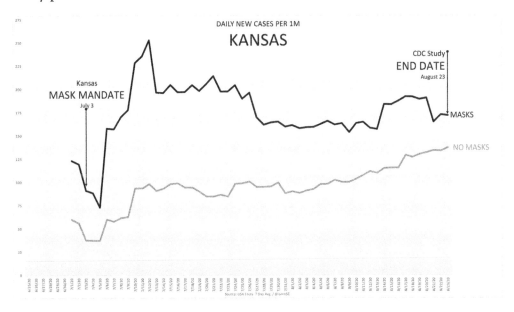

As you can see, the counties with mask mandates had more cases per capita than those without mask mandates.

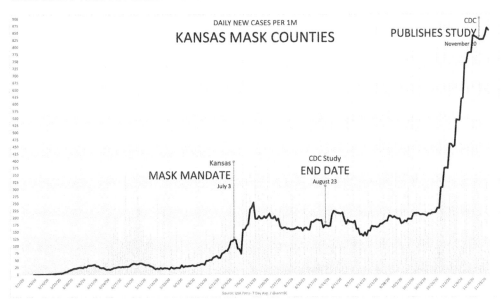

Here's what they did. Instead of comparing the case rate growth from July 3 when the mandate started, they chose to start by looking at the weekly case rate ending on July 9, after the masked counties had a huge increase. The seven-day average on July 3 was 91 per million. On July 9, it was 178 per million. They chose to start from 178. What that allowed them to do was claim a 6% decrease since the mask mandate because they got to ignore the 96% growth in the first week afterward, giving themselves a higher baseline to start from. If you take the starting date of July 3 and the ending date of August 23, the case rate growth in the masked counties was 89%. If you start on July 9, it's a 6% decrease.

Further, you can see what happened to cases when the winter season hit the upper Midwest. The CDC cut off their study before the seasonal bump but released it well after cases rose. The CDC had this data but chose not to qualify their results nor pull the entire study. Any time a study of this nature is completed and future data negates the conclusions, the study is scrapped. In this case, it was released with no acknowledgment of what happened following the study period.

From the time the study ended through year-end, cases were about the same (actually lower) in the mask-mandated versus non-mandated counties. The burden is not on the non-masked counties to be better; having the same results nullifies the value masks are bringing to the table. The CDC had this data for three subsequent months before releasing this study. I went to my primary care physician in late fall 2020 and we discussed masks. He mentioned this Kansas study. I asked him if he knew what the data was after the study cutoff date, and he did not. If there is one thing COVID-19 and the lockdowns should teach us, it's that we should fact-check data ourselves before running with anything provided from just one source.

The CDC study should not have been released. Once released, it should have been retracted like this study published in medRxiv.[54] In 2020 a group of doctors conducted a study of the relationship between wearing masks and decreased hospitalizations in 1,083 counties in the US. It was published and then withdrawn because, after the study, those counties increased hospitalizations, invalidating their initial results:

Danish Study in 2020

A group in Denmark did something every country should have done in 2020. They conducted an actual study later called "Effectiveness of Adding a Mask Recommendation to Other Public Health Measures to Prevent SARS-CoV-2 Infection in Danish Mask Wearers"[55] in April and May 2020 on face masks and whether or not they helped prevent people from getting COVID-19. 3,030 participants were assigned to wear masks and 2,994 were the control group not wearing masks. The Danes provided three-layer disposable surgical masks (like the one Dr. Redfield held in his Senate hearing) to the 3,030 wearers to maintain consistency.

4,862 of the original 6,024 participants completed the study. Following the study period, 42 people wearing masks got infected and 53 not wearing masks got infected. In the end, 1.8% of the mask wearers got infected, and 2.2% of non-mask wearers got infected, statistically even. This was the only study completed worldwide on the efficacy of masks through the first year of the pandemic.

US Marines Study

From May 12 to July 15, 2020, the U.S. Marines Corps conducted a study called COVID-19 Health Action Response for Marines (CHARM) with 1,848 volunteered recruits:[56]

- 133 participants (7.2%) were born outside the United States
- 1,672 (90.5%) were male, 176 (9.5%) were female
- 463 (25.1%) identified as Hispanic, and 271 (14.7%) identified as Black
- The mean age of the participants was 19 years (range, 18 to 31), and 1544 (83.5%) were 18 to 20 years of age. Of the 1813 participants who underwent serologic testing at enrollment, 105 (5.8%) had serum specimens that were positive for SARS-CoV-2–specific antibodies.

All recruits wore double-layered cloth masks at all times indoors and outdoors, except when sleeping or eating; practiced social distancing of at least 6 feet; were not allowed to leave campus; did not have access to personal electronics and other items that might contribute to surface transmission, and routinely washed their hands. They slept in double-occupancy rooms with sinks, ate in shared dining facilities, and used shared bathrooms. All recruits cleaned their rooms daily, sanitized bathrooms after each use with bleach wipes, and ate pre-plated meals in a dining hall that was cleaned with bleach after each platoon had eaten. Most instruction and exercises were conducted outdoors. All movement of recruits was supervised, and unidirectional flow was implemented, with designated building entry and exit points to minimize contact among persons. Bottom line: they were in a far more controlled environment than the vast majority of Americans during the 2020-2021 lockdowns.

Before the study began, 1% of the recruits had tested positive for COVID-19, and of that, 94% had no symptoms. By the time the study wrapped up fourteen days later, an additional 1.9% of the quarantined recruits tested positive. Of 1,544 recruits that did not participate but had test results available, an additional 1.7% of them tested positive. With tighter control measures than most had, there was more (really about even) infection in the quarantine group. It was hypothesized that when one got in various platoons, spread was more likely with the confinement. The real takeaway is that in this very controlled study, lockdowns and masks did not do better than nothing.

Public Health England

Public Health England is an executive agency of the Department of Health and Social Care in the United Kingdom. In a 17-page June 2020 study, they tried to answer two questions: 1) What is the effectiveness of face coverings to reduce the spread of COVID-19 in the community? and 2) What is the efficacy of different types of face coverings designed for use in community settings? Considering the UK had one of the tightest lockdowns throughout the pandemic, their findings just three months into the pandemic are startling.[57] Emphasis added.

- 28 studies were identified, but none of them provided high-level evidence, and 15 were non-peer-reviewed preprints (search up to 5 June 2020). *The evidence was mainly theoretical* (based on modeling or laboratory studies) and epidemiological (*highly subject to confounders*).
- There is weak evidence from epidemiological and modeling studies that mask-wearing in the community may contribute to reducing the spread of COVID-19 and that early intervention may result in a lower peak infection rate.
- Evidence from modeling studies suggests that beneficial effects of wearing masks may be increased when combined with other non-pharmaceutical interventions, such as hand washing and social distancing.
- *Limited and weak evidence from laboratory studies* suggests that materials such as cotton and polyester might block droplets with a filtering efficiency similar to medical masks when folded in 2 or 3 layers.

Downsides of Wearing Masks

When we were in Jackson Hole, WY, in July 2020, we counted a third of the drivers wearing masks in their cars while in the national park. Some climbers wore them. While visiting campuses throughout 2020 and 2021, nearly all students were seen wearing them walking outdoors around campus. In spite of the bad rap college students got in the fall of 2020, the vast majority were pretty good rule-followers. In Dallas, even before the state mandate happened, people were outdoors walking their dogs wearing them on hundred-degree days.

There is nothing wrong with any of these scenarios. If it made the users feel more comfortable, that's their choice. Maybe wearing masks in cars should have been discouraged; a man wearing an N95 while driving passed out and got in a car accident.[58] Logic does tell us that it can be a distraction. There was an article on *MSN* analyzing why you should, or when you should, wear a mask in your car. The problem with these jumping-the-shark commentaries is representing SARS-CoV-2 was blowing around outdoors like pollen in the wind, seeping in the air vents while driving was irresponsible. That the CDC didn't provide some grounding on that was reckless throughout the lockdowns.

Most of my focus was on studying data to determine if face masks blocked the transmission of the COVID-19 virus. If they did, you can make an extremely strong argument that regardless of the consequences of wearing masks, it's in the personal and public health interest to do so. I'd back that argument. Considering the data didn't show wearing masks demonstrably did anything to block the spread of the virus, it's worth looking at the downsides of wearing them. This wasn't about freedom of choice or the hassle of wearing them, two arguments frequently made. It was about science. There are some legitimate costs to wearing masks.

Oxygen Deprivation

Wearing a mask reduces the oxygen saturation measurably after thirty minutes.[59] We normally breathe in air comprised of about 20.9% oxygen. The oxygen saturation in our blood should be over 95%; our bodies do a good job of getting most of the oxygen out of the air we breathe. Breathing in air with a lower than 19.5% oxygen level is unhealthy, and our exhale is 16% oxygen. Repeated breathing from a mask does reduce the oxygen intake. Performing strenuous activities, work, or athletics wearing a mask was just insane.[60, 61] Wearing an N95, the oxygen intake drops to 17% or so.

Mask Traps

The data isn't conclusive, and to be honest, with hundreds of millions of people wearing masks nearly all the time in 2020 and 2021, the conclusion that masks trap *dangerous* amounts of bacteria and even viral concentrations seems weak. If this point were valid, the data points would be strong. Some (will cite examples) do believe masks are harmful in these areas. One thing indisputable: masks were unclean as used by most people: thrown in purses, car seats/consoles/floors. Using those to filter the air we breathe was not ideal.

The National Institute of Health ran this 2018 analysis on bacteria and surgical masks: "Surgical masks as source of bacterial contamination during operative procedures."[62] Their findings:

- The bacterial count on the surface of surgical masks increased with extended operating times; significant difference was found between the

4-to-6-hour and 0-hour groups, significant after 2 hours. The longer one operated with a surgical mask, the more bacteria accumulated. Additionally, the bacterial count of the external surface of the second mask (if swapped out, from touching) was significantly higher than that of the first one.

- Conclusion: The source of bacterial contamination in surgical masks was the body surface of the surgeons rather than the operating environment.

Children and Face Masks

In December 2020, a woman and her husband were kicked off a United Airlines flight when their daughter refused to wear a mask. You can find the video with an easy search. The parents tried diligently to get her to comply, but she was two years old. Any parent knows that could happen to any of us. In March 2021, a group was kicked off (flight eventually canceled) a Frontier flight because a 15-month-old was not wearing a mask. Nearly all schools required kids in school face-to-face to wear a mask. Many required athletes to wear a mask. While performing. What was the science on kids and masks before COVID-19?

First, recall from chapter one that pandemic planning assumed that kids would be the primary age segment spreading it like they are for seasonal flu. With COVID-19, kids were low spreaders and not getting sick from it, less some outliers. Why require kids two and older to wear them? Aside from the little-risk factors, we saw parents and kids both opt out of school where they had the opportunity for in-person learning because of the restrictions and mask-wearing.

In September 2020, the *Brussells Times* ran a story called "Mandatory masks in school are a 'major threat' to children's development, doctors warn."[63] Seventy doctors wrote an open letter to Flemish Education Minister Ben Weyts to stop requiring kids to wear face masks. Some of their observations include:

- Children experienced anxiety and sleep problems as well as behavioral disorders and germaphobia, and an increase in domestic violence, isolation, and deprivation.
- "Mandatory face masks in schools are a major threat to their development. It ignores the essential needs of the growing child. The well-being of children and young people is highly dependent on emotional attachment to others. The face mask requirement makes school a threatening and unsafe environment, where emotional closeness becomes difficult."
- "There is no large-scale evidence that wearing face masks in a non-professional environment has any positive effect on the spread of viruses, let alone on general health. Nor is there any legal basis for implementing this requirement. Meanwhile, it is clear that healthy children living through COVID-19 heal without complications as standard and that they subsequently contribute to the protection of their fellow human

beings by increasing group immunity. The only sensible measure to prevent serious illness and mortality caused by COVID-19 is to isolate individual teachers and individual children at increased risk."

Maskless Crimes

In September 2020, an Ohio mom was in the stands watching her son play football, distanced from others and not wearing a mask. She was confronted by a police officer and told to wear it, and she refused, saying she had asthma. A mild altercation arose, she resisted, and the officer tasered her. While this was going on, a nearby fan was also not wearing a mask, and as the officer handcuffed her and took her away, he was not wearing a mask.[64] What science supported the requirement that a person in this circumstance, socially distanced outdoors, needed to wear a mask? No science ever supported this.

Also, in September 2020, a mom flew from Chicago to Fort Myers and got kicked off a Southwest Airlines flight. On the flight down, her two-year-old son was wearing his mask on and off while also eating. The mother said the flight crew was working with her and understanding. On the return flight, the toddler was not wearing his mask consistently while snacking. The flight crew on this return flight wasn't having any of it.

In a statement, Southwest said it "requires all customers over the age of two to wear a face-covering or face mask while traveling to help prevent the transmission of COVID-19," and "if a customer is unable to wear a face-covering for any reason, Southwest regrets that we are unable to transport the individual." The flight turned around and kicked them off. "We got our luggage, packed up, went back through security, and paid almost $600 for an American flight home," the mother said. On that flight, she said, her son slept maskless. American Airlines doesn't require masks until age 3.[65] I flew several times during the lockdowns and spoke to some pilots and flight attendants throughout. It seems how strictly masks were enforced on flights was highly dependent on the flight crew.

There was zero science in existence that showed that two-year-olds were spreaders of or at risk of COVID-19. There was no science that showed people needed to wear masks on flights. It's one of the absolute safest places to be in this environment.

In February 2021, a New Jersey man was headed down to Tampa to work security for the Super Bowl. He tried to board his United flight wearing an elaborate filtering face mask that looked like something out of Star Wars.[66] He had just spent $85, and if you watch one of the interviews with him, he's clearly not a mask or COVID-19-denier. United would not allow his mask to be worn and made him wear one of their surgical masks. Then he was denied the ability to bring his mask on board at all and kicked off the flight.

When you see interviews with people, you can sometimes tell some are antagonistic and asking for trouble. In the case of this man and the couple who were also kicked off a United flight because their two-year-old wasn't wearing a mask, it's pretty clear from the videos that there is no reason they should have been denied service. Side note: try to find a flight that resulted in a string of hospitalizations or deaths from an illness sourced from a passenger. You'll have to go back to Patrick Dempsey's character flying to Boston in the movie *Outbreak*.

In January 2021, varsity baseball players from John Burroughs High School in Burbank, CA, took pictures as their tradition, and those pictures were posted on a team social media site. The pictures resulted in them being suspended for two weeks in March and nearly canceled their season.[67] Their crime? They posed without masks, violating state and county health orders.

The Texas Announcement

Florida reopened without a statewide mask mandate at the end of September 2020. Within that, counties and cities were able to mandate their own capacity restrictions and the wearing of masks. Some counties required masks and some did not. Governor Ron DeSantis prevented fines and penalties against those not wearing masks, but the real penalty was not being served. If you chose not to wear a mask in Orlando, you would not be allowed service at a restaurant or hotel. In most cases, hanging out at the pool was okay without a mask.

When we traveled to Jackson Hole in the summer of 2020, Teton County had a mask mandate. We were staying in Teton Village and got takeout one night. We went into the empty bar area at a lodge. The bar was closed and twenty or so tables there were completely empty. We unpacked our dinner and sat at an empty table to eat. A staff member told us we'd have to eat outside because we'd be unmasked eating. We did, no objection. Afterward, we went to the crowded indoor pool. No masks were required and none were worn. Did you know the virus spread more in an empty restaurant while eating than it did laughing, raising your voice to talk, and horsing around in a crowded indoor pool area? Meanwhile, Teton County had nine COVID-19 deaths one year into the pandemic.

Governor Greg Abbott sent shockwaves through the country when he announced on March 2, 2021, that Texas would lift all restrictions and mask mandates a week later. Further, no city or county would be able to enact their own restrictions unless COVID-19 hospitalizations exceeded 15% capacity in that area. We can debate whether that was the right number, but that is the metric that matters. Cases and death numbers, as we will see later, are very inaccurate. As a rule, the hospitalization number we see is about 2/3 caused by a real COVID-19 illness. Remember, we locked down to prevent the overflow of hospital beds, which never really happened. Certainly, a few hospitals were stretched for 3-4 weeks in many places at different times, but never were we overflowing. Texas businesses were allowed to keep their own requirements in place if they wanted. HEB announced immediately they would not require masks, and it was clear many national chains like Costco would for some time to come. Living in

Dallas, I never wore a mask again in Texas except at Costco, and I was frequently circulating.

Texas is the second-largest and most powerful state in the U.S. behind California. It's one thing when Iowa lifts all restrictions, quite another when Texas does. Nationally the U.S. had about 5% of total hospital beds occupied with CO-VID-19 patients (2/3 likely real). At what number do you go back to normal? New York City was under 1% when they would not send kids back to school in the fall of 2020. Texas lifting restrictions was the biggest step forward. President Biden called the decision by Texas and Mississippi governors "Neanderthal thinking."

If Texas remained on its trend of COVID-19 activity without masks and closures, how would other states justify it? You can picture Governor Newsom or Cuomo calling the White House or CDC in a panic. You can picture someone from the White House calling the CDC in a panic: "Do something! You must put something out that shows this is a mistake, or they're all going to open up by May 1!" Texas continued to bottom out on all COVID-19 activity. Other states followed, as did the CDC, as meekly as they could on May 13, 2021.

CDC Jumps The Shark Again

Three days after the Texas announcement, the CDC released this study: "Association of State-Issued Mask Mandates and Allowing On-Premises Restaurant Dining with County-Level COVID-19 Case and Death Growth Rates — United States, March 1–December 31, 2020."[68] Below are some key findings:

- Mask mandates were associated with decreases in daily COVID-19 case and death growth rates 1–20, 21–40, 41–60, 61–80, and 81–100 days after implementation.
- Allowing any on-premises dining at restaurants was associated with increases in daily COVID-19 case growth rates 41–60, 61–80, and 81–100 days after reopening and increases in daily COVID-19 death growth rates 61–80 and 81–100 days after reopening.
- Implementing mask mandates was associated with reduced SARS-CoV-2 transmission, whereas reopening restaurants for on-premises dining was associated with increased transmission.

How much of an increase? Twice as much? Three to four times more? Ten times more? To write a paper and publish it, it had to offer some very material differences in COVID-19 activity. They couldn't jump the shark three times in six months, could they? If you play poker at all, you can relate to the expression that the CDC became "pot-committed." They had invested so much in the lockdown pot that they had to see it through. On they went with these startling conclusions from their ten-month study on mask-wearing and indoor dining:

- Masks were associated with a .5% decrease in COVID-19 cases in days 1-20 and 1.8% in days 21-100 following mask mandates in 2,313 counties (73% of all counties). .5% and 1.8%.
- Indoor dining was associated with a 1% decrease in COVID-19 cases
- Indoor dining was associated with a ~2.6% increase in COVID-19 deaths
- "Mask mandates were associated with statistically significant decreases in county-level daily COVID-19 case and death growth rates within 20 days of implementation. Allowing on-premises restaurant dining was associated with increases in county-level case and death growth rates within 41–80 days after reopening. State mask mandates and prohibiting on-premises dining at restaurants help limit potential exposure to SARS-CoV-2, reducing community transmission of COVID-19."

The CDC is stating that not wearing masks and dining indoors caused about a one percent increase in cases and thus drew the conclusion that everyone should wear masks and not eat inside a restaurant. Any community college freshman stats student could tell you that one percent is within a margin of error and not real-world-significant. They are further concluding that these NPIs contributed an additional 2.6% in COVID-19 deaths. It doesn't pass the logic test. Half the deaths were to people at life expectancy with multiple underlying conditions. These are not people going out to dinner. You can argue that people in contact with them could've caught it and passed it on to those at risk. That is possible. This is where you encourage those individuals to practice more personal responsibility, not close hundreds of thousands of businesses indefinitely.

Most large media outlets pounced on Texas and reported on the CDC findings as justification. Here are two *New York Times* articles that ran right after the CDC study[69]:

The Virus Spread Where Restaurants Reopened or Mask Mandates Were Absent

C.D.C. researchers found that coronavirus infections and death rates rose in U.S. counties permitting in-person dining or not requiring masks.

The C.D.C. links restaurant dining and a lack of mask mandates to the virus's spread in the U.S.

March 5, 2021
By Roni Caryn Rabin

The *Washington Post* ran this headline right after the Texas order.[70]

The Washington Post
Democracy Dies in Darkness
Sections ≡

Opinion: When states unmask, we know what happens next

In it, writer James Downie wrote, "The science is clear: As [Jake] Tapper noted, a new CDC study released last week found case numbers and deaths "slowed significantly" within three weeks of mask mandates being imposed, while eased restrictions on dining increase both cases and deaths." That "slowed significantly" he referenced was the 1% decrease in cases. The media was shaping the fear in Americans. Rarely were major media outlets contextualizing the data or showing an actual balance between COVID-19 health and public health.

Actual Face Mask Science After COVID-19

On May 25, 2021, Damian D. Guerra and Daniel J. Guerra published "Mask mandate and use efficacy in state-level COVID-19 containment."[71] In *medRxiv*. This was the first study of U.S. data comparing mask efficacy and COVID-19 cases. Their conclusion was that case growth was not significantly different between areas that mandated masks and those that did not. The researchers found higher mask was not correlated to lower case growth rates, smaller surges, or less fall-winter growth at the end of 2020. They stated there is "inferential but not demonstrable evidence that face masks reduce SARS-CoV-2 transmission." This means it feels like masks should've worked and done something, but there was no data to support that feeling.

The pandemic officially ended on May 14, 2021, when the CDC removed their face mask and social distancing recommendations for those vaccinated.

Prior to the announcement, a third of the country was already completely mask-free. With the vaccines taking root and nothing adverse happening anywhere without masks, they caught up and called it a day. Almost. The CDC changed its recommendation on July 29, 2021, suggesting vaccinated individuals should wear masks. Why? Because many vaccinated people were becoming active cases. The pandemic was still over; we were nowhere near 7.4% of all deaths contributed by COVID-19. Kids were still "required" to wear them if not vaccinated, and Dr. Fauci was still recommending them for school in the fall.

Opening restaurants and lifting mask mandates should never have been a civil liberties or freedom argument. If COVID-19 was a harsh Category Five pandemic as outlined in the CDC playbook we saw, you could make a strong argument for some non-pharmaceutical interventions: some closed businesses and schools (for a while), wearing masks (if they scientifically worked), stricter social distancing and definitely quarantining the sick. With COVID-19, we had neither a category five (or four or three) pandemic nor very many interventions that worked. That this went on for a year and a half wasn't following the path of science, it was taking a detour with a machete, cutting out new territory, and ending up on the edge of a cliff.

Key Takeaways:
- Most of America wore face masks throughout the pandemic.
- COVID-19 case and death data throughout the pandemic were not reduced by wearing face masks.
- Face mask science AC (after COVID-19) was based more on opinion than actual scientific studies.
- The CDC failed America on the efficacy of face masks.

CHAPTER 4
Original Sin:
Ignoring The Cruise Ships

After writing *COVID-19: Lockdowns on Trial* in 2020, I was called to do several hundred interviews in 2020 and 2021 on the lockdowns. Nearly every interviewer began by asking me how I got involved, given my past writing work was completely unrelated to health, politics, or social issues. Each time I explained how I was following the quarantined cruise ships recreationally and that when the Imperial College model came out, the two didn't reconcile. If the model triggering the lockdowns was accurate, we should have lost 155 lives on those two cruise ships. We lost ten. It was then obvious how far off the models were. Interviewers would pause and always remark, "I never thought of that. No one ever talks about that." I wrote a piece called "Original Sin" for *Rational Ground*, and it caught so much attention on Twitter when posted that it crashed their website for the first time.

The science ignoring the data from the cruise ships was our original sin. Had we followed the cruise ship data more carefully, we would have known three things: the young and healthy were not statistically at risk; most people that contract SARS-CoV-2 don't get sick; the elderly and mostly those with underlying conditions were by far the most at risk. Much of this chapter and the next are taken from the self-published *COVID-19: Lockdowns on Trial* because they are so relevant to how we got here.

It's the mid-1980s. Many questions are swirling about HIV, the human immunodeficiency virus. Health experts, scientists, and governments around the world are all curious to learn about the spread of the virus. Dr. Fauci himself speculated in 1983 that HIV could be transmitted by skin-to-skin touch. They know it's predominately sexually transmitted. Nearly all cases at this time are between gay men, and curiosity is piqued around its ease of spread, spread within heterosexuals, and any other ways it can get from person to person.

They decided to set up a scientific experiment. They recruited 2,000 single swingers to go on a cruise for three weeks. They chose an even balance of men and women, encouraged bisexual passengers and people of all races, age 18-80.

The cruise staff of 500 was not allowed to have any sexual contact with the passengers. The ship was at sea for twenty-one days. At the end of the cruise, they interviewed each passenger and traced everyone's contact, whether sexual, skin-to-skin social touch, who participated in what, and then tested everyone when they ported in and for the next twelve months.

Can you imagine a better scientific experiment? A large, controlled environment with limited variables, it was the optimum petri dish for testing virus spread among people. No, this didn't actually happen, but it did happen by accident more than once in February 2020. Incredible insight into the spread of the virus was gained. However, little of the learnings were factored into the policy decisions leaders made and the media encouraged in March 2020.

Diamond Princess

The Diamond Princess cruise ship was first launched in 2004 by the Carnival Corporation. Carnival owns multiple cruise lines. Princess was made famous by the television show *The Love Boat* back in the 1970s and 1980s. The Diamond Princess accommodates 2,670 passengers and is supported by 1,100 crew members. It's a city on the sea if you've been—countless dining opportunities, a casino, live entertainment, multiple pools, sports activities, and interesting places to visit on the port days.

On January 20, 2020, the Diamond Princess left Yokohama, Japan, at full capacity for a fourteen-day cruise. Passengers were surely excited to visit ports in China, Vietnam, and Taiwan. On January 27, a passenger left the cruise ship in Hong Kong. That passenger was diagnosed with COVID-19 on February 1. By February 4, the cruise itinerary was canceled. On that day, ten people positive for COVID-19 were released for medical care, and by February 6, forty-one people tested positive. What followed was a near-month-long quarantine.[72]

Many in the media and medical community criticized the cruise ship quarantine. Unfairly. If you imagine being in the decision-making capacity, there are limited choices. Data was not really known about the ability to spread and the lethality of the virus. At this point, it was new to the world for thirty days and had not yet really impacted anywhere outside China. As many in the world sat locked down in their own homes from March to June 2020, pause for a moment to imagine being quarantined on a cruise ship.

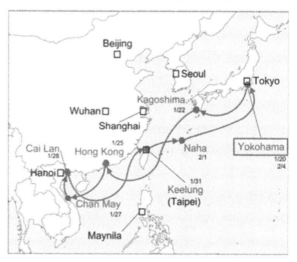

Nearly all the rooms are small. Many have balconies, but more do not. The casino is now closed. Live group entertainment is canceled. You know some portion of the people with whom you are seeing and interacting have the new virus. You don't really know how contagious or dangerous it is, but the actions taken are extreme, and you've seen *Outbreak* and *Contagion*. If there's a moment a situation seems unbearable, other than prison, it's hard to imagine something more difficult than those days. Not just the confinement but the uncertainty of what will happen.

The Center for Mathematical Modeling for Infectious Diseases performed a detailed study of the Diamond Princess passenger demographics, published on March 23, 2020.[73] Below is the make-up of the passengers:

Age	Passengers	COVID-19 Positive w/Symptoms	COVID-19 Positive w/No Symptoms	Deaths
0 - 9	16	0	1	0
10-19	23	2	3	0
20 - 29	347	25	3	0
30 - 39	428	27	7	0
40 - 49	334	19	8	0
50 - 59	398	28	31	0
60 - 69	923	76	101	0
70 - 79	1015	95	139	6
80 - 89	216	29	25	1
Totals	3711	301	318	7

The passengers and crew gave the world an unexpected gift of data about COVID-19. It was the best possible [accidental] controlled experiment a scientist could hope for to study the spread and impact of anything. From that cruise, we saw 3,711 people on board, and a quarter for certain caught COVID-19 or were carrying SARS-CoV-2. Half were asymptomatic, apparently immune to it like the millions we would see later. Seven elderly passengers died from it. Of those seven, two were an elderly Japanese couple in their 80's with underlying conditions.[74] It's very sad to see that a couple enjoying an elaborate vacation would not survive it due to this unforeseen occurrence. The other five passengers that did not survive were all over 70 as well.

This was one excellent data point. It offered up that COVID-19 is threatening to the elderly and, moreover, those with an underlying condition.

On March 27, 2020, the *Lancet* published an analysis by Dimple D Rajgor, Meng Har Lee, Sophia Archuleta, Natasha Bagdasarian, and Swee Chye Quek where they concluded the COVID-19 death rate to be a little worse than the flu but not as bad as the SARS threat a decade earlier:

> *A unique situation has arisen for quite an accurate estimate of the CFR [case fatality rate] of COVID-19. Among individuals onboard the Diamond Princess cruise ship, data on the denominator are fairly robust. The outbreak of COVID-19 led passengers to be quarantined between Jan 20 and Feb 29, 2020. This scenario provided a population living in a defined territory without most other confounders, such as imported cases, defaulters of screening, or lack of testing capability. 3,711 passengers and crew were on board, of whom 705 became sick and tested positive for COVID-19, and seven died, 6 giving a CFR of 0·99%. If the passengers onboard were generally of an older age, the CFR in a healthy, younger population could be lower.*
>
> *Although highly transmissible, the CFR of COVID-19 appears to be lower than that of SARS (9·5%) and Middle East respiratory syndrome (34·4%), but higher than that of influenza (0·1%).*[75]

The Grand Princess

The Grand Princess launched in 1997. I've been on one cruise on this ship, and I recall it was the second voyage of the Grand Princess, the largest cruise ship at that time. We took a cruise in the Mediterranean Sea, beginning in Istanbul and ending in Venice. It was a great experience, though cramped in our lower interior room. We had three channels on the little television: a movie channel, a BBC news channel, and a channel looping *The Love Boat* episodes, unfortunately the same six episodes for twelve days. The cost of my cruise was bumped with my almost-daily $200 donation at the blackjack table.

The Grand Princess is about the same capacity as the Diamond Princess. On February 11, 2020, the ship sailed out of San Francisco/Oakland to several ports in Mexico. It returned to San Francisco for the next voyage on February 21, bound for Hawaii, Mexico, and back to the Bay area. On March 14, 2020, the *Guardian* had a very appropriate headline about this cruise:

"From Paradise To Coronavirus: The Grand Princess And The Cruise From Hell"[76]

A 71-year-old man from California disembarked the February 11 cruise positive with COVID-19 and passed it on to passengers or crew on the February 21 cruise. The *Guardian* reported that the cruise infection was connected to the first positive-tested American from Washington state. About sixty passengers remained on the ship from the February 11 cruise to the February 21 cruise. Back-to-back cruises on the same ship? Those cruise lovers must have had their fill for a lifetime by the time this was over weeks later.

On March 4, that elderly man from the first cruise died, and the overlap passengers were quarantined by the ship to their rooms. Imagine that experience for a moment. 2,500 passengers able to move about except you. You're not sure what you may have. You're getting spotty news reports and you have to contend with that confined to a four hundred square foot cabin room.

By now, all passengers knew a bit of what was going on. Again, for the non-quarantined passengers, you don't know how serious it is, but it's something big. It's all over the news. You're out of control. You walk around the ship and look at each passenger as if they may be a contagious leper. You see the food you get, and before eating, you're thinking it was prepared by staff from the previous cruise, sharing rooms, handling your food. You walk up and down stairs and double-take at the handrails. You opt to take an elevator, look at the buttons, and put your finger behind your sleeve to touch a button.

You go to your room, stare at the four walls, you turn on the television. The news channel is pounding information on the very crisis you are in. You've exhausted the content on the other channels. You're glued to information, but it all feels unsettling. Anxiety is building, and while it's not solitary confinement in prison, to a non-prisoner, it feels that way.

The ship stayed at sea in the Pacific for four days awaiting its fate by the U.S. government. Anyone stuck in a plane for an hour or two looping around in bad weather waiting to land knows the anxiety. This was for days. It's not as confined as an airplane but factoring in the length of time and uncertainty of the virus, a much worse experience.

When the ship entered the San Francisco Bay on March 9, it was covered on the news like the Bronco chase decades earlier. News media painted a picture as if the leper colony from *Ben-Hur* was porting in. But what was actually discovered? Hundreds were tested, hundreds declined to be tested. Those testing positive or declining tests were sent to be quarantined at various military bases around the country. According to the CDC, 469 people were tested and 16% (78) were positive.[77] Two people, both in their sixties and together, died by the end of the month. Later a Philippine crew member died in early April.

Two cruise ships offered very controlled environments to observe the spread and impact of the virus. There was a medium spread of a virus that we would learn was more contagious than seasonal flu viruses. It's aggressive to the elderly and those with underlying conditions, primarily respiratory-related, and leaves the younger age groups with flu-like or no symptoms. Later data would show this was much less dangerous to young people than the flu.

The Ruby Princess

The Ruby Princess was launched in 2008 and is about the same size as the Diamond and Grand Princess ships. The Ruby was the third Princess cruise that experienced an outbreak of COVID-19. An estimated 2,647 passengers and another thousand crew members boarded the ship on March 8, 2020, in Sydney, Australia, on their way to New Zealand for a thirteen-day cruise.[78] 900 of the guests were from overseas, the rest Australians. Before they left, a few hundred were spot tested for COVID-19 and the tests came back negative.[79]

On March 15, the Australian government announced they were ordering fourteen-day quarantine for those entering from another country. The ship decided that evening to get back to Sydney as soon as possible. It ported in on March 19. The number of passengers with ILI (influenza-like-illness) was about 1%, not terribly alarming. The passengers, some symptomatic from something and some already testing positive for COVID-19, all went about their way from Sydney. Many were from Australia, and many flew off around the world.

The data from the Ruby Princess is much looser than that from the Grand or Diamond cruises. The Ruby was not quarantined and much of the data was pieced together after the fact, where other variables could have impacted the results. Still, it's one more interesting piece of pre-lockdown data. By April 2, a third of the Australian passengers had tested positive for COVID-19. This could include (and likely did for some) infections that occurred after the cruise. The ship's crew remained on board and eighteen of the 1,000 members tested positive, a very low and almost unbelievable percentage considering the circumstances.

The reported death toll "associated" with this cruise was twenty-eight. The data is very loose on cause and effect, but does suggest a higher toll than the tighter records from the Diamond and Grand Princesses.

The Aircraft Carriers

Life on an aircraft carrier is in no way similar to the experience of taking a cruise vacation. Sailors are living in cramped quarters practicing whatever the opposite of social distancing is. Hallways are cramped and staircases are like going up and down Teewinot. Most are working long days and not going to the flight deck to enjoy the fresh air breeze and ocean views. The flight decks are restricted and potentially dangerous, so only required authorized personnel go above deck. Windy conditions and airflow from the jets create a risky environment requiring much training and structure for the sailors. The flight deck perches sixty-five feet above the ocean.

USS Theodore Roosevelt

In late March, the USS Theodore Roosevelt ported into Guam and announced a few dozen sailors tested positive for SARS-CoV-2 or COVID-19. Nearly 5,000 people were on board, larger than either of the cruise

ship populations. In stark contrast, these were predominantly very healthy, fit young men and women. This provided a very different and still controlled petri dish study on the spread and impact of COVID-19. 1,271 sailors ended up testing positive for SARS-CoV-2.[80]

76% of those sailors were asymptomatic at the time of testing. Over the course of the study period, 55% showed some kind of symptom. The remaining sailors had no symptoms for the entire study period. Six sailors were hospitalized. A 41-year-old petty officer died from complications associated with COVID-19 after being found unresponsive while in isolation housing during a medical check.[81] Reporting has not identified if he had underlying conditions. A Department of Defense inspector general found the ship to be in violation of social distancing throughout the outbreak. Not sure how you effectively social distance close to 5,000 people on an aircraft carrier with the conditions just looser than a submarine.

Four of the U.S Navy ships wound up with coronavirus breakouts, with one death and thousands testing positive. This is another sampling of the virus acting like an aggressive flu strain but not any more dangerous to the young and healthy. The USS Theodore Roosevelt data was not critically analyzed by leaders supporting lockdowns. The data showed it would not be a significant hospitalization and death threat to the young and healthy.

Charles de Gaulle

In mid-April 2020, the French announced their aircraft carrier, Charles de Gaulle with 2,000 crew members, had been infected with the virus. After testing over 1,700 of the sailors, 1,121 tested positive for SARS-CoV-2.[82] 24% were asymptomatic. Thirty-one were hospitalized and one was in intensive care. None died.

If you take the data from the cruise ships and aircraft carriers, a broad sampling of ages and health conditions, you have about 14,000 people exposed and eleven fatalities. The rate of infection would be much less than that in the general population. At that rate, of the 326,000,000 Americans, we would experience a likely fatality rate of about .07%. That translates to about 228,000 predictive COVID-19 deaths in the United States. I calculated that in April 2020 in *Lockdowns on Trial*. That number is nearly spot on to the COVID-19-caused excess deaths one year through the pandemic. Would Americans have supported the shutdown of society and the economy for a year for a Category Two pandemic? Or, would they have forged on and isolated those that mirrored the eleven that lost their lives?

CHAPTER 5
The Models

Imperial College

The Imperial Institute was created in 1887 in London as a graduation of the Westminster Hospital Medical School in 1834, the Royal College of Chemistry in 1845, and St. Mary's Hospital Medical School in 1854. Imperial College was officially founded in 1907. *Top Universities* ranked Imperial as the ninth-best university in the world with a large emphasis on science and medicine.[83] *U.S. News and World Report* ranked Imperial twentieth worldwide.[84] In 2020, Imperial had a student body of around 20,000, about half in graduate work and half in undergraduate.

Professor Neil Ferguson was the Vice-Dean at the Faculty of Medicine, School of Public Health at Imperial College in 2020. Ferguson achieved a master's in physics from Lady Margaret Hall, Oxford, and a doctorate in theoretical physics at Linacre College, Oxford. Ferguson has been considered a mathematical and epidemiology expert and authority since his early 30's (born in 1968).

When the swine flu broke out in 2009, he wrote a piece for the *Lancet* called "Closure of schools during an influenza pandemic."[85] In it, he opined on school closures as a way to mitigate the spread of the flu and wrote on the opportunity costs on health care workers (for example, figuring out childcare while caring for the sick). Side question: did you notice throughout all the school closures, they talked more about logistics, lunches, etc. more than lost education? Within academic standards, Ferguson was considered a genius at epidemiology and mathematical modeling.

A theory or model embraced by many epidemiologists is called "herd immunity." That happens when enough of the population develops natural or vaccinated immunity and there just aren't enough people to keep spreading it. The infected are cared for if necessary, recover, develop antibodies for the virus and then won't spread it or be symptomatic in the future. Controlled herd immunity is when a subset of the population is allowed to or will catch a virus and develop immunity in a tiered way, so not everyone in a community catches it at once and overwhelms the healthcare system, and stunts the spread to the vulnerable.

Flashback for a moment to 2005. In 2005, there was a breakout of the H5N1 bird flu. Back then, David Nabarro was a senior expert at the World Health Organization. The *Guardian* reported then that Nabarro said the outbreak, which had killed a few dozen people in Asia, could result in a "range of deaths could be anything between five and 150 million."[86] In the same article, Neil Ferguson is quoted with his analysis below.

Quoting the *Guardian*, "Last month Neil Ferguson, a professor of mathematical biology at Imperial College London, told *Guardian Unlimited* that up to 200 million people could be killed. Around 40 million people died in the 1918 Spanish flu outbreak, said Prof. Ferguson. There are six times more people on the planet now, so you could scale it up to around 200 million people probably."[87]

Reaching back a little further in 2002, there was a potential disease associated with BSE-infected cows and potentially sheep. Professor Ferguson was conducting analysis then and shared this: "Our latest analysis shows that the current risk from sheep could be greater than that from cattle, due to the more intensive controls in place to protect human health from exposure to infected cattle, as compared with sheep. The Imperial College team predicted that the future number of deaths from Creutzfeldt-Jakob disease (vCJD) due to exposure to BSE in beef was likely to lie between 50 and 50,000. In the "worst-case" scenario of a growing sheep epidemic, the range of future numbers of death increased to between 110,000 and 150,000."[88] It never happened.

Imperial College COVID-19 Model

Ferguson authored a COVID-19 model in early March 2020, predicting 500,000 deaths in Great Britain and 2,200,000 deaths in America unless the populations enacted strict social distancing, broad testing, and quarantining for those positive with the virus. It became the foundational document and roadmap for Great Britain and the United States, countries that would effectively lock down their citizens to prevent an overwhelming of healthcare facilities all at once.

According to an Imperial College analysis on March 17, they interpreted the model as follows:

In the first scenario, they show that interventions could slow down the spread of the infection but would not completely interrupt its spread. They found this would reduce the demand on the healthcare system while protecting those most at risk of severe disease. Such epidemics are predicted to peak over a three to four-month period during the spring/summer.

In the second scenario, more intensive interventions could interrupt transmission and reduce case numbers to low levels. However, once these interventions are relaxed, case numbers are predicted to rise. This gives rise to lower case numbers, but the risk of a later epidemic in the winter months unless the interventions can be sustained.[89]

As we look at the model in assumptions and its output, here's a quick explanation. Ferguson and his team are among the most expert in this field. It's also easy to pick apart a model that falls apart after the fact. We've all made scaled-to-our-expertise models and assumptions that have failed. We've all had criticism of our work.

The Imperial College report called "Report 9: Impact of non-pharmaceutical interventions (NPIs) to reduce COVID-19 mortality and healthcare demand" opens with a callout that the COVID-19 pandemic is the most serious since the Spanish Flu.[90] Options were only suppression and mitigation. Suppression basically says the goal is to limit the reproduction of the virus spread, eliminating person-to-person contact. Mitigation doesn't focus on the spread, but the treatment through drugs, vaccines, etc., as a means to limit the impact.

The Imperial College predicted in a do-nothing scenario more than 500,000 COVID-19 deaths in Great Britain and 2,200,000 in the United States, both peaking in June 2020. Below is their chart, the lower line being the United States. For quick math translation, 17 deaths per 100,000 per day in the United States is over 50,000 deaths per day.

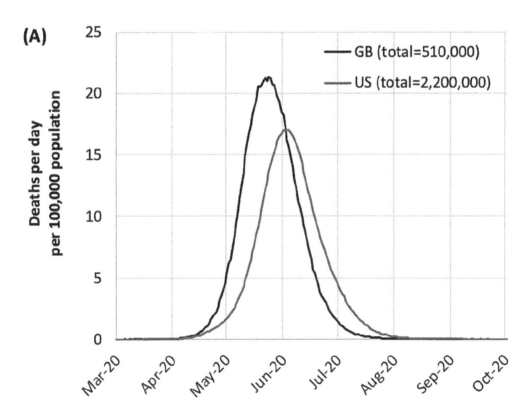

Model Assumptions

- *We assumed an incubation period of 5.1 days. Infectiousness is assumed to occur from 12 hours prior to the onset of symptoms for those that are symptomatic and from 4.6 days after infection in those that are asymptomatic with an infectiousness profile over time that results in a 6.5-day mean generation time.*

- *On recovery from infection, individuals are assumed to be immune to reinfection in the short term.*

- *Infection was assumed to be seeded in each country [GB and US] at an exponentially growing rate (with a doubling time of 5 days) from early January 2020, with the rate of seeding being calibrated to give local epidemics which reproduced the observed cumulative number of deaths in GB or the U.S. seen by 14th March 2020.*

- *We assume that 30% of those that are hospitalized will require critical care (invasive mechanical ventilation or ECMO) based on early reports from COVID-19 cases in the UK, China, and Italy (Professor Nicholas Hart, personal communication).*

- *Based on expert clinical opinion, we assume that 50% of those in critical care will die and an age-dependent proportion of those that do not require critical care die (calculated to match the overall IFR).*

- *We calculate bed demand numbers assuming a total duration of stay in the hospital of 8 days if critical care is not required and 16 days (with 10 days in ICU) if critical care is required. With 30% of hospitalized cases requiring critical care, we obtain an overall mean duration of hospitalization of 10.4 days, slightly shorter than the duration from hospital admission to discharge observed for COVID-19 cases internationally13 (who will have remained in hospital longer to ensure negative tests at discharge) but in line with estimates for general pneumonia admissions.*

- *Infection was assumed to be seeded in each country at an exponentially growing rate (with a doubling time of 5 days) from early January 2020, with the rate of seeding being calibrated to give local epidemics which reproduced the observed cumulative number of deaths in GB or the U.S. seen by 14th March 2020.*

- *In the (unlikely) absence of any control measures or spontaneous changes in individual behavior, we would expect a peak in mortality (daily deaths) to occur after approximately 3 months. In such scenarios, we predict 81% of the GB and U.S. populations would be infected over the course of the epidemic.*

Below are the mathematical projections for hospitalizations and deaths applied to the United States in that do-nothing scenario:

Age-group (years)	% Symptomatic cases requiring hospitalization	% Hospitalized cases requiring critical care	Infection Fatality Ratio	Total U.S. Population	Fatalities
0-9	0.1%	5.0%	0.002%	40,000,000	648
10-19	0.3%	5.0%	0.006%	42,000,000	2,041
20-29	1.2%	5.0%	0.03%	45,400,000	11,032
30-39	3.2%	5.0%	0.08%	43,700,000	28,318
40-49	4.9%	6.3%	0.15%	40,600,000	49,329
50-59	10.2%	12.2%	0.6%	42,800,000	208,008
60-69	16.6%	27.40%	2.2%	37,300,000	664,686
70-79	24.3%	43.2%	5.1%	22,700,000	937,737
80+	27.3%	70.9%	9.3%	12,700,000	956,691

Population data from Statista1: https://www.statista.com/statistics/241488/population-of-the-us-by-sex-and-age/

Not all the model assumptions are easily available. One assumption was that 81% of the population would end up infected. In applying their assumptions to the U.S. population, it predicts a worst-case scenario of 2.8 MM deaths. Imperial College came up with 2.2MM deaths. Uncovering exactly how the 2.2MM number was derived is not broken down in the model released on March 17. The code behind the model was later identified as flawed in a peer group review. On the next page is their model predicting hospitalizations compared to capacity in the United States. If you look at the "Do nothing" line, you can see a peak need for critical care (ICU) hospital beds of approximately 900,000 at one time (~275 x (326,000,000 U.S. population/per 100,000 people)). Even with social distancing, case isolation, quarantining, closing schools, and more, about 300,000 ICU beds would be needed on the peak day.

US Hospital Capacity

According to the American Hospital Association, the United States had the following 2020 hospital capacity:

- **6,146** - total number of all U.S. hospitals
- **924,107** - total staffed beds
- **55,663** - medical-surgical intensive care 4 beds
- **15,160** - cardiac intensive care 5 beds
- **22,721** - neonatal intensive care 6 beds
- **5,115** - pediatric intensive care 7 beds

- **7,419** - other intensive care 9 beds
- **36,353,946** - total annual admissions in all U.S. hospitals

US hospitals had a total of 924,107 staffed beds and around 90,000 ICU beds in 2020.

Can you see the three-fold ICU shortfall in a best-case scenario and ten-fold shortfall in a do-nothing scenario? This is exactly what led government leaders to panic and not just lockdown businesses and schools, but hospitals and all non-emergency non-COVID-19-related treatment.

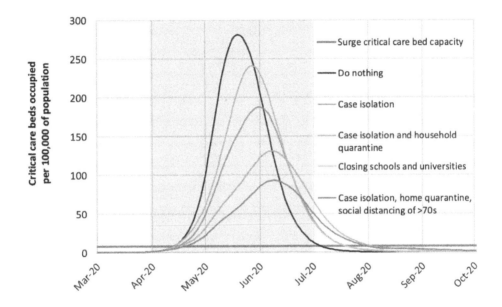

The lines in descending order are: do nothing; closing schools and universities; case isolation; case isolation and household quarantine; case isolation, home quarantine, social distancing of those over 70, and the bottom flat line is ICU capacity.

We later saw this gross miscalculation is what triggered the economic collapse as well as a collapse of the healthcare industry. Hospitals went empty nearly everywhere other than the greater New York City area and a handful in Detroit and New Orleans for about three weeks, creating a vacuum of revenues lost and thousands of healthcare workers laid off, and millions going without their non-COVID-19 treatments. In the summer of 2020, several southern states got their "wave," never stretched over capacity. In the winter of 2020-2021, COVID-19 hospitalizations reached their pandemic peak, about 132,000 at their highest. That represented less than 15% of all national capacity. The major flaw in the model? They did not realize the very high majority of healthy infected Americans would never see the inside of a hospital.

Cruise Ship Comparison

However, that model seems implausible given one important actual study we all had access to before this model came out: the cruise ships. The cruise ships provided a perfect analysis of how the virus spreads, who is likely to get infected, hospitalized, and who is not likely to survive. Ignoring that data went on to creating the worst world social and economic collapse in American history. Going back to the data from the Diamond Princess cruise ship, this is the age stratification spread of the virus:

Age	Passengers	COVID-19 Positive w/ Symptoms	COVID-19 Positive w/No Symptoms	Deaths
0 - 9	16	0	1	0
10-19	23	2	3	0
20 - 29	347	25	3	0
30 - 39	428	27	7	0
40 - 49	334	19	8	0
50 - 59	398	28	31	0
60 - 69	923	76	101	0
70 - 79	1015	95	139	6
80 - 89	216	29	25	1
Totals	3700	301	318	7

The data above is for the Diamond Princess only. Specifics for the Grand Princess are not released at this level of detail because many did not test. Given the two cruises had nearly identical populations of guests and crew, for this exercise, let's extrapolate and double the population spreads of the Diamond Princess to represent both, adding in three deaths from the Grand Princess.

Age	Combined Passengers	Actual Cruise Ship Deaths	Imperial College Predictive Deaths
0-9	32	0	0
10-19	46	0	0
20-29	694	0	0
30-39	856	0	1
40-49	668	0	1
50-59	796	1	4
60-69	1846	2	33
70-79	2030	6	84
80-89	432	1	33
Totals	7400	10	155

Based on the Imperial College infection rate of .81 and their fatality rate of each age group, the Diamond Princess and Grand Princess cruise ships should have resulted in 155 deaths. Remember, the Imperial College worst-case scenario was in a do-nothing action. This is effectively what happened on the cruise ships because they were infected and spreading before practicing distancing/quarantining and had inferior mitigation capabilities compared to the experience one with symptomatic conditions would receive.

According to the *Telegraph*, Professor Ferguson's "report so shook the Prime Minister and his advisers that it reportedly prompted them to shift tack, moving from gradually attempting to achieve "herd immunity" to a lockdown of most businesses, with people only allowed to leave their homes under limited circumstances."[91]

Based perhaps on the Imperial College model, *U.S. News and World Report* reported on March 30, 2020, the following:

- "A person's odds for death after infection with the new coronavirus also rose with age. An estimated 0.031% of people in their 20s will die, the new analysis found, compared to 7.8% of people over 80."[92]
- 7.8% of people over 80: 990,000 deaths.
- .031% of people in their 20's: 14,075 deaths.

Someone's laptop needed to be taken away. Or maybe they should take a cruise.

In an ironic closure to Professor Ferguson's role in the pandemic and lockdowns, Ferguson himself violated the UK lockdown and quarantine order he lectured the public about many times. He met on more than one occasion a married woman with whom he was having an affair, resigning in disgrace on May 5, 2020. On June 2, 2020, Ferguson commented on Sweden's lack of lockdown compared to Great Britain's severe lockdown. His conclusion was that Sweden had the "same effect" as countries that did lockdowns, invalidating the effectiveness of the lockdowns.[93]

Oxford University

Sunetra Gupta is a professor of Theoretical Epidemiology at Oxford University's Department of Zoology. Gupta graduated from Princeton University in 1987 and later with a doctorate from Imperial College. Shortly after the Imperial College model was released and acted upon, Gupta led an Oxford study refuting the conclusions and predicted the COVID-19 impact would be much less devastating, releasing this just one week after the release of the Imperial College model.

Two core assumptions made the Oxford model much more conservative. First, they assumed only 0.1% of the population was in a high-risk category. Second, they believed that the first transmissions occurred days before the first case was detected. They also concluded that the epidemics in Italy and the UK began at least a month before the first reported deaths and had already inched toward herd immunity.[94]

What that means is that the UK and, soon to follow, the United States, would enact lockdown measures when the curve was already secured. Reality ended up supporting this model. By the time the United States was locked down, in an effort to slow down the curve, the spring curve was already set in motion.

The curve talked about is the steep curve in the models above ICU capacity that could overwhelm hospitals. This panic is what caused healthcare and political leaders to rush for ventilators and get a Navy ship to New York to cover hospital bed shortfalls. In the end, only the New York City area was overwhelmed while still not running out of hospital beds and having thousands of ventilators to spare.

As a researcher without medical training, studying this has been a fascinating journey. You will often hear people in the media and in social circles dismiss anyone's opinion if they are not a "subject matter expert." You hear this all the time from the media and from partisan critics. But still, did the model that triggered our economies and schools to shut down and disrupt life of world-history proportions ever make sense? Perhaps being so close to a situation can prevent looking at data and models objectively, looking at conclusions, and asking, *does this make sense?*

The data out of Wuhan was spotty early on, it may be forever in what is widely released. But the data from the cruise ships told us there was no way that there was a materially vulnerable group other than the elderly or those with specific comorbidities.

Using the word "materially" is a touchy word to use, but it's not fair to 1) play odds for other illnesses and solutions while factoring in a macro-impact, which the medical community and government do all the time, and 2) make the grandest domestic decision in United States history that would crush economies, put tens of millions out of work, prompt domestic violence, stunt student learning, and have countless other impacts.

There is a scene in the movie, *WarGames*, near the end when the missiles were on radar heading for the United States. Barry Corbin's character, General Jack Beringer, was ready to release U.S. missiles on the Soviet Union in response, real missile launches. The man that created the wargames was John Wood's character, Dr. Stephen Falken. He leaned into the General and asked if this made any sense and encouraged him to hold off. General Beringer decided it did not make sense and did not launch the missiles. Unfortunately, though it did not make sense for the United States to usher in such severe countermeasures, those missiles were launched. Incredibly, the overstated model predicting would continue on.

Changing the Model

Just hours after Oxford released their model, suggesting this would not be the catastrophic event Imperial predicted, Imperial revised their model down to 20,000 deaths in the UK, with Professor Ferguson qualifying it by stating that half of those victims would probably have died in 2020 of other causes anyway.

On March 25, 2020, a day after Gupta's findings were circulated, Ferguson changed his modeling. Not a tweak, but drastically. *New Scientist* reported on March 25 (March 25!) that Ferguson said "expected increases in National Health Service capacity and ongoing restrictions to people's movements make him 'reasonably confident' the health service can cope when the predicted peak of the epidemic arrives in two or three weeks. UK deaths from the disease are now unlikely to exceed 20,000, he said, and could be much lower."[95]

In one week's time, one of the most elite and brightest scientists in the world (no sarcasm, he was revered as that) changed his forecast from 500,000 deaths to 20,000 or "much lower," reduced by a factor of 25. It's impossible to accept that social distancing could have such an impact on a model in a week's time.

The timeline for infection to symptoms to hospitalizations to intensive care to death is 10 to 20 or more days. If the model was credible from the beginning, it would take at least two cycles of this to dent it, which means at least a month's time, to see if social distancing was working. The reason is that pre-social distancing infections were in motion.

Professors Dr. Eran Bendavid and Dr. Jay Bhattacharya from Stanford University published an article on March 24 in the *Washington Examiner* with a highly skeptical view of the Imperial model and opined that fear was based on bad data rather than probability modeling:

> *So if 100 million Americans ultimately get the disease, two million to four million could die. We believe that estimate is deeply flawed. The true fatality rate is the portion of those infected who die, not the deaths from identified positive cases.[96]*

> *The professors cited data from Iceland, China, the United States, and Italy, which is arguably the hardest-hit region when it comes to the coronavirus.*

> *On March 6, all 3,300 people of Vò were tested, and 90 were positive, a prevalence of 2.7%," the professors said. "Applying that prevalence to the whole province (population 955,000), which had 198 reported cases, suggests there were actually 26,000 infections at that time. That's more than 130-fold the number of actual reported cases. Since Italy's case fatality rate of 8% is estimated using the confirmed cases, the real fatality rate could, in fact, be closer to 0.06%.*

> *A universal quarantine may not be worth the costs it imposes on the economy, community, and individual mental and physical health. We should undertake immediate steps to evaluate the empirical basis of the current lockdowns.*

> *The conclusions drawn in that article played out spot-on a year later.*

The Institute for Health Metrics and Evaluation (IHME)

The Institute for Health Metrics and Evaluation (IHME) self-describes as an "independent population health research center at UW Medicine, part of the University of Washington, that provides rigorous and comparable measurement of the world's most important health problems and evaluates the strategies used to address them. IHME makes this information freely available so that policymakers have the evidence they need to make informed decisions about how to allocate resources to best improve population health."

The IHME became an authority of modeling that policymakers used as the United States entered its lockdown (the Imperial College Model prompted the lockdowns) and considered options and likely outcomes.[97] The IMHE model whitepaper detailed their assumptions and predictions on March 30, 2020.[98]

On March 29, 2020, the IHME released a projection of the resources required from that date through the summer of 2020. In it (chart on next page), they predicted a peak resource need on April 14, 2020. On that summit date, they predicted a need for 232,298 hospital beds, with a shortage of 49,292, and 34,754 ICU beds with an ICU bed shortage of 14,601. Also required were 18,767 invasive ventilators. Given the capacity listed previously, it's not clear where they saw the huge shortfall.

The IHME model predicted a COVID-19-related death total of anywhere from a low of 38,000 to a high of 162,000. When I saw that, it seemed low; I was calculating about 238,000 deaths then, but did not consider the effect on long-term care facilities. As an American locked down at the end of March, we're watching the news daily and hearing that just two weeks away, we will be crunched with a shortage of hospital capacity and ventilators, an early suspected reason Italy had so many deaths - not enough ventilators.

The closest thing to this model that many Americans are used to is seeing a massive, wide category-five hurricane hurling toward the coast days away, but you.

You can't leave your beachfront home made of straw. You see it coming and you helplessly wait with no actions you can take to prevent it. There just isn't enough time. Except, it would end up a category-two hurricane for the United States. On April 1, the model predicted New York state would have 50,000 hospitalizations, while in reality, they had 12,226 on April 1, a shortfall by a factor of four.[99] Again, you've got a time lapse between infection and hospitalization and then death. That gap is 10-14 days.

The model was rolled out based on data before the lockdowns occurred. If

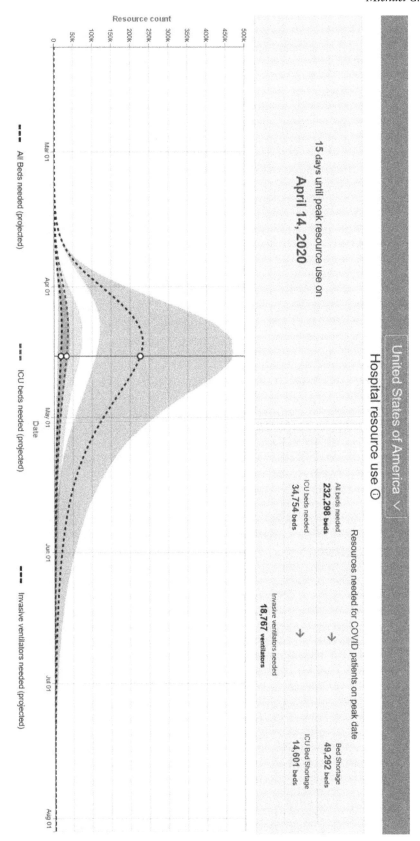

you lock down on March 20 (New York), the wheels from previous normal social behavior would be in motion. Therefore, hospitalizations and death should be close to something predictive and a curve softening would not be realized until the second or later weeks in April. If reality does not deliver, the model inputs or assumptions are flawed.

The *New York Times* reported on April 1 that the "number of confirmed or suspected coronavirus patients at Cedars-Sinai has grown from about 50 on March 17 to about 115 as of [March 31]."[100] This is a major hospital in Los Angeles with 886 hospital beds. California locked down its state on March 20. Twelve days after the largest state in America locked down, they saw, in a major hospital in a major city, an increase of about five hospitalizations per day. Five. Hospitalizations. Per. Day. On top of that, the growth was flat, not exponential like models predicted.

Remember, considering infections occur, a few days pass, then you go to the hospital, any normal pre-social distancing interactions would be accounted for. Also, remember, cases were not hospitalizations. It did not mean people were sick. They are positive tests where there may be no or only casual symptoms. Non-hospitalized cases are good things; they drive the denominator (deaths/those infected) down and illustrate a lower lethality to the infection.

Models in Play

On April 2, 2020, the IHME predicted 56,000 New York state hospitalizations and 11,000 ICU beds, while the reality was 13,400 hospitalizations and 3,400 ICU beds used. The actual data seen was collapsing to a fraction of the predictions within days, even the same day.

April 4, 2020: the IHME predicted for New York state 65,400 hospitalizations and 12,000 ICU beds while the reality was 15,905 hospitalizations and 4,100 ICU beds used. The model was consistent with the April 2 model data but shockingly not adjusting for reality. Keep in mind the IHME model from the University of Washington created these projections after and accounting for lockdowns, including in New York on March 20.

Imagine following the Major League Baseball (MLB) channel. They are predicting the outcome of a game, but not updating their prediction or presenting the score *during* the game. It would take all of a minute for baseball fans to lose confidence in them, either because they weren't updating the actual score or weren't adjusting outcomes based on what was going on during the game. Perhaps Jonah Hill's character in the movie, *Moneyball*, should join the CDC or IHME.

April 5, 2020: the IMHE model began adjusting data a little more to reality. It reduced the number of peak hospitalizations from 262,000 to 141,000, a 46% reduction in days! ICU needs were reduced from a peak of 39,700 to 29,200, cut by a quarter. Pause for just a moment to consider how large a 46% reduction in hospital capacity needs really is. In a week, their prediction was cut almost in half. By now, the model was factoring in lockdown measures, and by this date, the course had been set to where lockdowns and social distancing would barely have kicked in yet. The current state and model adjustment did not make sense if they believed in the first model.

Two days later, the IMHE model revised its data again and new projections were: hospitalizations reduced from 141,000 down to 90,000 and deaths reduced from 80,000 to 60,000. At this point, we are now in the territory of fewer COV-ID-19 deaths than the flu season two years prior, though that was never realistic. America is now locked down with a depression-level economic ruin as a fallout of state policies.

The death estimation of 60,000 was as absurd as the high estimation of hospital bed usage. Why? Data from the cruise ships. On a one-page piece of paper and the calculator on my phone, I came up with 238,000 likely deaths. Not factoring in nursing home deaths, it was the most accurate prediction we had. If you take the likely real number of COVID-19 deaths we will examine later and subtract long-term-care-facility deaths, this was laser-accurate. It did not occur to me in April 2020 when I modeled that nursing homes would be as ravaged as they were. That is documented in *Lockdowns on Trial* published early summer 2020, no revisionism here.

IHME Models in 4th Quarter 2020

The IHME made later model projections in 2020. The absurdity continued. Below is their late 2020 model predicting Sweden to experience essentially a redux of the spring in the winter of 2020-2021 if they, well, do what they had been doing all along. On that, they were fairly accurate. The chart of Sweden's COVID-19 deaths is below. The absurd part is that universal masking would flatten the death curve to about zero. Why? Because the death data in other strictly masked countries had an identical curve. If masks were effective at blocking COVID-19, why did other countries mandating them not do better?

In America, the IHME predicted that without universal mask-wearing and

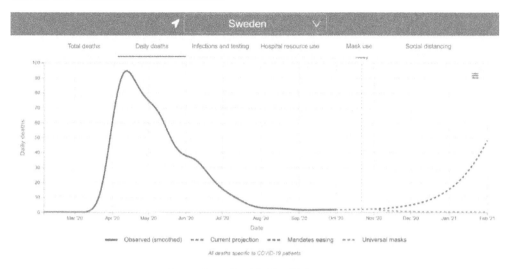

Source: https://covid19.healthdata.org

an easing of lockdowns, we will experience daily deaths of COVID-19 far in excess of the spring. In the fourth quarter of 2020 and the first quarter of 2021, Americans wore masks in indoor settings about 90% of the time. Schools were closed in most places. Where open, fewer than 50% of the students attended face-to-face. NPIs the IHME said were needed to avoid the curves below were in action. And still, the hospitalization prediction in the models below were nearly spot-on even with all the NPIs used.

In early 2021, the United States peaked with 132,000 COVID-19 hospital-

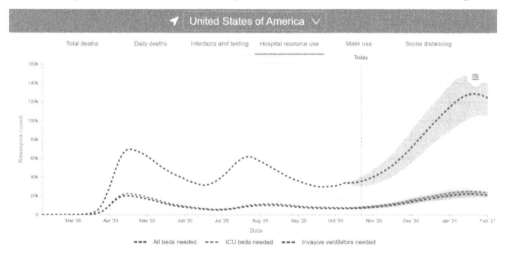

Source: https://covid19.healthdata.org

izations.[101] Their hospitalization modeling was accurate, but for some reason, their modeling grossly overstated the impact masks had on this in America, in Sweden, and everywhere. Mask-wearing simply did not impact the infections, hospitalizations, and deaths. We wish it did. It would have been an easy fix. The data just doesn't support it anywhere.

With masks adopted and worn in 90% of America, we did reach a death rate

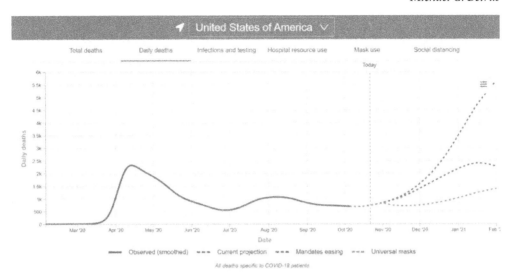

Source: https://covid19.healthdata.org

close to the "Current projection" trend line above. The model projection above suggested half the number of deaths realized with universal masks. The data just never showed suppressed COVID-19 activity by wearing masks.

May 6 IHME Revelation

The IHME changed its modeling and view of COVID-19 mortality on May 6, 2021. "Estimation of total mortality due to COVID-19"[102] was their post-pandemic analysis of total COVID-19 deaths. The modeling report begins with, "As of today, we are switching to a new approach that relies on the estimation of total mortality due to COVID-19." At a time when the official COVID-19 death count in the U.S. was about 600,000, the IHME stated actual COVID-19 mortality was over 900,000. They are subtly suggesting actual COVID-19 deaths may be even lower than the 400,000 estimated here.

Their assumptions: "Excess mortality is influenced by six drivers of all-cause mortality that relate to the pandemic and the social distancing mandates that came with the pandemic. These six drivers are:

1. The total COVID-19 death rate, that is, all deaths directly related to CO-VID-19 infection.
2. The increase in mortality due to needed health care being delayed or deferred during the pandemic.
3. The increase in mortality is due to increases in mental health disorders, including depression, increased alcohol use, and increased opioid use.
4. The reduction in mortality due to decreases in injuries because of general reductions in mobility associated with social distancing mandates.
5. The reductions in mortality are due to reduced transmission of other

viruses, most notably influenza, respiratory syncytial virus, and measles.

6. The reductions in mortality due to some chronic conditions, such as cardiovascular disease and chronic respiratory disease that occur when frail individuals who would have died from these conditions died earlier from COVID-19 instead."

What they did was batch all deaths attributed to COVID-19 and the lockdowns together as an overall pandemic loss. They attributed at least 300,000 and up to 500,000 excess deaths to the pandemic, but not the COVID-19 disease. You can see they are recognizing a material number of lockdown deaths due to delayed healthcare and deaths of despair. We will never know the exact number of deaths caused because of COVID-19 and how many were caused by the lockdowns. What we do know is the latter number is huge, and the lockdowns did not work to suppress the first number.

CHAPTER 6
The United States Locks Down

On February 1, 2020, Americans woke up to headlines that flights to and from China were canceled over some virus from Wuhan, China. Still, most Americans were not thinking about SARS-CoV-2. The Super Bowl was the evening of February 2, and Kansas City fans finally found peace of mind. The sports world was still reeling from Kobe Bryant's untimely passing. The Democrats were beginning the process to select their presidential nominee and that was consuming news. Socialist populist Bernie Sanders was looking like the sure bet to win that nomination and challenge Donald Trump for the presidency in November.

Many countries ceased flights to and from China, Taiwan, and Hong Kong. Still, it was viewed at the time as more preventive than anything. On February 3, 2020, the *New York Times* ran an article with this sub-headline: "The C.D.C. is testing three patients in the city for coronavirus. Should New Yorkers be worried, and what could happen next?"[103] What indeed. No one could have imagined what would unfold in New York in just weeks and impact years.

Further in that article was this: "Public health officials note that the ordinary flu has proved to be far more dangerous so far. Across the country, the C.D.C. says 68 children have died of the flu this year, and the agency estimates 10,000 adults have died. The coronavirus has not yet caused a single death in the United States, officials said. At a news conference, Mayor Bill de Blasio said transmission of the new coronavirus required "substantial contact with someone who already has it," adding that "you don't get it from touching a surface." This is no indictment of the *Times* or the mayor. It simply was not viewed as a threat at the time.

The coronavirus was more a headline in February 2020 than an apparent health risk to Americans until American-Chinese supply chains began to fracture and the stock market crashed at the end of the month. In Europe, the wave was beginning to reach the border of many countries.

First COVID-19 Fatalities

Country	First COVID-19 Fatality
China	1/10/2020
United States	2/06/2020
Japan	2/12/2020
France	2/15/2020
Iran	2/18/2020
Italy	2/22/2020
Australia	2/29/2020
Sweden	3/10/2020
Spain	3/2/2020
United Kingdom	3/5/2020
Germany	3/8/2020

The first major international headline outside Wuhan came on February 5, 2020, when the Diamond Princess cruise ship was quarantined with cases identified. The World Health Organization named the disease sourced from SARS-CoV-2 and called it COVID-19.

By the end of February, the following countries had travel bans to and from China:

- **Australia** - any foreign nationals in mainland China were not allowed to enter Australia until fourteen days after they have left or transited through China. Australian citizens, permanent residents, and their families were able to enter but must isolate themselves for fourteen days if they've recently been to mainland China. The government has advised against any travel to mainland China.
- **Hong Kong** – quarantine required for anyone arriving from mainland China, including Hong Kong residents and visitors beginning February 8.
- **India** - existing visas are no longer valid for any foreign national traveling from China, and anyone traveling from China will be quarantined.
- **Japan** – foreign nationals who have visited China's Hubei province denied entry into Japan, and these limitations would be expanded.
- **New Zealand** - banned anyone traveling from China on February 3.
- **The Philippines** - Banned visitors from China, Hong Kong, and Macau. Any Philippine returning from China would be quarantined.
- **Saudi Arabia** - citizens banned travel to China and those trying to return would not be allowed.

- **South Korea** – no foreigners allowed entry that had visited or stayed in Hubei in the previous fourteen days.
- **Italy** – banned travel to and from China and entry from those coming from China on February 27. Italy would lock down many towns on February 23.
- **United States** – implemented restricted travel to and from China, Iran, Italy, and South Korea.

Also, companies around the globe began to stop business travel. For example, in February, Nestle stopped or severely limited international business travel for its nearly 300,000 employees. British American Tobacco Plc, Coca-Cola, Kraft Heinz, and many others followed suit. At this point, France had not canceled their spring fashion shows, but that was about to change. Amazon limited employee travel and Apple stopped employee travel to China except for emergency purposes, same for Facebook and Google. Microsoft instructed employees in China to work from home.

Expert Opinions At The Time

When January 2020 was winding down, most impacts of COVID-19 were unclear. At the time, President Trump's clamp on entrance to the United States from China was harshly criticized by many in the media and his political opposition. It was a bold move and other countries like Australia echoed the move. Critics saw it as a way for him to hurt China given the years of trade negotiations and disdain he exhibited for the US-China trade deficit, lost manufacturing jobs, and Chinese theft of intellectual property.

The WHO in Early 2020

World Health Organization comment on January 31, 2020:

Travel restrictions can cause more harm than good by hindering info-sharing, medical supply chains and harming economies. The WHO recommends introducing screening at official border crossings. It has warned that closing borders could accelerate the spread of the virus, with travelers entering countries unofficially. Just as the WHO condemned travel restrictions, the U.S. rushed in the opposite direction. [It is] certainly not a gesture of goodwill. - Foreign Ministry spokeswoman Hua Chunying [104]

The WHO did discourage travel bans in their playbook. Their justification for this condemnation was a little off base though. On what planet can closing borders accelerate the spread of anything? And, if your mission is health care and pandemic prevention, how much should a "gesture of goodwill" even factor in? Still, good for the WHO in one aspect. They were following their playbook we saw in chapter one. Too bad the playbooks were thrown out just weeks later.

Media Coverage

The media downplayed and largely dismissed the threat of the coronavirus in America in January 2020. On January 25, *NBC News* Medical Correspondent Dr. John Torres said, "You're hearing a lot of news about [COVID-19] right now, but the reality is comparing it to the flu, it's not even close to that stage." The point here is that a subject matter expert like Torres did not see this coming.

On January 31, Dr. Sanjay Gupta was on *CNN* interviewed by Alisyn Camerota and she said, "…there's an important context we need to keep this in, that the flu is more deadly [than COVID-19]", to which he replied, "This is one of the ironies that keeps coming up. Take a look at the numbers." He was referencing the number of flu deaths compared to COVID-19. However, it's easy to see news opinion people and a subject matter expert not seeing the eventual impact COVID-19 would have on the United States and the world.

On February 1, 2020, former vice president Joe Biden tweeted…

"We are in the midst of a crisis with the coronavirus. We need to lead the way with science — not Donald Trump's record of hysteria, xenophobia, and fear-mongering. He is the worst possible person to lead our country through a global health emergency."[105]

…in response to the halt on China travelers to America. Looking back, it's hard to view the policy as xenophobic. Future President Biden would go on throughout the 2020 presidential campaign and deny that comment was about the travel ban, but it's pretty clear, combined with the tweet coming the day after President Trump's travel ban between China and the United States. President Biden later banned travel to more than one country in 2021.

The Economy Before The Lockdowns

These headlines tell you a lot about the state of the economy as 2020 was beginning:

- *Unemployment was holding strong in January 2020, hovering around the 50-year low of 3.6%[106]*
- *Colorado unemployment rate reaches a historic low of 2.5%; State's tight labor market enters a third year[107]*
- *Utah's unemployment rate is now at an all-time low[108]*
- *US weekly jobless claims increase less than expected[109]*
- *Florida's unemployment rate hits record low[110]*
- *New jobless claims fall 5th straight week to 204,000 in sign of strong U.S. labor market[111]*
- *Washington state unemployment rate hits new low[112]*
- *Michigan's seasonally adjusted unemployment rate crept down one-tenth of a percentage point to 3.9 percent last month, with payroll jobs increasing by 5,000 in December[113]*

- *California unemployment holds at record low 3.9 percent in December; Employers add 12,600 nonfarm jobs as record job expansion continues*[114]
- *Dow Jones Industrial Average closes above 29,000 for first time*[115]

The Lockdown

On December 3, 1979, The Who played a concert in Cincinnati, Ohio, at a downtown arena similar to today's basketball arenas. Just a young boy at the time, I had listened to the album they were promoting, Who Are You, on an eight-track cassette until the tape got tangled up in the player. The Who was one of the biggest musical draws in the world. They sold general admission tickets to this concert.

The doors were supposed to open at 3:00 pm and did not open until after 7:00 pm. One set of doors opened earlier than others, and fans from the back began pushing forward to get in. Eventually, the push into the funnel of two open doors crushed fans, and eleven died of asphyxiation. An uncontrollable flood can break any system. That would not happen at a concert again. I later saw The Who with general admission at the Pontiac Silverdome (80,000+ fans) and entry was smooth.

With the panic-inducing Imperial College model seeming hauntingly real, the United States and governments across the world were faced with challenging options. With no vaccine in hand and sure-thing treatments still unknown, what do you do? The panic by mid-March was what would happen if all the hospitals and ICUs were slammed at the same time. As we saw in the models, the worst case at the peak of the then-respected Imperial College model was a nine-fold shortfall.

Why We Locked Down

The purpose of the lockdown was not to stop the virus spread. The purpose was to slow it down so the hospitalizations did not exceed capacity, like preventing the fan rush at the Cincinnati Who concert. The puzzling thing after observing the data from the cruise ships was that it seemed illogical that there would be such an outbreak of hospitalizations or realized COVID-19 deaths. By April 7, it was clear there would be plenty of hospital capacity for COVID-19 patients. By mid-April, hospitals were going broke from their inability to serve non-COVID-19 patients and the lack of COVID-19 patients.

The insanity reached a new level in American history in late April. Hospitals were not overwhelmed. In fact, they never reached capacity with COVID-19 patients. Later many were overwhelmed for three to four weeks at a given community's peak of COVID-19 hospitalizations. As hospitals stayed empty and were going broke, the curve was flat, and states remained closed as unemployment claims reached forty million. Forty million. It's a hard number to grasp, but that is about 25% of the workforce.

On March 11, 2020, my son traveled with his college baseball team to California for a weekend series. By the morning of March 12, they announced the game that evening would be played without fans. By late afternoon they canceled the weekend series. On the evening of March 13, the season was canceled, and he came home to finish up the semester online and at home. It was still unclear exactly how this would impact Americans, and if it so, how bad it was going to get.

The NBA suspended their season on March 11. The NCAA tournament was canceled on March 12, disappointing for this Michigan State alumni - it may just have been our year. On March 14, Vail Resorts closed most of their ski resorts, which is most of the ski resorts. On March 17, The Rolling Stones canceled their spring tour in America. I would miss out on my sixteenth and final Rolling Stones concert. The summer Olympics, the French Open, the Kentucky Derby, the NHL, the PGA Tour, Major League Baseball, everything was canceled or postponed. Americans were not yet in a lockdown, nor had they experienced any real health impacts as it thundered in with an emptiness of perhaps an impending new reality.

President Trump declared that all flights to and from 26 countries in Europe would cease on March 11. Those countries included: Austria, Belgium, Czech Republic, Denmark, Estonia, Finland, France, Germany, Greece, Hungary, Iceland, Italy, Latvia, Liechtenstein, Lithuania, Luxembourg, Malta, Netherlands, Norway, Poland, Portugal, Slovakia, Slovenia, Spain, Sweden, and Switzerland. The United Kingdom was added days later.

Before official lockdowns by state, city, or county were rolled out, many businesses took the cue from the travel bans and fear of an outbreak and took their own preventive measures. Retailers began temporarily closing stores. By March 20, Nike, Patagonia, Neiman Marcus, The Gap, and hundreds of shopping malls closed. Grocery stores' inventory were washed out from the sea of shoppers stocking up. The unusual item in short supply? Toilet paper became a hot commodity and sales exploded. Hopefully, savvy investors got out of airline stocks and into Procter and Gamble or Kimberly Clark in time. P&G stock cratered like many stocks but jumped up 30% within thirty days, as did Kimberly Clark.

The First Lockdown: California

California became the first state to lockdown on March 20, 2020. Illinois and New York followed immediately. It was a surreal headline to digest. California. Forty million people. The largest state and economy in the United States. On its own, the fifth largest economy in the world shut down. This had to be the hardest and most consequential decision California Governor Gavin Newsom would make in his life.

"Essential" businesses remained open. The sixteen critical infrastructure sectors were: chemical, commercial facilities, communications, critical manufacturing, dams, defense industrial base, emergency services, energy, financial service, food and agriculture, government facilities, health care and public health, information technology, nuclear reactors, materials and waste, transportation systems and water and wastewater systems.

Many businesses and employees could fit in these broad sector classifications. Examples of non-essential businesses closed by most of the state lockdowns include:

Entertainment venues: nightclubs; bowling alleys; arcades; concert venues; theaters, auditoriums, and performing arts centers; tourist attractions (including museums and planetariums); racetracks; indoor children's play areas; adult entertainment venues; casinos and bingo halls.

Athletic facilities and activities: fitness centers and commercial gyms; spas and public or commercial swimming pools; yoga, barre, and spin facilities.

Spectator sports: sports that involved interaction with another person of closer than 6 feet; activities that required the use of shared sporting apparatus and equipment; activities on commercial or public playground equipment.

Close-contact service providers: barbershops; hair salons; waxing salons; nail salons and spas; body-art facilities and tattoo services; tanning salons; massage therapy and massage services.

Retail stores: furniture and home-furnishings stores; clothing, shoe, and clothing-accessory stores; jewelry, luggage, and leather goods stores; department stores; sporting goods stores; book, craft, and music stores.

Most states closed indoor dining, churches, and the businesses listed above in late March. Reopenings began in late April in Georgia and then Texas, with others following to varying degrees in May and June. Statewide mask mandates took root in the spring of 2020. Schools remained closed in the spring of 2020 and when they reopened in the fall of 2020, they were either completely remote or optionally remote. When optionally remote, we rarely saw over 50% face-to-face attendance throughout the 2020-2021 school year. When COVID-19 activity spiked in the fall of 2020, many states resumed closing indoor dining and other retailers.

Below is when each state locked down if they did. All states closed schools in March 2020.

State	Lockdown Date in 2020	Restrictions
Alabama	March 28	Stay-at-home order a week after closing all non-essential businesses. Beaches closed.

Alaska	March 28	Shelter at home and closed all non-essential businesses; travel ban.
Arizona	March 24	Stay-at-home order; closed all non-essential businesses.
Arkansas	March 15	Indoor dining closed.
California	March 20	Stay-at-home order; closed all non-essential businesses.
Colorado	March 25	Stay-at-home order; closed all non-essential businesses.
Connecticut	March 23	Stay-at-home order; closed all non-essential businesses.
Delaware	March 24	Stay-at-home order; closed all non-essential businesses.
District of Columbia	March 16	Stay-at-home order; closed all non-essential businesses.
Florida	April 2	Stay-at-home order; closed all non-essential businesses.
Georgia	April 2	Stay-at-home order; closed all non-essential businesses.
Hawaii	March 25	Stay-at-home order; closed all non-essential businesses.
Idaho	March 25	Stay-at-home order; closed all non-essential businesses.
Illinois	March 20	Stay-at-home order; closed all non-essential businesses.
Indiana	March 25	Stay-at-home order; closed all non-essential businesses.
Iowa	March 17	Stay-at-home order; closed all non-essential businesses.
Kansas	March 30	Stay-at-home order; closed all non-essential businesses.
Kentucky	March 23	Stay-at-home order; closed all non-essential businesses.
Louisiana	March 22	Stay-at-home order; closed all non-essential businesses.
Maine	March 31	Stay-at-home order; closed all non-essential businesses.
Maryland	March 16: schools closed; March 30	Stay-at-home order; closed all non-essential businesses.
Massachusetts	March 15	Stay-at-home order; closed all non-essential businesses.

Michigan	March 23	Shelter-in-place order; closed all non-essential businesses.
Minnesota	March 25	Stay-at-home order; closed all non-essential businesses.
Mississippi	April 3	Shelter-in-place order; closed all non-essential businesses.
Missouri	April 6; many cities and counties issued local orders in March	Non-essential businesses with fewer than ten employees or customers remained open as long as they practice social distancing. Some cities and counties imposed more stringent lockdown rules than the state.
Montana	March 16: schools closed; March 28	Limiting all non-essential businesses. Outdoor activities allowed with social distancing; indoor dining closed.
Nebraska	No state order; schools closed March 13	Some businesses required to halt operations, including indoor dining, more social distancing requirements than a lockdown.
Nevada	March 18	Closed schools and non-essential businesses.
New Hampshire	March 16 schools closed; March 27	Beaches and non-essential businesses closed.
New Jersey	March 21	Stay-at-home order; closed all non-essential businesses.
New Mexico	March 24	Stay-at-home order; closed all non-essential businesses.
New York	March 22	Stay-at-home order; closed all non-essential businesses.
North Carolina	March 30	Stay-at-home order; closed all non-essential businesses.
North Dakota	March 19	Closed bars, restaurants, gyms, and movie theaters to on-site business.
Ohio	March 23	Stay-at-home order; closing all non-essential businesses.
Oklahoma	No state order; many cities and counties issued local orders in March	Many non-essential businesses closed.
Oregon	March 23	Stay-at-home order; closed all non-essential businesses.
Pennsylvania	April 1; schools closed March 13	Stay-at-home order; closed all non-essential businesses.

Rhode Island	March 28; schools closed March 13	Stay-at-home order; closed all non-essential businesses.
South Carolina	April 7; schools closed March 15	Stay-at-home order; closed some non-essential businesses and did require social distancing.
South Dakota	No state order; schools closed March 13	
Tennessee	March 31	Stay-at-home order; closed all non-essential businesses.
Texas	April 2; schools closed March 20	Stay-at-home order; closed all non-essential businesses.
Utah	No state order; many cities and counties issued local orders; schools closed March 16	
Vermont	March 24	Stay-at-home order; closed all non-essential businesses.
Virginia	March 30	Stay-at-home order; closed all non-essential businesses.
Washington	March 23	Stay-at-home order; closed all non-essential businesses.
West Virginia	March 24	Some non-essential businesses closed.
Wisconsin	March 25	Safer-at-home order; closed all non-essential businesses.
Wyoming	No state order; many cities and counties issued local orders; schools closed March 16	Prohibited gatherings of ten people or more in a single room or confined space (including outdoors) and closed bars, restaurants, coffee shops, and some personal services businesses.

Nearly all the orders initially called for a two-to-three-week lockdown to "flatten the curve." This is where the catchphrase "Wait two more weeks!" was born. The first curve to flatten was a potential overflow of hospitalizations. The second curve to flatten was cases, which is what propelled lockdowns for months. In late 2020 there was a real curve of hospitalizations (about 14% of total capacity), and it evaporated like past pandemic curves within a few weeks. The lockdowns went from flattening these curves to a Zero-COVID objective.

In late April 2020, Georgia reopened some of the closed businesses, and Texas soon followed. Many states followed in May and early June. Holdouts included California, Illinois, Michigan, and others. Reopenings were highly correlated to Republican-led states for reasons we will review later. Combined with limited re-openings and a summer swell in the southern states of COVID-19 activity, mask mandates took root in many states that had avoided issuing them. Blue states, red states, all-in 39 states issued mandates at one time or another and most kept them going well into 2021.

Lockdown Lunacy

Sometimes the lockdown orders went a little (a lot) over the top with both certain restrictions and how they were enforced by law enforcement. Sometimes the media went off without data support on a lack of lockdown measures. We could fill a book with just stories like these. When you read through some of these cases, you can see how far we lost our way from the intent of basically "laying low" to prevent a catastrophic overflow of hospitalizations.

California

On April 2, 2020, one of the more interesting violators of the stay-at-home order was arrested, demonstrating the ridiculousness of lockdown orders and police-state some were heading. A young man was seen paddle-boarding off Malibu Beach and was reported. The Lost Hills Sheriff's office was called and the man was pursued until he came to shore. The man was arrested for Disobeying a Lifeguard 17.12.115 LACC and Violation of Government Code 8665.[116] The "perpetrator" was transported to Lost Hills Sheriff's Station, where he was booked and released on a promise to appear.

He was arrested and faced up to a $1,000 fine and or up to six months in jail. How far would the state go to enforce this law while others could access hiking trails while keeping social distance? What about where people in other states could freely do this type of activity that wasn't against the law? Meanwhile, California released 3,500 nonviolent inmates within the next sixty days, and New York City had already released 900 people as of March 31. As states were releasing convicted criminals serving time, this surfer was arrested for getting some time in the outdoors by himself.

On April 10, Riverside County, California, launched an app that could be downloaded from the Apple Store or Google Play for residents to report on stay-at-home violations. Users could upload a picture of the violation and the idea was that law enforcement pursue the perpetrators.[117]

After five weeks of shutdown, San Clemente, in Orange County, voted to open their beaches. April 25, 2020, was unseasonably warm in southern California. Tens of thousands of people showed up on beaches in Orange County, making headlines nationally. People were getting antsy and ready to move on. They'd been cooped up for over a month, nothing was happening in California, there was no hospitalization wave or even trickle, and some demonstrated they were ready to get back to normal.

On April 24, Los Angeles Mayor Eric Garcetti said, "There is a direct correlation between what you do this weekend and how long this will take and how many lives we will lose. If you stay home this weekend, our case numbers will drop, and we will stop the spread of this virus."[118] It was more like a parent scolding a rebellious teen than a healthcare initiative. Hospitals were still empty, and each day new data was showing more people had COVID-19 and the fatality rate was lower than initially thought. Young people were at no measurable risk of becoming ill nor transmit the virus. And yet, some politicians continued to double down on lockdown measures.

In response to the beachgoers the weekend of April 25, Governor Newsom closed just Orange County beaches the next weekend, for May 2-3. You children listen to me or else! That weekend a few thousand protesters gathered at Huntington Beach to express their displeasure at the governor's order. In addition, local governments at Huntington Beach and Dana Point began a legal challenge against both the governor and the state, as well as a restraining order. Into 2021 Governor Newsom was subject to a recall over his handling of the pandemic.

Still, on this date, hospitals were empty, and California's fatality rate was 58 COVID-19 deaths per one million people. A year later, after the tightest lockdown in the country, that number was 1,500 per million, about the U.S. average. Millions of people were out of work in California, out of school, young people at no real risk, and yet the governor was now doubling down on principle, as science had left his side. There is a big distinction between COVID-19 risk and supporting the lockdowns. As real as COVID-19 was to millions getting sick and a few hundred thousand deaths, the lockdowns were far too an extreme ongoing policy.

Colorado

One of the craziest lockdown violation stories came out of Colorado on April 7, 2020. Former Colorado State Patrol Trooper Matt Mooney, 33, was playing t-ball with his six-year-old daughter at a near-empty softball field. This struck a chord with me because baseball was our family life for a decade, and at my son's same age, we were at fields practicing a good four days a week. Matt was instructed by police on the scene to leave and that the park was closed, though it was open. When he didn't and apparently resisted giving his identification, probably due to the lack of cause in the first place, the police arrested him in front of his daughter, releasing him not long after at the scene.

Never mind that the police were wrong about the park being closed. This really demonstrated an overreach in actual application and the spirit of the law. In reality, Colorado was in no crisis. A man was getting outdoors with his daughter. Hoping this would help illuminate the absurdity of the lockdowns, nothing really changed.

Florida Reopening

Critics started a Twitter hashtag called *#FloridaMorons* that trended when Jacksonville's mayor Lenny Curry reopened the beaches on April 17, 2020. Mainstream media outlets crucified the mayor for the decision, led by headlines like this from the *Washington Post*: "In Florida, we love our beaches. Thanks to our governor, now we can die for them,"[119] by Diane Roberts, a journalist and professor of English at Florida State University. In the article, Roberts slammed Governor DeSantis and President Trump, largely with the claim that "how can we open the beaches until we know how many people have [SARS-CoV-2]?" With hospitals empty, when do you open the beaches? Would Roberts suggest they wait until next April?

Illinois

In late March 2020, an Illinois man had some COVID-19-like symptoms and was ordered to self-isolate.[120] He was not tested for COVID-19. For some reason, he posted that on Facebook. A few days into his self-quarantine, he decided to visit his in-laws. On the way, he stopped in a gas station so his son could use the restroom. A clerk at the gas station recognized him and recalled his Facebook post. That escalated and the Jasper County state's attorney's office charged Liddle with reckless conduct, a misdemeanor. The charge was later dismissed. At the time, there were no COVID-19 cases or deaths in that or the adjacent county.

Kentucky

Kentucky made its biggest COVID-19 headline around Easter services on April 12, 2020. Kentucky Governor Andy Beshear issued a warning that anyone who violates the state's stay-at-home order was subject to a 14-day mandatory self-quarantine.[121] The state would record license plate information of people seen attending mass gatherings and turn that information over to local public health officials. Quarantine notices would then be delivered in person. This warning sparked controversy between supporters of the policy and those feeling like attending service on the most important Christian holiday in a drive-in way was government overreach.

Kentucky Senator Rand Paul tweeted this in response: "Taking license plates at church? Quarantining someone for being Christian on Easter Sunday? Someone needs to take a step back here." On Fire Christian Church sued Louisville Mayor Greg Fischer and the city after Fischer prepared to enforce the governor's order. U.S. District Judge Justin Walker sided with the church, saying that the city is prohibited from "enforcing; attempting to enforce; threatening to enforce, or otherwise requiring compliance with any prohibition on drive-in church services at On Fire."[122]

Michigan

On March 23, 2020, Governor Whitmer issued a stay-at-home order to lockdown the state. Michigan residents experienced one of the harshest lockdowns in the country in 2020.

Soon after Whitmer's lockdown order, controversy swirled. Joe Biden had announced in a debate leading up to Super Tuesday that he would, if the Democrat nominee, select a female running mate. Immediately shortlists were created and debated, and Governor Whitmer emerged on the shortlist. Whitmer was the Democrat representative to deliver President Trump's State of the Union address opposition party response, speaking in East Lansing, Michigan.

It started on March 17, 2020, when Whitmer was interviewed on *MSNBC* and said, "the federal government did not take this seriously early enough... to hear the leader of the federal government tell us to work around the federal government because it's too slow is kind of mind-boggling, to be honest." Her response was referring to a comment President Trump made on March 16, suggesting governors take the lead on securing their own healthcare equipment such as ventilators. Governors are elected to manage their state needs, and playing this out, a governor would identify needs and then fill those needs through the federal government, other states, or the private sector.

On March 20, President Trump and his team were delivering their daily briefing on the COVID-19 crisis. Those press briefings became lengthy each day. In most press briefings and even at rallies, President Trump spoke extemporaneously. He offered up that hydroxychloroquine, a malaria treatment drug, might be effective for treating COVID-19. He was criticized sharply by his critics for this, and Dr. Anthony Fauci was less than committal on its benefit. The *Washington Post* referred to his comment as recommending snake oil.[123]

Whitmer reacted swiftly and on March 24, Michigan's Department of Licensing and Regulatory Affairs sent a letter warning health care providers not to prescribe hydroxychloroquine.[124] The letter stated:

> *Prescribing hydroxychloroquine or chloroquine without further proof of efficacy for treating COVID-19 or with the intent to stockpile the drug may create a shortage for patients with lupus, rheumatoid arthritis, or other ailments for which chloroquine and hydroxychloroquine are proven treatments. Reports of this conduct will be evaluated and may be further investigated for administrative action. Prescribing any kind of prescription must also be associated with medical documentation showing proof of the medical necessity and medical condition for which the patient is being treated. Again, these are drugs that have not been proven scientifically or medically to treat COVID-19.*

If President Trump said, "Drink water to hydrate!" the opposing party would have banned or sin-taxed bottled water. That's where we were in 2020. This political sparring was taking place center stage in a healthcare crisis with no known sure-thing treatments.

On April 1, the *New York Times* ran this headline: "A group of moderately ill people were given hydroxychloroquine, which appeared to ease their symptoms quickly, but more research is needed."[125] On April 2, the *New York Post* ran this: "Of 2,171 physicians surveyed, 37 percent rated hydroxychloroquine the "most effective therapy" for combating the potentially deadly illness."[126]

On April 2, Whitmer reversed her stance, saying this: "The fear that a pronouncement at the federal level might create some hoarding was something that we were very concerned about because we do have Michigan patients that have been prescribed this drug pre-COVID-19 that we wanted to make sure still had access to their medication," she said. "But I think that, as we know, this is a novel virus, and we have to have the mindset that we're going to be willing to explore what possibilities there are in terms of improving testing, in terms of testing for antibodies ... so we know who is immune, [and are] testing drugs and therapies in the process."[127] It's okay to buy bottled water again. That was quick.

Politics were shining brightly as Whitmer was trying to gain points by standing up to President Trump. However, as Whitmer stated above, it was a novel virus. In the midst of a crisis, many patients would try something with a reasonable chance of improving their condition. Why not? The treatments used in New York in the early days of the pandemic were practically barbaric. It's the difference between being a peace-time politician and a war-time politician. There was fury all over the world to try new treatments to find the right solution while a vaccine was unavailable.

Karen Whitsett was a Democrat state representative in Michigan from Detroit. She contracted COVID-19 in April 2020. Feeling ill, she took hydroxychloroquine to ease her symptoms. She described it as a miracle drug. Whitsett said, "I really want to say that you have to give this an opportunity. For me, it saved my life. I only can go by what it is that I have gone through and what my story is, and I can't speak for anyone else. So that's not what I'm trying to do here. I'm only speaking for myself. I did have a difficult time, even that day, obtaining the medication because of an order that was put down in my state. And it was on that day, so you can imagine how terrified I was that I had to beg and plead and go through a whole lot to try to get the medication. If President Trump had not talked about this, it wouldn't have been something that would be accessible for anyone to be able to get right now."[128]

On April 14, Whitsett personally thanked President Trump and Vice President Pence. On April 25, Detroit's 13th Congressional District Democratic formally censured Whitsett and withheld any future endorsements of the lawmaker for breaking protocol by meeting the president.[129] No water for you, Whitsett! A censure is when a political party publicly reprimands a politician. The censure stated Whitsett "misrepresented the needs and priorities" of Democratic leadership to the president and public.[130] Politicians from both parties would say we were at war with COVID-19, but they believed it when it was convenient, stopping short of war declarations in favor of partisan politics.

On April 10, Governor Gretchen Whitmer expanded Michigan's stay-at-home order, prohibiting Michiganders from visiting family or friends with exceptions for providing care and preventing residents from traveling between different residences they may own. Michigan's dense population resides in the southeast, but many have homes in rural areas, around the Great Lakes, and getaway spots like Charlevoix and Traverse City in the north.

The order banned the use of motorboats, golfing, and sales of carpeting, flooring, furniture, garden supplies, or paint. It prevented people from moving between homes in the state. Garden supplies banned from purchase at Home Depot or Ace Hardware? Paint? Seriously? When you're locked down for weeks and prohibited from some DIY projects? Many drove to Toledo for those things.

On May 24, Governor Whitmer's husband claimed executive privilege against the lockdown.[131] He requested a marina put their boat in the water in northern Michigan so they could go boating over Memorial Day weekend. After all the strict lockdown measures, one of the tightest and longest in the country, the first family demonstrated the rules didn't apply to them. This really shows that these measures were not necessary or mission-critical in the first place. This is one in a long line of lockdown hypocrites violating their own orders.

New Jersey

New Jersey's lockdown took an interesting turn on April 18, 2020. New Jersey Governor Phil Murphy shut down people viewing a tulip farm festival, an in-vehicle drive-by activity. Murphy banned gatherings of more than ten people, like most states. That led to some arrests of people violating those orders claiming they were an infringement of rights. Considering the real crisis hitting the New York area, it is reasonable to understand locking down like they did when they did. However, the tulip ban took it to a new level.

To put this in some context, New Jersey residents remained able to shop at Walmart and Target, interacting pretty much as they had in the past, normal. To ban a drive-through activity like this, particularly when the hospitalizations and deaths were on the sharp decline, brought government overreach to an absurd level. Governor Murphy was one of the very last to remove face mask mandates in his state, well after the CDC removed their face mask recommendation in May 2021.

Texas

As Texas was reopening in the spring of 2020, one salon owner had had enough. In the highest-profile Texas arrest and jailing in recent memory, Shelley Luther was guilty of opening her salon before the May 8 date allowed by Texas order. Luther closed her salon on March 22, like everyone else. On April 24 police officers visited her salon and issued her a citation and told her to close. It was open but was respecting social distancing. I visited her salon. The seating is indeed spaced out well beyond six feet.

Luther did not and was arrested and arraigned on May 5.[132] The Dallas judge gave her the option to apologize and admit wrongdoing and she would not be fined or serve time in jail. She declined on principle and said she would not apologize for opening her business to feed her children. She went immediately to a sheriff's jail to serve her one-week term. Luther explained to the judge, "I have to disagree with you, sir, when you say that I'm selfish because feeding my kids is not selfish. If you think the law's more important than kids getting fed, then please go ahead with your decision. But I am not going to shut the salon."

The story took a happy turn for Luther. She was released after two days served. Supporters set up a Go Fund Me page and she was hailed a hero by many in the community.

Robin Torres spent five weeks in the Hidalgo County jail after a police officer caught him smoking and drinking a Busch Light beer outside a convenience store just after 11 p.m. on April 3. Arrested on a public intoxication charge and for violation of the stay-home orders, Torres couldn't afford to pay the $150 he owed on his bond. He wasn't released until early May.[133]

Wisconsin

On April 29, while many states were opening up and some never locked down in the first place, with hospitals empty and no health crisis going on in Wisconsin, the Calumet County Sheriff's Department in Wisconsin showed up at a mother's home and reprimanded her for allowing her daughter to play at a neighbor's home for a play date. They badgered her for not strictly following the "Safer-At-Home" order. The crime was allowing two kids to play together.[134]

Other Crimes Against the Stay-At-Home Orders

In Faribault County, Minnesota, Winnebago police officers found four men playing cards and drinking inside a bar. According to the criminal complaint, the bar owner said they didn't need to listen to the officer – calling it communism. The bar owner was cited for violating the executive order.[135]

Greensboro, North Carolina, police charged seven people for violating stay-at-home orders on March 30, 2020. Police said the seven individuals were protesting *outside* an A Woman's Choice clinic. Greensboro police officers tried to gain voluntary compliance before charging the protestors with violation of

Guilford County's stay-at-home order and resisting, delaying, and obstructing a public officer.[136]

Lockdown measures were in effect to varying degrees for a year and a half as of this writing. Well-intentioned guidelines turned so political. They did not follow the science, for certain after May 2020, when so much was known. People supported them in large numbers because they were afraid because the media drove it home, and dissenters were either canceled or demonized. Democrat versus Republican politics and state and local leaders refusing to fold their hands perpetuated what should have been a four-week shutdown into something fictional for many, many months. When the death totals missed the model projections by wide margins, how COVID-19 deaths were counted brought more controversy.

CHAPTER 7
Counting COVID-19 Deaths

Counting COVID-19 cases and deaths dominated the world view in 2020 and 2021. It was impossible to turn on the news without seeing a partial screen of COVID-19 cases and deaths in haunting big red letters. If you were burned out of television news, you may have turned to online news. When you opened any news outlet online, the first thing you saw was COVID-19 data. There was little wonder why so many people were afraid to leave their house, travel, or send their kids to school. Where the media, politicians, and healthcare organizations failed Americans was in contextualizing the data.

Some of the brightest people I knew really did not understand the risk. They knew the numbers, broadly anyway, but didn't have perspective. It reminded me of seeing *Jaws* at the theater when I was a kid. If that was your source for risk and safety swimming in the ocean, you'd never go in. Many didn't after that movie.

In May 2021, David Leonhardt of the *New York Times* wrote an opinion piece called "A Misleading C.D.C. Number."[137] He made a great, if not delayed, observation: "The Centers for Disease Control and Prevention announced that "less than 10 percent" of COVID-19 transmission was occurring outdoors. In truth, the share of transmission that has occurred outdoors seems to be below 1 percent and may be below 0.1 percent. Saying that less than 10 percent of COVID-19 transmission occurs outdoors is akin to saying that sharks attack fewer than 20,000 swimmers a year. (The actual worldwide number is around 150.) It's both true and deceiving." That pretty much exemplifies how the risk and counting of COVID-19 deaths was portrayed during the pandemic. It also exemplifies how poorly the CDC did in providing science-based recommendations to Americans.

CDC Guidelines

In a March 24, 2020 memo, the CDC called for this in its directive to health-care providers classifying COVID-19 deaths:

> *Will COVID-19 be the underlying cause? The underlying cause depends upon what and where conditions are reported on the death certificate. However, the rules for coding and selection of the underlying cause of death are expected to result in COVID-19 being the underlying cause more often than not.*
>
> *Should 'COVID-19' be reported on the death certificate only with a confirmed test? COVID-19 should be reported on the death certificate for all decedents where the disease caused or is assumed to have caused or contributed to death. Certifiers should include as much detail as possible based on their knowledge of the case, medical records, laboratory testing, etc. If the decedent had other chronic conditions such as COPD or asthma that may have also contributed, these conditions can be reported in Part II.*[138]

The CDC instructed *probable* deaths in the official death count total. Steven Schwartz was the Director of Vital Statistics at the CDC. On March 4, 2020, he sent a memo to hospital administrators advising them to code COVID-19 as the cause of death if it was the known cause or likely cause of death. On March 24, he sent another note guiding administrators that COVID-19 is expected to more often than not be the cause of death. The CDC counted anyone that died *with* COVID-19 as a COVID-19 death, even if that was not the cause of death. Then they counted anyone who *may have had* COVID-19 as a COVID-19 death, but not verified through a test.[139]

Given the policy making and public concern for real data, the guidance should have been something like, "If you code a cause of death to COVID-19, it should be verified that both the patient tested positive for the virus and you concluded it was the primary cause of death." Otherwise, the integrity of the data is fractured. Had anyone that signed off on any death certificate with COVID-19 on it had to take a lie detector test and be personally liable had COVID-19 not been the primary cause, we would have seen at least 30% fewer COVID-19 deaths. One data advisor to the White House told me it would have been closer to 50% fewer official COVID-19 deaths than 30%.

Given the overlap of deaths with other health issues like a cardiac arrest or cancer, or even car accidents, all of which were counted as COVID-19 deaths as long as they carried the virus, the only way to measure the real impact COVID-19 had on America and the world is to look at all-cause mortalities year-over-year.

Excess deaths went up significantly in 2020 and early 2021 in every state. When conclusive data is available for all-cause mortality death increases in America, it may end up over a million throughout the pandemic, at least through official CDC benchmarks. On a four-year average into 2023, given the lives COVID-19 claimed, there is a good chance deaths *from* COVID-19 will be matched by excess deaths caused by the lockdowns, and we will visit that in more detail later. Further, there is a very good chance the total deaths will end up at no excess due to COVID-19 as a disease because of pull-forward deaths. With so many losing their lives near their life expectancy, we may well see a decline of excess deaths in late 2021 and 2022.

The data reporting on COVID-19 deaths is not clean but is directionally accurate. Here are the variable considerations on the reported COVID-19 deaths' reliability of accuracy and how they may raise or lower actual COVID-19-caused fatalities. The net is a high probability that COVID-19 deaths were overstated due to other conditions or causes.

Unreported COVID-19 deaths	↑
Counting "probable" COVID-19 deaths	↓
Lower than usual classified influenza deaths	↓
Lower than usual classified pneumonia deaths	↓
COVID-19 positive deaths by other causes (like a car crash)	↓
Other comorbidities causing the COVID-19 death	↓

COVID-19 Death Data

Below is the age stratification of COVID-19 deaths in the United States from the beginning through March 31, 2021. 47% of all deaths were to victims over age 80, who make up less than five percent of the population. 73% were over age 70, and 88% were over age 60. 39% of Americans were under age 40 and comprised about 4% of all COVID-19 deaths. Those from birth to college age were statistically zero, sixty times more at risk of dying in a car accident, homicide, suicide, or overdose.

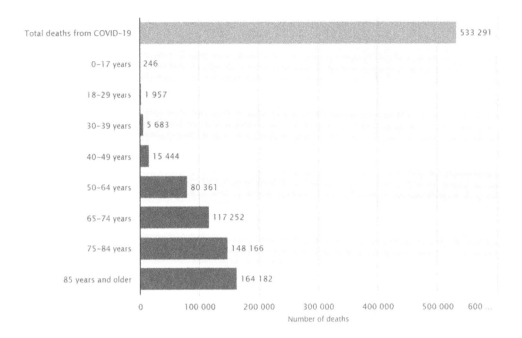

Total deaths from COVID-19 — 533 291
0–17 years — 246
18–29 years — 1 957
30–39 years — 5 683
40–49 years — 15 444
50–64 years — 80 361
65–74 years — 117 252
75–84 years — 148 166
85 years and older — 164 182

Number of deaths

Source: Statista March 31, 2021

Over 95% of COVID-19 deaths occurred in concert with two to three combined comorbidities. Chronic kidney disease was most common, according to some studies. Diabetes, hypertension, and cancer were also prominent as underlying conditions. According to the CDC, for people under 44 years old, obesity was the most common underlying condition.[140] It was probably closer to 50-55 years old. Obesity affects the respiratory and immune systems making a person more vulnerable to the effects of COVID-19. Obesity is associated with other comorbidities, including those at the top of the COVID-19 underlying condition list: hypertension, cardiovascular diseases, diabetes mellitus, and vitamin D deficiency. The CDC reported that 78% of COVID-19 hospitalizations were associated with obesity. Patients with intellectual disabilities were twice as likely to be hospitalized from COVID-19 and three times more likely to not survive.[141]

There are two parts of a death certificate identifying the cause of death and contributing factors. The first part lists the immediate cause of death followed by any conditions that led to the immediate cause. An example is a patient who died from pneumonia while they had COVID-19. COVID-19 gets listed under that as an underlying condition that led to death. That is reasonable; most COVID-19 deaths associated with pneumonia were likely real COVID-19 deaths.

The second part lists conditions that did not set off medical events that led to death but *may have* contributed in some other way. In these cases, a person died that was probably going to die with or without COVID-19. It's these cases and the probables that should be excluded from the COVID-19 counts for a truer reflection of the impact of the disease. There were thousands of these cases in the United States.

Overcounting Fatalities

When the lockdowns began on March 19, 2020, in California and followed by most states within ten days, the projection of American deaths was 2.2MM lives lost by August 2020. On that date, the Imperial College model was the standard. By March 26, the projection of lives lost was down to 150,000-200,000. Within days the estimation dropped from the IHME model to a range of 38,000 to 162,000. That was really an absurdly low projection. At this point, states locked down, millions lost their jobs, schools were closed, and hundreds of millions of Americans stayed at home.

The counting of COVID-19 fatalities went from positive COVID-19 tests in those who died to those who died with a probability they had COVID-19. By doing that, the fatality counts elevated and therefore inched closer to the projections that prompted the lockdowns. Inched, they never got close. On the other side of the death equation, we saw higher than average deaths in homes, suggesting people died with COVID-19 who were not tested nor hospitalized, a reasonable assertion. That likely happened in March and even April 2020, but not after. The reason is the sensitivity was too great. There was a lot of extra federal government money available for COVID-19 patients and deaths. It's nearly impossible a material number of real COVID-19 hospitalizations and deaths went uncounted after mid-April 2020.

The *New York Times* reported on April 14, 2020 that Dr. Oxiris Barbot, the commissioner of the city Health Department said, "'Three thousand more people died in New York City between March 11 and April 13 than would have been expected during the same time period in an ordinary year.'"[142] Dr. Barbot was saying that, at that time, New York was up 3,000 all-cause deaths year-over-year while New York was reporting more than 10,000 COVID-19 deaths in the same period.

On April 13, New York state reported more than 3,700 COVID-19 fatalities for that day, which was elevated with victims who did not test positive for COVID-19 but were presumed to have died with it *over the previous month*. Their otherwise highest reported fatality day was a fifth of that. This inclusion bumped up the total number of New York fatalities which grew the United States total 17%, all in one day.

Can you see how the data loses some integrity and you aren't really sure what the real numbers are? Dr. Barbot raised an excellent statistic in identifying that New York was a net 3,000 up in deaths in the same period compared to more than three times that in COVID-19 deaths. In the next chapter, you will see how this displaced usual deaths of other causes.

On May 11, the *Washington Post* reported that Dr. Deborah Birx felt the CDC was using methods of tracking that may be inflating the COVID-19 fatality counts by as much as 25%. "There is nothing from the CDC that I can trust," Birx reportedly said, according to two of the Post's sources. It's a very indicting comment coming from perhaps the number two medical expert leading the COVID-19 response from the federal government in 2020, along with Anthony Fauci and Robert Redfield.

Dr. Scott Jensen is a Minnesota physician and a state senator. He gave an example of a patient who died while having the flu. Jensen said typically, if the patient had symptoms like a fever and cough (flu-like symptoms), he would code the death as "respiratory arrest. I've never been encouraged to [notate 'influenza']. I would probably write 'respiratory arrest' to be the top line, and the underlying cause of this disease would be pneumonia ... I might well put emphysema or congestive heart failure, but I would never put influenza down as the underlying cause of death, and yet that's what we are being asked to do here."

Jensen then told the interviewer that under the CDC guidelines, a patient who died after being hit by a bus and tested positive for coronavirus would be listed as a COVID-19 death, regardless of trauma from the bus accident causing death. Further, he called out that "Right now Medicare has determined that if you have a COVID-19 admission to the hospital, you'll get paid $13,000 [compared to a standard $5,000]. If that COVID-19 patient goes on a ventilator, you get $39,000, three times as much. Nobody can tell me, after 35 years in the world of medicine, that sometimes those kinds of things [have] impact on what we do."[143]

The CARES Act government bailout initiative paid by another estimate a 20% increase in Medicare reimbursements for COVID-19 hospitalizations. The add-on was authorized by the coronavirus stimulus package signed into law on March 27. *Revcycle Intelligence* noted that even with higher payouts for COVID-19 patients, the costs associated with treatments are greater, in which case hospitals would lose money overall per patient.[144] In speaking with several physicians, they all doubted hospitals were changing death classifications for financial gain. However, I personally saw reports where an attending physician did not classify COVID-19 as a hospitalization cause but was overridden by an administrator. That is anecdotal and no scaled conclusions are drawn.

Pennsylvania

Pennsylvania followed New York's lead and began including "probable" COVID-19 deaths in their count around April 21, 2020. That resulted in ballooning their total death count by nearly double in a couple of days. After some scrutiny and criticism, the Pennsylvania Department of Health (DOH) backtracked and removed the "probables" in their tally.[145]

None of these dirty-data observations is meant to suggest that COVID-19 was not a huge health event. It was and spending any time in each community for the four to six weeks when they experienced their surge would validate that. There were many COVID-19 deniers that talked about how deaths were greatly exaggerated and that this was basically a bad flu. Emergency department doctors and nurses would've laughed those conjectures out of the room. Data integrity inspires confidence and adjusting death counts by 10% or 20%, or even 40%, doesn't change the bigger picture of the virus's effect.

Colorado

If you think government agencies would not try to overcount COVID-19 fatalities, consider what happened in Colorado at the end of April 2020. The Colorado Department of Public Health and Environment reclassified three deaths at a Centennial nursing home as COVID-19 deaths. Attending physicians ruled all three were not related to coronavirus, and yet their cause of death was overridden.[146]

The unsettling part of this is that, eventually, stories like this always come out. The counting of nursing home deaths in New York is the grandest example of this. Data integrity is everything for citizens to have confidence in their government, health organizations, and the media. Why overstate the COVID-19 deaths? The best news everyone can get is that we dodged one and that the coronavirus pandemic was less dangerous than anyone thought. The problem is that it would require most health and government officials to admit the lockdowns were overblown, with 40 million jobs lost and the greatest domestic crisis in American history since the Civil War and with the Great Depression.

On May 13, 2020, near Durango, CO, another controversy erupted because a 35-year-old man died from alcohol poisoning, with a .55% blood-alcohol level, seven times the legal limit. In the autopsy, the man tested positive for COVID-19 and was counted as a COVID-19 death. Should this be counted as a COVID-19 death if he died with it but not from it?[147]

If he died with HIV but from a car crash, is it an HIV death? These may be outliers, but they're the ones we heard about. If tens of millions of people had COVID-19 or a positive test in their history by even summer 2020, entirely likely, then many deaths could be COVID-19 deaths.

On May 15, 2020, Colorado began to change their coding of COVID-19 deaths, breaking it up into people who died from COVID-19 and people who died with COVID-19. In one day, the state's COVID-19 fatalities dropped 25%. The next day Colorado Governor Jared Polis blasted the way the CDC was counting COVID-19 deaths as it was not reflecting accurately who was dying from the illness. He pointed to the Durango alcohol poisoning death and called it a point of reckoning.

Milwaukee

On September 30, 2020, Milwaukee Chief Medical Examiner Dr. Brian Peterson reported that COVID-19 deaths were overstated.[148] Peterson said of the state coding deaths: "They're simply lumping everything into one basket, so if they have COVID anywhere on a death certificate, they're calling that a COVID-related death. I don't believe that's true." He estimated a 20% overstatement of COVID-19 deaths in Wisconsin.

Some people believed that COVID-19 should not be a cause of death in the counts if the person died over life expectancy. Others believed that long-term care facility patients should not be counted because they may have been within six months of passing. Some felt if COVID-19 was not the single cause of death, it should not be counted. I don't subscribe to any of these. If COVID-19 accelerated a condition to a quicker passing, it's a COVID-19 death regardless of age. If a victim was severely obese or had a serious kidney function condition, and they caught COVID-19, and their bodies were not strong enough to get over it, that's a COVID-19 death.

Where we should scrutinize COVID-19 death counts is if they were 1) a probable and 2) they died of a cause that is unrelated to what we know is a COVID-19 type of death. An example of the latter may be if someone died of a cardiac arrest while positive with the virus. Another is if they died days or weeks later from something with a positive test in their history. If a COVID-19 death required death certificate matching long after the fact, it likely wasn't a real COVID-19 death.

Dade County (Miami), Iowa, and North Dakota did some parsing out of COVID-19 patients. They at one time separated those hospitalized with COVID-19 versus from COVID-19. If you looked into North Dakota data in fall 2020, you can see a break, a decrease, in COVID-19 counts after they separated those out. That's a reasonable way to count since, at that time, there were easily over 100 million Americans that had SARS-CoV-2 in their history. When those three communities separated out their COVID-19 cases, they showed a reduction of between 28-42% in their totals. Combined with the CDC and others like Dr. Birx saying COVID-19 numbers could be inflated by about 25%, our working number here is a conservative 30% inflation. That means we are working off a premise that 70% of the reported COVID-19 hospitalizations and deaths are valid and should be counted as such. It's still a huge number, so no minimizing the impact of the pandemic. What it contextualizes is the excess death impact and the number of deaths due to the lockdowns, which is also a huge number, as we will see later.

Undercounting Fatalities

While overcounting fatalities was uncovered with hard data, other data suggested that early (February and March 2020) COVID-19 deaths were undercounted. The challenge with analyzing these deaths, and even those caused by the flu is, did the patient die with the virus or because of the virus?

Two things could account for this. First, the patient died from COVID-19 but was not tested. Second, they died from something else because they did not get normal health care for their ailment because they either could not get in to see their healthcare provider, or they were afraid to do so for fear of catching COVID-19.

While the premise in this book is that the actual COVID-19 risk and deaths never backed up the models, nor the economic and social lockdowns, there's little doubt the actual deaths with COVID-19 could have been higher than those reported, perhaps by 10-15%, from fatalities that occurred in February and March 2020. It's doubtful they were undercounted after mid-April because probables were included, as well as so much attention brought to all death classifications and the reimbursements at stake. However, it's then lower than reported because many died *with* COVID-19 but not *from* it.

Why Counting Mattered

Future Hall of Famer Justin Verlander pitched opening day for the Houston Astros (play along even though he was out for 2021 after arm surgery). He got shelled in his first outing, giving up nine runs in three innings, ballooning his earned run average to 27.00. He was benched for months after that. It didn't matter that this was just one bad outing against a career ERA of 3.33 and an Astros career ERA of about 2.50. Verlander sat on the bench, itching to get back on the mound, but because of the one bad opening day performance, his coach sat him out in fear of another bad outing. His track record didn't matter.

Like Verlander's bad outing, the initial outbreak in New York shellshocked America into fear of another bad outing, thus putting Americans on the bench for much of 2020 and 2021. If you watched television news, read the newspaper, visited online news sites, or read social media, it was hard to understand what really happened.

CHAPTER 8
Lockdown and Excess Deaths in America

medRxiv reported this commentary on the accuracy of counting COVID-19 deaths:

> Deaths attributed to COVID-19 are difficult to measure accurately. Problems with testing affect not only confirmed cases, but also attributed deaths. Besides, testing is not enough to determine the cause of death, as some patients may die while infected with SARS-CoV-2, but not due to it. Due to constraints health systems are facing across the world, it is likely that a precise attribution of cause of death is not possible.[149]

The United States loses about 8,000 people on average every day. With muddy COVID-19 fatality data, the best way to determine COVID-19's impact is to compare year-over-year all-cause deaths. The CDC data used for analysis compares deaths to a five-year average.

In 2018, 2,839,205 registered deaths occurred in the United States, according to the CDC.[150] In 2019, 2,854,838 died. The unusually high-death flu season in 2018 helped account for higher age-adjusted deaths. However, though the absolute number of people dying increased in 2019, the age-adjusted number of deaths actually decreased. This gets a little complicated. You may be wondering how you have more people die one year, but there's a decrease in age-adjusted mortality. The simple explanation is, more people fell into older age ranges in 2019, so more were expected to die. While more people did actually die, fewer died based on the population age than were expected. This builds up an insensitive term called dry timber. When there is a buildup of people that would be expected to lose their life and did not, a bad flu or certainly something like COVID-19 catches it up. That is a large reason why Sweden had more COVID-19 deaths than neighboring Finland and Norway. Sweden was riding fewer all-cause deaths the previous couple of years.

In 2020, approximately 3,358,814 registered deaths occurred in the United States, and age-adjusted deaths were 829 per 100,000. Age-adjusted, 346,500 more people died in 2020 than in 2018, and 376,200 more than in 2019.

To analyze the impact of COVID-19 and the lockdowns in 2020, we simply look at three basic statistics to determine the overall risk of COVID-19 compared to the consequences of the lockdowns:

A. Excess deaths
B. Excess deaths caused by COVID-19
C. Excess deaths not caused by COVID-19

A minus C equals excess deaths caused by COVID-19, and B minus C equals the net impact of COVID-19 relative to the lockdowns. The reasoning is, had we not locked down, the lockdown deaths would not have occurred. For example, suppose we had 400,000 excess deaths during the pandemic. Then suppose we had 100,000 excess deaths not attributed to COVID-19, perhaps untreated ailments, abandonment, suicides, overdoses, etc. If we had 300,000 real COVID-19 extra deaths then would be expected, and the lockdowns cost another 100,000 lives; the net is 200,000. The net effect would be 200,000 COVID-19 deaths. These are examples, not the real numbers.

Think of it simply, like this example. Suppose you could drive further than your local grocery store to buy fruits and vegetables at a farmer's market. You go to the market and you buy some lettuce, cucumbers, apples, and berries and save $10 compared to buying at Kroger. However, because it's further away, you spend an extra $5 in gas to get there. Did you save $10? No, because the cost to save that $10 was $5, so you really saved $5. That's what happened in balancing the relationship between trying to save COVID-19 lives while costing other lives. Furthermore, in the real world of COVID-19, there's no evidence to support you could have saved that $10 by going further to the farmer's market. We essentially spent the $5 in gas and didn't save anything off the $10. For full disclosure, that last point is heavily debated. When you really study the deaths in the least restricted places, it doesn't pass the logic test that lockdowns prevented a material number of COVID-19 deaths and in no way a number surpassing lockdown deaths.

Another way to examine the impact of the lockdowns is life years lost. The median age of a COVID-19 death was 78-80 all over the world, right at life expectancy. The average age of a lockdown death was much younger. The data is still coming in at this writing, but 48 is a good working number. If 300,000 people lost their lives with an average of seven life years left, that's 2.1 million life years lost. If 100,000 people lost their lives with thirty years left, that's three million life years lost. What we will analyze and discuss is that the lockdown deaths were high and may end up exceeding COVID-19 deaths over the 2020s. Life years lost because of the lockdowns will exceed COVID-19 life years lost, and it won't be close.

This doesn't minimize the impact of COVID-19 in any way. Policy decisions are made around the greater good for every facet of our lives. America is much more generous in its health care approach than countries like Canada, the UK, Italy, and many others, with providing care more around humanity than life years. What we generally disregarded was the health impact on the people locked down and not at statistical risk of COVID-19. If you lock down a population with no collateral consequences (lost education, deaths of despair, untreated medical issues) and saved life years, it's a healthy debate if it was worth it.

If you lock down a population with consequences including more life years lost due to the lockdowns with little evidence the lockdowns saved COVID-19 lives, the primary objective, well, we're here to make sure this never happens again.

Below is a CDC graphic illustrating the excess deaths in America after six months of the pandemic.

Excess death analysis compares the number of people who died in America on average and compares that to the number of people who died in 2020, regardless of why they died. Figure 1 below is a chart illustrating some scale between COVID-19 deaths and all deaths in America: of the 4,162,418 deaths in America, official COVID-19 deaths are about 12.9% of that total. The CDC states here that 2/3 of excess deaths were from COVID-19 and 1/3 from something else. That something else was lockdown deaths.

Figure 1

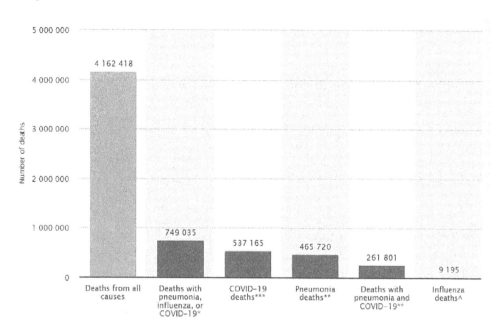

Number of deaths involving coronavirus disease 2019 (COVID-19), pneumonia, and influenza in the U.S. from February 1 to April 5, 2021. Source: https://www.statista.com/statistics/1113051/number-reported-deaths-from-covid-pneumonia-and-flu-us/

First, according to the CDC, through mid-April 2021, 491,148 Americans lost their lives where COVID-19 was the direct cause or primary underlying cause of death.[151] That number is directly taken from the CDC when at the time, the reported COVID-19 death count in America was 539,723. On this same date during this same period, the CDC reported a total of 609,142 excess deaths. In a 2020 analysis of COVID-19 deaths, the CDC reported that over 25% of COVID-19 deaths had no plausible chain-of-event condition associated with COVID-19.[152]

In the CDC October 2020 release on excess deaths, they reported 2/3 of excess deaths attributed to COVID-19 and 1/3 to anything else. Six months later, that was down to 20% caused by anything else. Their estimate on causal COVID-19 deaths was surely high because *probable* COVID-19 deaths and those with a past history of a positive test were counted at a time we likely had close to 200 million Americans that had caught SARS-CoV-2 sometime over the past fourteen months. If they died, it was a COVID-19 death. We also had spikes in other age groups not from COVID-19.

Here is the lockdown decision you are faced with; you get to be the judge. Keep in mind that we probably had more like 380,000 actual COVID-19 deaths based on how we counted COVID-19 deaths as seen in the previous chapter. For this exercise, we will round to 600,000 excess deaths through mid-April 2021,

400,000 from COVID-19 (only 25% inflation for overcounting from the official 540,000).

- 400,000 people died from COVID-19 (through mid-April 2021) and 200,000 died because of the lockdowns
- If we did not lock down, those extra 200,000 non-COVID-19 excess deaths would likely not have occurred, and there was no other social or healthcare reason for those deaths other than the lockdowns.
- We netted out 200,000 "saved" COVID-19 lives from the lockdowns. It's not 400,000 because we lost more lives that would not have died, so they are offsetting. The open argument is, would we have had more than 400,000 COVID-19 deaths had we not locked down?

Based on what we see in the Burden of Proof chapter, there was is not data-driven evidence that lockdowns saved any more lives than doing little more than protecting our long-term care facility residents and encouraging people to practice personal responsibility (see Florida, South Dakota, Oklahoma, Wyoming, etc.).

With little evidence and no data that strict lockdowns worked better than just a few mitigations, seeing a couple hundred thousand non-COVID-19 excess deaths, lost education for a year and a half, forty million people lose their jobs, hundreds of thousands of businesses close, and medical treatments paused for months, was it worth it? That's a call for you to make, but it sure seems like we incurred very high costs for saving lives that the data doesn't show could have been saved. COVID-19 was a natural disaster that could not be avoided, and as governors tried to stop it, they simply made a bad situation much worse. They turned a category two hurricane into a manmade category five hurricane.

Of the 41 million kids between ages 5-14, 5,556 died of something and of that, 1% died with SARS-CoV-2. By the time the pandemic ends, two kids in a million will have died *with* it, fewer *from* it. Based on youth samplings and estimated seroprevalence (the amount of infection in the population), we can make an educated assumption that at least eight million kids were infected by the fourth quarter of 2020. That made the infection fatality rate .00039%, or one in 205,000 that got infected died. 75% of those youths that died with COVID-19 were Black, Hispanic, or Native American; those minorities comprise 41% of the population in that age range.

Characteristic	No. (rate)*	
	Total deaths	COVID-19 deaths[§]
Total	3,358,814 (828.7)	377,883 (91.5)
Age group, yrs		
<1	19,146 (506.0)	43 (1.1)
1–4	3,469 (22.2)	24 (0.2)
5–14	5,556 (13.6)	67 (0.2)
15–24	35,470 (83.2)	587 (1.4)
25–34	72,678 (157.9)	2,527 (5.5)
35–44	103,389 (246.2)	6,617 (15.8)
45–54	189,397 (467.8)	17,905 (44.2)
55–64	436,886 (1,028.5)	44,631 (105.1)
65–74	669,316 (2,068.8)	80,617 (249.2)
75–84	816,307 (4,980.2)	104,212 (635.8)
≥85	1,007,114 (15,007.4)	120,648 (1,797.8)

Source: https://www.cdc.gov/mmwr/volumes/70/wr/mm7014e1.htm. The rate in parentheses is per 100,000. 2020 The COVID-19 death numbers are "gross," meaning any real or probable relationship to SARS-CoV-2.

Underlying Conditions

One consistent data point we learned from the cruise ships, the early breakout in Italy, and all the data well-documented in America was that COVID-19 was a discriminating disease. Unlike the Spanish Flu or HIV, which killed a wide demographic of people of all ages and health conditions, COVID-19 proved to be most dangerous to specific demographics: the elderly with frail immune systems and those suffering from specific chronic conditions. Of patients hospitalized, the breakdown in underlying conditions was:

Hypertension	49.7%
Obesity	48.3%
Diabetes	28.3%
Serious heart conditions	27.8%
Chronic lung disease	34.6%

Source: https://www.cdc.gov/coronavirus/2019-ncov/need-extra-precautions/groups-at-higher-risk.html

A *Reuters* article stated that "some 97% of those killed by COVID-19 in Louisiana had a pre-existing condition, according to the state health department. Diabetes was seen in 40% of the deaths, obesity in 25%, chronic kidney disease in 23%, and cardiac problems in 21%."[153]

Obesity

CNBC reported this study from the CDC in March 2021: "CDC study finds about 78% of people hospitalized for Covid were overweight or obese."[154] Of the thousands of COVID-19 hospitalizations they traced in late 2020, 28% were overweight and 50% were obese. A 5-foot-10-inch man at 175 pounds and a 5-foot-4-inch woman at 146 pounds are both considered overweight with BMIs of just over 25, according to the CDC's BMI calculator. A man and woman of the same heights would be considered obese at 210 pounds and 175 pounds, respectively.

Below is a chart mapping obesity percentages of the population in each country. Two of the wealthiest countries on the globe are shaded the darkest, the highest rate of obesity. Lighter shades below representing less obesity resulted in fewer COVID-19 effects. With the exception of Japan and South Korea, you can see a correlation between obesity and wealthier nations.

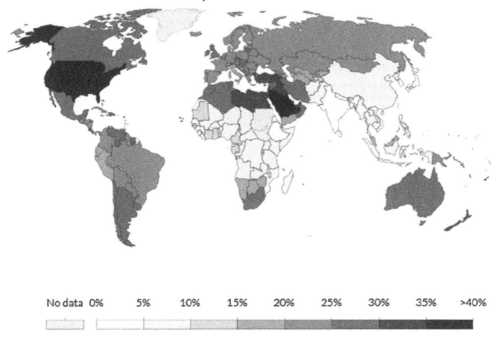

No data 0%   5%   10%   15%   20%   25%   30%   35%   >40%

Source: https://www.ehn.org/obesity-coronavirus-2645861896.html

As part of the COVID-19 response team at O'Connor Hospital in San Jose, California, Nivedita Lakhera wasn't prepared to see her intensive care unit filled with so many young patients. Many of those patients had no medical condition other than obesity. "They are young and coming to the ER and just dropping dead," she says. Some doctors said that some of their sickest patients are those under 60 who are obese.[155]

America has one of the highest obesity rates in the world. Obesity was the number one underlying condition causing death from COVID-19 in victims under age 65. In the United States, more than 40% of adults have a body mass index (BMI) greater than 30, the threshold for obesity. Nearly 10% are "severely obese," meaning they have a BMI greater than 40, according to the CDC.

What is obesity? Below is a BMI chart. In reviewing it, the beginning of the overweight boxes fringe on what would be normal. For myself, I fell into the last "normal" box on a row and feel I need to put on some weight. My son, a D1 college athlete, has 3% body fat and he too is on the last "normal" box on his row, so the chart is not hard and fast. About 40% of Americans are in the obese or extremely obese boxes on the chart. When I mentioned that data to many of the physicians with whom I spoke in researching this book, each rolled their eyes at me and shook their heads; they knew. That's with many of them falling into those same right-hand boxes by their own admission.

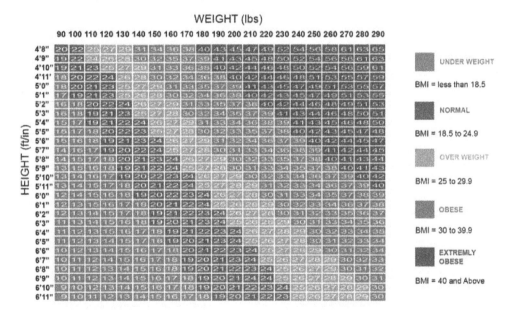

COVID-19 caused strokes at a much higher than usual rate in people under 50 who were obese. Usually, strokes occur from blood clots in arteries, but doctors were seeing clots in veins in COVID-19 patients.[156] This is correlated to the reports of vaccines causing blood clot issues in the spring of 2021. COVID-19 caused blood clotting; it's little surprise that the vaccines caused similar side effects as well.

For more validation on how much obesity correlates to the risk of COVID-19, here is a look at the highest and lowest obese countries. Countries with less than 10% of their populations clinically obese include:

Nearly all African nations
Thailand	10.0%
Indonesia	6.9%
Philippines	6.4%
China	6.2%
Singapore	6.1%
Afghanistan	5.5%
South Korea	5.0%
Japan	4.3%
Nepal	4.1%
Cambodia	3.9%
India	3.9%
Bangladesh	3.6%

Not one of these countries saw even 200 COVID-19 deaths per million at a time when the United States was at 1,750 deaths per million. India finally reached 300 deaths per million in the summer of 2021. They finally got their wave in May and June 2021.

Countries with obesity rates over 20% and high COVID-19 death rates include:
USA	36.2%
Jordan	35.5%
Canada	29.4%
Mexico	28.9%
Argentina	28.3%
South Africa	28.3%
Chile	28.0%
Uruguay	27.9%
United Kingdom	27.8%
Hungary	26.4%
Czechia	26.0%
Iran	25.8%
Costa Rica	25.7%
Ireland	25.3%
Bulgaria	25.0%
Belgium	22.0%
France	21.6%
Sweden	20.6%
Italy	19.9%

Source: *https://obesity.procon.org/global-obesity-levels/*

These countries were all among the leaders in COVID-19 deaths per capita, some at the very top of the list. There were many high obesity countries that did not experience high death rates, such as Saudi Arabia (same obesity rate as the US), Turkey, Australia, and New Zealand. What this shows is that having a high obesity rate did not guarantee a high death rate, but having a low obesity rate did seem to guarantee a low death rate.

Other Causes of Excess Deaths

The United States loses more than 80,000 people to diabetes any given year.[157] The combination of diabetes deaths with and without COVID-19 exceeded 100,000 in 2020.

The United States had 4,162,418 deaths in this period, February 1, 2020 to April 5, 2021. Here is the additional context:

- 749,035 people died with either pneumonia, the flu, or COVID-19 or a combination, 18% of all deaths.
- In 2019, somewhere between 34,000 and over 50,000 people died from the flu compared to under 10,000 during the pandemic, through two flu seasons, where that number would normally hover close to 100,000.
- Many that would have died of the flu died from COVID-19. This is one reason not all COVID-19 deaths were excess deaths: that and the older age of most victims.

Dr. Fauci made repeated comments in 2021 that social distancing and masks should remain in place forever. He stated these behaviors stunted flu illnesses and that was why flu deaths disappeared. However, COVID-19 highjacked the flu all over the world. Influenza and COVID-19 transmission is the same. If face masks, closed restaurants, and schools suppressed the flu, why not COVID-19? One may argue that closed schools suppressed the flu in the US, but the same thing happened in Europe with kids in class.

Finally, look at the chart illustrating the displacement of cause of deaths in New York state. This should leave little doubt while some COVID-19 deaths may not have been counted, more were overcounted or double-counted in concert with other causes. This is a small snapshot of New York's initial wave:

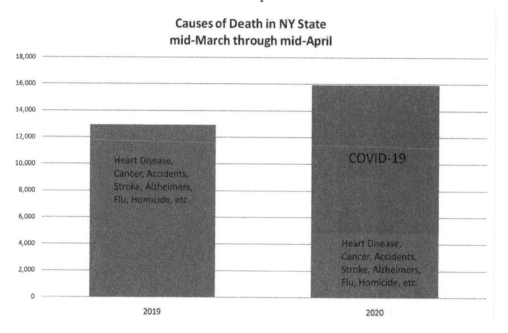

Source: CDC NY mortality stats & https://www.nytimes.com/2020/04/14/nyregion/new-york-coronavirus-deaths.html

Future Excess Deaths Not From COVID-19

The CDC recommended in March 2020 the deferment of in-person care for non-COVID-19, non-emergency healthcare. The puzzling thing about a sweeping policy like that is that in March, and April, and May, and every month since the pandemic began, hospitals were much more empty than full of COVID-19 and all patients.

Why not specify a threshold for ceasing non-COVID-19 healthcare? Why not set up places for dedicated non-COVID-19 treatment? Some surgeons told me it was impractical because of geography and doctors dedicated to certain facilities. I countered with the pandemic was treated like war-time in the measures taken. If war-time, reallocate everyone temporarily to get non-COVID-19 patients scheduled care.

Routine screenings and even treatments for existing conditions were largely suspended all over the country. The county where I live in metro Dallas had less than half the U.S. average deaths per capita. No hospital was pushed. In a county more populated than either of the Dakotas, we had an average of two COVID-19 deaths a day. Why was every healthcare provider shut down for routine care?

In South Carolina, a 700-bed hospital was not seeing non-emergency CO-VID-19 patients during the lockdowns. They were down to 60% occupancy.[158] They did not see more than ten COVID-19 patients at one time. People with inflamed appendixes, infected gallbladders, bowel obstructions, chest pains, and stroke symptoms had all vanished. They either were not admitted by their physicians or were too afraid to go be seen. That same hospital saw an 80% drop in possible stroke victims over the previous period.

The *Journal of the American College of Cardiology* reported a 38% decrease in patients being treated for a life-threatening event known as a STEMI — the blockage of one of the major arteries that supplies oxygen-rich blood to the heart. Plaque in arteries wasn't vanishing. Cancer was not magically disappearing, nor did cancer patients magically stopped needing treatments. Conditions would progress and lead to preventable deaths in the future.

The *San Francisco Chronicle* reported a new future casualty of the lockdowns: sexually transmitted diseases. Testing for STDs dropped sharply during the period when most non-essential health issues were sidelined. I always laughed at that term, "non-essential surgeries and tests." The term makes it sound like face-lifts were put on hold. STD cases plummeted during the lockdowns, creating another future problem.[159]

Cancer

Nathan Hyatt is a mathematician and graduate of Ohio Northern University. He has been an educator in math for over twenty years and was one of the first to uncover a sharp decrease in cancer screenings and diagnoses during the lockdowns. His work found its way into the White House in the summer of 2020. Nathan turned me on to several studies supporting this. The *JAMA Network* published a study about 278,778 patients receiving cancer treatments from Qwest Diagnostics for breast, colorectal, lung, pancreatic, gastric, and esophageal cancer during the initial lockdown period.[160] They found that treatments decreased by 46%. 46%! Cancer screening rates for breast, colorectal, and prostate cancer were down over nine million in 2020 compared to 2019.[161] Much of this was made up later in 2020, while still down about 15% year-over-year, leading to probabilities that these decreases will increase future cancer deaths because of the lockdowns.

The number of cancer diagnoses was also down significantly. On the low-end, lung cancer diagnoses were down 16% and breast cancer diagnoses down 42% on the high-end. The UK saw a 75% decrease in cancer treatment referrals during the lockdowns. Undiagnosed and untreated cancer throughout the lockdowns will cost tens of thousands of excess cancer deaths in the future. A pool of doctors reported this in The *Lancet Oncology*:

Substantial increases in the number of avoidable cancer deaths in England are to be expected as a result of diagnostic delays due to the COVID-19 pandemic in the UK. Urgent policy interventions are necessary, particularly the need to manage the backlog within routine diagnostic services to mitigate the expected impact of the COVID-19 pandemic on patients with cancer.[162]

In the summer of 2020, over six thousand people in the UK were on hold for cancer treatments.[163] A million women missed mammogram testing, which they estimate will result in thousands of later-stage diagnoses. *BMJ Open* reported a 70% decrease in cancer diagnoses in the UK as well.[164]

In the United States, the UW Carbone Cancer Center, the National Comprehensive Cancer Network, the American Cancer Society, and 76 other organizations signed a letter to the public urging them to resume cancer screenings and treatments during the pandemic.[165] The title of the letter was "Major U.S. Cancer Centers Endorse Goal of Resuming Cancer Screening and Treatment During the COVID-19 Pandemic." The date? January 28, 2021, a full eleven months into the pandemic. One study showed cancer screenings were down 17.2% year-over-year ending in October 2020.[166] Like Emily Oster observed, it's not what one study says; it's what most studies say.

Below is a chart of a single hospital system in New England called Massachusetts General Brigham.[167] There they saw far fewer cancer screenings and diagnoses during the mid-2020 study period. Extrapolate that nationally, and especially in large-populated states with severe lockdowns like New York, the mid-Atlantic, the west coast, and Midwest states like Illinois and Michigan.

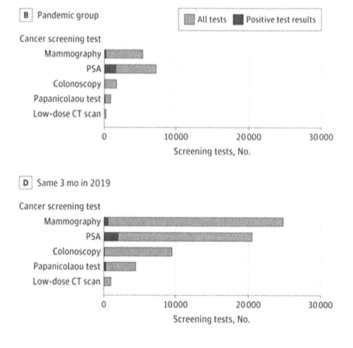

Even in large, less stringent states like Florida and Texas, the cancer screenings and diagnoses were way down.

These are significant decreases from the previous year and only included some cancers, not all. Long-term effects of delayed non-COVID-19 healthcare will be felt for years and contribute to tens of thousands of excess deaths. The *Epic Health Research Network* reported colon, breast, and cervical cancer screenings were down about 90% in the early lockdowns and still down a third in the summer of 2020.[168] Compounding this were sharp decreases in cancer research funding and clinical trials, reported to be down 60% in the *Lancet Oncology*.[169]

Studies like this are available from around the world. If cancer screenings dropped because people were unable and then afraid to get tested, as well as cancer treatments dropping, you can see how this will result in tens of thousands or more excess deaths from the lockdowns that have nothing to do with COVID-19. Add to that decreased trials and research, and the long-term effects will be far-reaching.

What percent of official COVID-19 deaths were really caused by COVID-19?

Through 2020, the United States recorded 345,323 lives lost to COVID-19. By the end of 2021, that will nearly triple. One debate that went on throughout the pandemic was, how many of those are real COVID-19-caused deaths? The reason for the debate is that we knew many of those deaths were probables or that people died *with* SARS-CoV-2 and not *from* COVID-19.

In September 2020, there was a release from the CDC that stated that only 6% of the victims of this coronavirus died exclusively from it. Many pounced on this as validation that it was much less dangerous than thought and that only about 10,000 people to date had actually died from COVID-19. That line of thinking was wishful thinking but completely inaccurate. There was no doubt COVID-19 caused many more deaths than that.

However, of the COVID-19 deaths with or likely with COVID-19 that were reported in the United States after a year, the actual number was substantially lower. This is why. The deaths recorded as COVID-19 are categorized with sole cause, primary cause, and tertiary cause of deaths from the virus. That is identified on a death certificate. Below is a breakdown after analyzing through the Morbidity and Mortality Weekly Report by the CDC and reconciling that with other excess deaths:

- 19% of excess deaths are from COVID-19 alone. Based on the 609,142 excess deaths from February 2020 through March 2021, that is 115,737 lives lost almost solely to COVID-19.
- 27% of excess deaths where COVID-19 was the primary cause of death with other underlying conditions as secondary contributors to death. That is another 164,468 lives lost to COVID-19.

- Those two groupings combined are about 280,000 real lives lost to CO-VID-19 of the 530,000 reported at the time. The median age of these victims was around 83 years old.

23% more of the excess deaths died with SARS-CoV-2 but not as a sole or primary cause of death. Examples of this could be a car crash victim or someone that died from a heart attack that carried the virus, and often nosocomial infections. These are infections that are contracted within a hospital. Transmission usually occurs via healthcare workers, patients, hospital equipment, or interventional procedures. A patient comes in with an ailment, and while in the hospital, they catch the virus and may or may not have been sick from it, but were in for something else. This represents 140,103/609,142 excess deaths and are much lower confidence to attribute to COVID-19 death counts. These deaths would have happened anyway had they caught the virus or not.

Now we see a certain 280,000 of the 600,000 excess deaths in 2020. What about the rest? There are another 300,000 deaths to account for. Many of these are COVID-19 deaths, but many of these are also lockdown deaths.

Lockdown Deaths

Deaths not attributed to COVID-19 spiked in 2020-2021 due to the lockdowns in three major areas: people dying due to abandonment, untreated medical conditions, and unintended injuries (overdoses among them). Conceptually, you look at the 530,000 COVID-19 deaths and decide if they were preventable. Then you look at the extra 200,000 non-COVID-19 excess deaths and determine if the effort was worth it in causing more life-years lost. That is the argument: COVID-19 deaths were not preventable and, in trying to do so, caused many more deaths. In trying to prevent them, governments made the situation even worse.

Another way to look at it is, would we have had 200,000 more COVID-19 deaths had we not locked down? Would we be worse off if we had 200,000 more COVID-19 deaths at that health condition and age stratification and 200,000 fewer lockdown deaths at the younger, healthier age group? These are very complex decisions, and when making decisions "for the greater good," there is always fallout.

That's your call to make; everyone sees it differently. After doing hundreds of interviews on the lockdowns and receiving hundreds of reader emails, it's clear there are some that believe there is no such thing as a lockdown death. However, they are real. They are as real as COVID-19 deaths. Neither is a hoax, both are huge numbers, and one was controllable.

The *JAMA Network* is a medical journal published by the American Medical Association and has published hundreds of articles and studies about COVID-19. On October 20, 2020, they published an analysis on excess deaths called "Excess Deaths From COVID-19 and Other Causes, March-July 2020."[170] In that, they looked at excess deaths by state and by cause and made the following determinations:

- Between March 1 and August 1, 2020, 1,336,561 deaths occurred in the US, a 20% increase over expected deaths. The ten states with the highest per capita rate of excess deaths were New York, New Jersey, Massachusetts, Louisiana, Arizona, Mississippi, Maryland, Delaware, Rhode Island, and Michigan, the highest at +65%.
- Of the 225,530 excess deaths, 150,541 (67%) were attributed to COVID-19.
- Other deaths attributed to causes *other than COVID-19* had two causes reaching statistical significance. Mortality rates for heart disease increased and mortality rates for Alzheimer disease/dementia doubled.

Within that, here are select states that had high excess deaths in 2020 and the percent that came from *something other than COVID-19*, what we will call lockdown deaths. Again, the percentages listed below are the percentage of excess deaths not from COVID-19, but from the lockdowns:

United States:	33%
Ohio:	48%
Texas:	44%
Florida:	40%
California:	39%
Illinois:	34%
Michigan:	33%
New Jersey:	22%
New York:	22%

Below is an excellent graphic illustrating the breakdown of excess deaths in the United States. Deaths by dementia, malignant neoplasms (cancer), and circulatory diseases are all up not from COVID-19 but from the lockdowns. Scientists reporting in a University of Leeds report believed many excess deaths "were caused by people not seeking emergency hospital treatment for a heart attack or other acute cardiovascular illness requiring urgent medical attention, either because they were afraid of contracting COVID-19 or were not referred for treatment."[171]

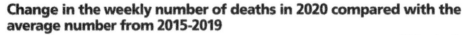

Change in the weekly number of deaths in 2020 compared with the average number from 2015-2019

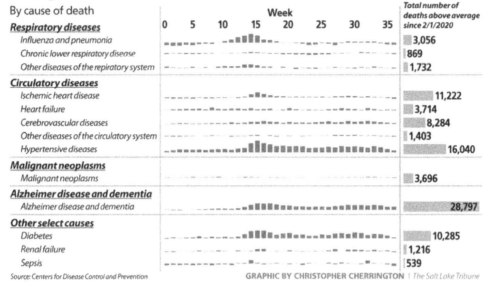

By cause of death	Week 0–35	Total number of deaths above average since 2/1/2020
Respiratory diseases		
Influenza and pneumonia		3,056
Chronic lower respiratory disease		869
Other diseases of the repiratory system		1,732
Circulatory diseases		
Ischemic heart disease		11,222
Heart failure		3,714
Cerebrovascular diseases		8,284
Other diseases of the circulatory system		1,403
Hypertensive diseases		16,040
Malignant neoplasms		
Malignant neoplasms		3,696
Alzheimer disease and dementia		
Alzheimer disease and dementia		28,797
Other select causes		
Diabetes		10,285
Renal failure		1,216
Sepsis		539

Source: Centers for Disease Control and Prevention

GRAPHIC BY CHRISTOPHER CHERRINGTON | *The Salt Lake Tribune*

Christopher Cherrington | The Salt Lake Tribune

Deaths by Abandonment

Below you can see an analysis published by Quartz that illustrates the high increase in deaths by Alzheimer's and dementia. [172] In long-term care facilities, people with dementia were left alone more and, as a result, saw significant increases in their loss of life. Lockdown deaths. According to Katherine Ellen Foley in that analysis:

> *The pandemic dramatically disrupted dementia care. Nursing homes struggled with staffing and adequate PPE for employees. The atmosphere was tense—a factor that could put residents at a higher risk of dying on its own. Routine check-ups were foregone or conducted over the phone or computer—an imperfect medium new to both patients and providers.*
>
> *The pandemic isn't just a respiratory illness. By straining resources and access to healthcare, it has indirectly killed thousands. As the U.S. health care system continues to battle Covid-19, it will have to pay attention to the gaps and inequalities revealed by all the pandemic's impacts.*

US weekly deaths from Alzheimer's and other dementias

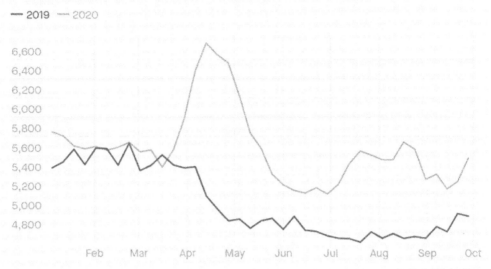

Quartz | qz.com | Data: US Centers for Disease Control and Prevention | Note: Deaths from recent weeks are likely to be incomplete as reports are delayed

Revisiting Michael Osterholm's group at the University of Minnesota, the Center for Infectious Disease Research and Policy published "Intellectual disability, obesity tied to COVID-19 hospitalization, death" in March 2021.[173] Patients with intellectual disabilities were twice as likely in their age group to be susceptible to hospitalization, intensive care, and death as those without. Intellectual disability trumped other underlying conditions such as congestive heart disease, kidney failure or lung disease, everything except old age. Once again, you can see COVID-19 was not a sweeping general threat to all Americans. It was noticeably aggressive to narrow segments of the population, never warranting one-size-fits-all lockdowns.

To net this out, people in long-term care facilities, those with intellectual disabilities, and those over 75 years old were at measurable risk. Less those people, we'd barely know there was a pandemic. That is in no way minimizing this; my family lost someone to COVID-19 with Down's syndrome in a care facility. It is stating unequivocally that some of the measures, like locking kids out of school and shutting down restaurants, were the most reckless, unscientific policies of our time.

The CDC reported 42,000 deaths above normal for Alzheimer's and dementia patients during 2020.[174] With tight visitation and care restrictions in 2021, like 2020, that excess number will likely be replicated in 2021. These were not all COVID-19 deaths, though some were. Contributing factors into the many non-COVID-19 deaths, the lockdown deaths, were less medical care, less healthcare attention and staff to do so, and loneliness, feeling abandoned. I have to believe that if many of us were relegated to a care facility and were prevented from seeing outsiders for months, we'd give up too. I would. My family had an elderly relative that suffered a stroke in Michigan in the spring of 2021 days after receiving his second vaccine shot. He was rehabbing in a care facility and we were not permitted to see him. We walked outside to his first-floor window and called him, talking on the phone through a closed window. No visitors were allowed.

Younger People and Excess Deaths

Below are two CDC charts showing excess deaths in Americans age 0-44. Look closely at the under-25 chart.[175] Excess deaths in 2020 through September were actually 2% below average. The spike in May to July is also interesting, making you wonder if any deaths were spiked due to untreated ailments or were depression-oriented. Still, with all deaths *below average* for those under age 25 makes you really wonder about closing schools. One in a million kids died with SARS-CoV-2 and all-cause deaths were below average, and tens of millions of kids were away from school for a year and a half.

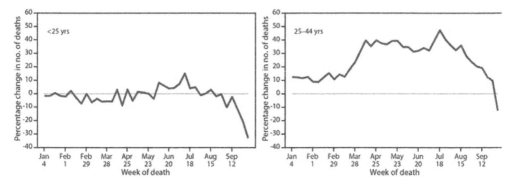

The second chart is more telling for those ages 25-44. 5,834 deaths were with SARS-CoV-2 in this age bracket of the total 121,447 total deaths. Adults ages 25–44 years experienced the largest average percentage increase (26.4%) in the number of deaths from all causes from late January through October 3, 2020, of any age bracket. We know that this age bracket is highly unaffected by COVID-19; 2.5% of all COVID-19 deaths came from those aged 25-44.

Those ages 25-44 generally lack the comorbidities seen in most COVID-19 deaths, so that was likely not the cause. And, the excess deaths were up to 15,000 more than the 5,834 COVID-19 deaths. These excess deaths are likely deaths of despair, including from alcohol/drug abuse and violence.

In 2020, a cause of death labeled "Unintentional Injuries" was up over 20,000 over the previous two-year average. Unintentional injuries include overdoses, drownings, car accidents, etc. It's typically a top-five leading cause of death category.

Looking Forward

Based on the excess death outlook for the second half of 2021 at the time of this writing (June 2021), it appears that excess deaths are already trending below average. It can take up to a couple of months for all deaths to be counted, but there are already indicators of fewer deaths than the spring of 2020 and even fewer total deaths than the spring of 2019. If that trend holds, it will validate that COVID-19 mostly pulled forward deaths. What this means is that the pandemic mostly accelerated deaths that would have occurred within less than a year. That doesn't minimize the pandemic, but it does invalidate the lockdowns. A category two pandemic that mostly pulls forward deaths should never again trigger sweeping lockdowns as we saw in 2020 and 2021.

How lethal is COVID-19?

Contrary to what White House advisor Andy Slavitt and Dr. Anthony Fauci told us, we knew quite a bit about COVID-19 after a year and a half. Based on a half-million fatalities and hundreds of millions infected, the following groups of people are statistically unaffected:

- Young people under 18 were almost impregnable to COVID-19
- Anyone under sixty and in excellent health was at no *measurable* risk
- Those under seventy and in great health were at *very little risk*

We also knew the following groups are at risk:

- Those over 80 in any health condition were at *measurable risk*
- Those 70-80 in any health condition were at *some risk*
- Severe obesity and COVID-19 could cause a stroke, the most at-risk condition under 50
- Those with severe kidney failures, hypertension, severe diabetes, chronic lung and respiratory conditions were at measurable risk

One metric used for virus lethality is the infection fatality rate (IFR). If 1,000,000 people contract a virus and 100,000 die from it, the fatality rate is 10%, which is very high. If you look at the official numbers after a year of COVID-19, there were about 30,000,000 official "cases" and 500,000 deaths, a 1.6% fatality rate, also very high. It was not an evenly stratified fatality rate risk, though. The IFR in younger people was mathematically zero, and the IFR in older people was higher.

However, many more people contracted the virus and were not sick at all or only mildly sick, in which case they were not tested. In September 2020, the WHO estimated 750,000,000 people worldwide had contracted the virus. The official number was 42,000,000. That's an 18-fold increase. The CDC often estimated seven times more Americans caught the virus than the official count.

A year into COVID-19, we had at least 175,000,000 infections, which calculates to an IFR of .28%, very low relative to the lockdown measures taken. If you believe COVID-19 deaths are somewhat overcounted, the IFR drops to .2%, and that really is close to the IFR for COVID-19. It's awfully hard to believe any lockdown measure is warranted other than isolating those known to be at risk.

CHAPTER 9
Nursing Homes

Nursing home residents proved to be most vulnerable to COVID-19. Nursing homes became the hotbed for the virus spread and the source of most deaths. In Europe, it's estimated more than half of the deaths were residents of long-term care facilities, which was during that first wave.[176] In America, the data was not tied together in one reliable data source, meaning the data was loose and reported state-by-state. It was significant and likely a good 50% of all COVID-19 deaths too. In April 2021, the official count was 33% of all COVID-19 deaths were sourced from nursing homes. There was very low confidence that the percentage was accurate.

When looking at states in the northeast, most were 50% or more. New York and New Jersey are listed at 31% and 33%. Back in June 2020, New York was reporting 27%. It defied all logic. The data from New York that 96% of their COVID-19 deaths were from victims with three or more comorbidities and an average age of close to 80. Those are people that live in long-term care facilities.

The following states required nursing homes to accept new or existing COVID-19 patients in the spring of 2020: New York, Michigan, California, New Jersey, and Pennsylvania. What was someone thinking to require a sick patient with a spreadable disease like COVID-19 to be brought into the most vulnerable population group already known to everyone by March 2020? A grade-school kid looking at the death data out of the cruise ships, and particularly Italy, could see that by March. Italy was ravaged early on solely because COVID-19 spread like wildfire through low-end care facilities.

There were two known Laws of COVID-19 known by March 2020:
1. Elderly people with underlying conditions were at serious risk of dying to COVID-19
2. Kids were at statistically zero risk to COVID-19

These governors managed to keep kids out of school for a year and a half while requiring sick COVID-19 patients into the lion's den. It's still hard to believe a year and a half later these two policies existed, with every data point of science indicating what awful policies these were. Why the media didn't put so much coverage on this to drive polls to have these governors resign is unfathomable. Actually, it is fathomable, and we will see why later on in chapter eighteen.

No one following this closely believed the data out of New York. Janice Dean, from *Fox News*, lost both her in-laws to COVID-19 in a New York care facility and was really the only person in the media beating on this story for months. When the story about Governor Andrew Cuomo broke in January, it made huge headlines. Likely no one was more gratified than Dean. Still, to people studying this, it was a non-story. We knew that data was inaccurate at best, corrupt at worst.

The Most Flawed Policy

On March 25, 2020, the New York Department of Health issued an order requiring nursing homes to take in COVID-19 patients. The other states listed above did as well. Patients went into nursing homes, spread it to other patients and staff. It spread more, the treatment was less effective than it was at the end of the pandemic, and thousands of patients died, waiting like sitting ducks in these care facilities. One of those patients was a cousin of mine in Detroit; thank you, Governor Whitmer. That loss wasn't the governor's fault, but her nursing home policy combined with banning DIY purchases during the lockdown may have been the most out of touch policy in the world.

A quick side note on the blame on the governors. While the policy was maybe the most abhorrent of any COVID-19 policy (let's close gyms and playgrounds but send sick people to mingle with the vulnerable!), it wasn't just the governors. In fact, it may even be less on the governors than the "public health experts." This may not have been intuitive to a governor, who was not a healthcare expert and rushing around in a frenzy during those days trying to figure out what to do with models projecting millions of lives lost. However, it should have been to the "public health experts."

Where were Dr. Fauci, Dr. Redfield, Dr. Birx, Dr. Adams, or the HHS secretaries for these states? Why were they never held accountable? These individuals should all be questioned, sanctioned, and probably fired for malpractice for not seeing this coming. You won't find the analysis on this in the media, but these are the most responsible individuals. Seeing Dr. Birx talk on *CNN* in 2021 about how most lives could have been saved had the federal government (read: President Trump) done better while she sat silently during these nursing home policies was maybe the most hypocritical display of a health care leader in memory.

On January 28, 2021, New York State Attorney General Letitia James released a report on nursing homes that suggested the state undercounted COVID-19 deaths from nursing homes and long-term care facility residents by as much as 50%. This was no surprise to those following the data.

Reporting at the Time

Below is some reporting on the impact on people living in long term care facilities:

- *Nursing Homes Are Starkly Vulnerable to Coronavirus"[177] on March 4, 2020. Perhaps someone should have gotten a New York Times subscription for Governor Cuomo.*

- *70% of Ohio coronavirus deaths have occurred in long-term care facilities[178]*

- *One-Third of All U.S. Coronavirus Deaths Are Nursing Home Residents or Workers; At least 25,600 residents and workers have died from the coronavirus at nursing homes and other long-term care facilities for older adults in the United States. The virus so far has infected more than 143,000 at some 7,500 facilities[179]*

- *Nearly 50% of California's COVID-19 deaths are residents, staff at nursing, care homes[180]*

- *Nursing homes account for 48% of all Illinois COVID-19 deaths[181]*

- *70% of Johnson County [southern part of metro Kansas City, KS] deaths were in at least eight different long-term care facilities[182]*

- *Elder Care Facilities In Mass. The Hardest, With More Than 1,300 Now Dead[183]*

- *Nursing homes account for one-third of Indiana coronavirus deaths[184]*

- *The deaths of 322 residents of nursing homes and senior care centers in Colorado have been linked to COVID-19[185]*

- *40% of the COVID-19 deaths in Georgia were in long-term care facilities, including nursing homes, according to data from the Georgia Department of Community Health (DCH) and the Georgia Department of Public Health (DPH)[186]*

- *Louisiana has had 275 COVID-19 deaths among residents at long term care facilities and about 1,100 at the end of April[187]*

- *The WHO reported nursing homes linked to up to half of coronavirus deaths in Europe[188]*

- *In Michigan, more than 2,000 nursing home patients had COVID-19 at the end of April[189]*

- *Of Florida's first 1,074 COVID-19 deaths, 311 were long-term care residents, almost a third. This was much less than some states like Delaware (58%), Massachusetts (55%), and Colorado (50%)[190]*

- *Nearly 60 percent of Virginia's coronavirus deaths are in nursing homes, other long-term care facilities[191]*

- *Over 40% of Texas deaths were linked to nursing homes and long-term care facilities[192]*

- *68% of Pennsylvania's 3,106 COVID-19 deaths by early May were sourced from nursing homes and related facilities[193]*

- *Minnesota nursing homes, already the site of 81% of COVID-19 deaths, continue taking in infected patients."[194]*

- *U.S. Nursing Homes Have More Coronavirus Deaths Than All But 5 Countries, and the Counting Has Just Begun[195]*

- *Canada's nursing home crisis: 81 percent of coronavirus deaths are in long-term care facilities[196]*

- *Nursing home protections limit families who want to sue; As the coronavirus takes a devastating toll on seniors in nursing homes, many attorneys are turning down grieving families seeking to sue long-term care providers for wrongful death[197]*

- *How many COVID-related deaths occurred in Michigan nursing homes? Lawmakers, families want answers; No standard policy for reporting deaths[198]*

- *[Michigan Attorney General Dana] Nessel declines GOP request to probe Michigan COVID nursing home deaths[199]*

- *December [2021] Proved To Be Deadliest Month For Residents In Long-Term Care Facilities[200]*

- *In one week of the holiday month, the coronavirus killed more frail people in institutions than there are undergrads enrolled at Georgetown. The disease claimed the lives of just about more long-term residents in December than there are students enrolled at George Washington or Johns Hopkins[201]*

Below is a visual of the percent of nursing home deaths in states through March 2021.

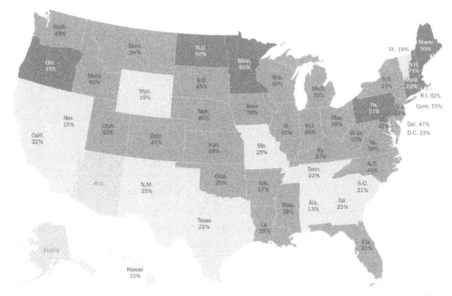

Source: https://www.nytimes.com/interactive/2020/us/coronavirus-nursing-homes.html

We will never know exactly the number of COVID-19 deaths that occurred in care facilities or were sourced there, but it's sad when you think of inconsistent care and the immobility of the residents. One woman lost her grandfather, a World War II veteran, to COVID-19 in a nursing home. She said that the residents were "sitting ducks" as this swept through his nursing home.

Upper Midwest and western states, including the Dakotas, Montana, Wisconsin, and Wyoming had high nursing home deaths to COVID-19, the highest number of victims in the fall of 2020. South Dakota had one in four nursing home residents catch COVID-19 and one in twenty die from it in November and December. From mid-October to mid-November, about 60,000 residents and another 60,000 staff were positive with COVID-19 nationally.

The *New York Times* analysis also identified a list of surge states — including Colorado, Iowa, Illinois, Nebraska, New Mexico, and Ohio — that experienced double the number of resident deaths, resident infections, and staff infections from mid-October to mid-November when compared with the previous month. Their skyrocketing rates put them all above the national average in all three categories.

Many states and nursing homes are not required to release this data and are not motivated to do so. Several states are indemnifying care facilities and their employees (who may have been sources of the spread), and many more are requesting their states to do so. There were hundreds of wrongful death lawsuits filed against facilities and employees through 2021, though many lawyers declined these cases because they didn't think they could win. If states did not indemnify nursing homes, fewer would exist by the end of 2021. It was a lose-lose situation.

What Happened in Nursing Homes?

Quality of life is usually better when you spend more money. First-class flying is better than coach. Most people prefer a Ritz Carlton over a Springhill Suites. Driving a Lexus is better than a Volkswagen. Going to a Beverly Hills physician is better than a Medicaid-servicing facility in Inglewood. It follows that being cared for in a more expensive facility is a better experience than a low-end facility. In 2020 we learned they were also safer.

The CDC released a study in September 2020 called "Association Between CMS Quality Ratings and COVID-19 Outbreaks in Nursing Homes — West Virginia, March 17–June 11, 2020."[202] Long-term care facilities are rated one to five stars, similar to how hotels are rated. The CDC study authors looked at 123 facilities in West Virginia for trends and correlations in the quality of the facility with COVID-19 outbreaks.

The breakdown of West Virginia facilities in the study was:
- 1 star, 20 facilities
- 2 star, 34 facilities
- 3 star, 28 facilities
- 4 star, 22 facilities
- 5 star, 18 facilities
- 1 facility unrated

Differences that distinguish the ratings are health inspections, staffing, and quality measures. Can you see where this is going? Half the nursing home outbreaks in West Virginia were in one-star facilities. Half the infections in just 16% of the facilities. No five-star facilities had an outbreak, and only one four-star facility did.

The outbreak facilities had four times the number of substantiated documented complaints. The outbreak facilities had deficiencies in every category: quality of life; care planning; nurse and physician services; nutrition and dietary; and several other categories. The point in this is not to criticize the one-star facilities but rather give some context on what was happening. There is no easy resolution to something like this. If someone doesn't have the resources and needs care, they are bound to a low-end facility. The one-star facilities don't have the resources to provide better care.

The U.S. Senate Committee on Finance held a hearing on March 17, 2021[203] to probe why there were so many nursing home deaths. A certified nurse assistant (among others) testified the following:

- When COVID first hit, we lost over 20 plus residents in just over a month. A CNA at my facility died, too, and she was one of the first nursing home workers to die of COVID in Rhode Island.
- We were extremely short-staffed, too. At one point, I was caring for 26 critically ill residents with only the help of one other CNA, a nurse, and a housekeeper. My residents couldn't eat or drink without help. They couldn't move or get out of bed by themselves. They all required oxygen changes every 15 minutes. And because they had Alzheimer's, sometimes they would get very scared or angry.
- It was horrifying. But management didn't seem to be too concerned when my coworkers and I told them what was going on. We pleaded for more staff on each shift, but they said they couldn't find anyone. And so our residents and staff kept getting sick. They kept dying.
- Despite my years of training and the love I have for my residents, there was nothing I could do to help them. Our residents felt so alone. Because we were dressed head to toe in protective gear, they couldn't tell who we were. They deserved so much better than what we were able to provide with so few staff and resources.

Why did this happen? Senator Elizabeth Warren voiced displeasure at the mountain of CARES Act funding that did not find its way toward more resources and staffing at facilities amidst an outpouring of taxpayer-funded relief allocated to them. Warren called out that the CEO of the facility where the testifying nurse assistant served received a multi-million-dollar retention bonus.

There is nothing wrong with CEOs earning a lot more than rank and file staff. NBC News did a hit job on the HCA Healthcare CEO, earning much more than a technician there.[204] If you're not going to get upset at Justin Verlander or Miguel Cabrera earning 300 times more than the person selling game tickets, then don't get upset at CEOs earning a lot more. However, if the company, in this case, this long-term care facility channeled government money in the form of a bailout to executive pay rather than its intended purpose, it's wrong.

Nursing homes were ravaged because they had extremely vulnerable residents. Low-end facilities lacked staff, cleanliness, space, ventilation (think the opposite of airplane air circulation and ventilation), and on top of that, many had positive patients there. In most cases, nursing homes took their existing residents back even if positive with COVID-19 and even if they did not admit new patients.

The long-term care facility situation was a no-win tragedy situation for everyone. Even if patients did not get infected, they were not allowed visitation from family members. Think about that for a moment. You're eighty years old. You're in poor health. You're limited to television someone else sets up; it's unlikely any are using tablets to binge on Netflix. You may not even be able to go outside. You're likely wearing a face mask all the time. You're lonely for weeks and then months and then well over a year. At some point, you're maybe even hoping to get COVID-19 to get it over with. I think I would have.

CHAPTER 10
The Burden of Proof

An unimaginable thing happened in 2020: the default of American life turned upside down during the pandemic. There are many things we assume as norms or even rights. People accused of crimes are presumed innocent; the burden is on the prosecution to prove they did something wrong. People are granted a driver's license if they pass a test and get it taken away only when they do something wrong. Every child gets to go to school and is only removed if they do something wrong.

Every person has rights to do what everyone else can do unless they do something to have those rights taken away. In March 2020, when COVID-19 reached America, the default shifted from freedom to locked down. The default for a year was not to be in school, eat out, work out, work period, but to stay at home. Most states practiced this for well over a year straight, including California, Hawaii, New York, New Jersey, and many others. Each time cases or hospitalizations crept up, state or local leaders shut down schools, indoor dining, set capacity restrictions on nearly everything and required wearing face masks (sometimes in each person's own house).

This is not an argument about civil liberties or freedom. If these restrictions worked and states that ratcheted their communities down had suppressed COVID-19 activity, you could make an argument the interventions were warranted. Outside of the four to five weeks when COVID-19 hit each community (and most were untouched to where you'd not even know COVID-19 existed), nothing was happening. Still, the default was Close Schools!, Close Restaurants!, Mask Up!, and many other restrictions.

Did the restrictions work? "Experts" will tell you they helped, that things would have been far worse had they not tied their states down. You have to ask yourself....if masks worked, why didn't they work? Why didn't states or countries that had better than 90% adoption suppress it? Why did their hospitalizations and deaths exactly mirror so many places that did next to nothing? If closing California schools worked, why didn't they have any better pediatric results than anyone else? Spoiler alert on this one; pediatric illnesses from COVID-19 all over the world were too few to measure any trends anywhere. But their teachers working from home fared no better than their peers in class every day.

The data around COVID-19 hospitalizations and deaths had wild margins of error, up to 40% inaccuracies in some places. A White House data advisor told me it was up to 50%. The working number in this research is 30%. The inaccuracies spawned from mostly two things: the inclusion of untested *probable* hospitalizations and deaths, including those that died after testing positive within weeks or months but died of something else. Yes, the stories you heard about the gun or car accident victim counted as a COVID-19 death are outliers. What aren't outliers are the tens of thousands of people that died from real health issues, including issues like cardiac arrests, cancer deaths - things that had nothing to do with COVID-19. Remember, the number one source of COVID-19 hospitalizations and deaths was nosocomial infections gained in healthcare settings.

The other consequence discussed here is lockdown deaths. There is no doubt that tens or hundreds of thousands of people died prematurely from untreated ailments, avoidance of healthcare out of fear of getting COVID-19, and to a lesser degree, things like overdoses and suicides. Because of all the looseness in reporting, the highest integrity data point measuring the pandemic and lockdown impacts is looking at how many people in total died against expectations. If three million people died annually from 2015-2019 and then 3.5 million people died in 2020 and 2021, the increase is obvious. This is how we measure the pandemic and interventions holistically.

If California had fewer COVID-19 deaths per capita than South Dakota, but 3% more total excess deaths during the pandemic from all causes amidst the strictest lockdowns, was it worth it? Well, that's a no-brainer. A better comparison may be Idaho and neighboring Oregon and Washington. Idaho was much less restricted; kids were mostly in class if they wanted, whereas the two states to their west were almost California-tight. Idaho had about 14% excess deaths compared to about 8% in Oregon and Washington. Were the mitigations worth it? That's for you to decide. Here we will show many comparisons that suggest hard locking down produced no better results than doing little more than protecting the vulnerable and letting the populations practice personal responsibility without government mandates.

The burden was not on open states like South Dakota, Nebraska, Wyoming, Oklahoma, or Florida to do better. The burden was on states mandating a bunch of restrictions to do better. If lockdown measures work, their results should be a lot better. Then we can analyze if certain mitigations are worth it. Hypothetically, if open schools resulted in a 10% increase in pediatric deaths, we have a cause and effect to weigh. Then you decide, are open schools worth 10,000 more kids' lives lost? If open restaurants were known to result in 50% more deaths in a community, once again, we can analyze if closing was worth it. If either of those things played out and the data proved the cause and effect, closed schools and closed indoor dining would have had a higher approval rating than eliminating taxes.

Fourteen months into the pandemic, the United States was +14% in all-cause deaths, meaning 14% more died than expected. Low-restricted South Dakota, Oklahoma, Florida, Nebraska, Florida, and others should have far surpassed locked down states in all-cause deaths. South Dakota was +17% in excess deaths since the pandemic began. States doing worse than South Dakota that locked down harder included New Jersey (+27%), Arizona (+24%), New Mexico (+24%), Texas (+24%), California (+22%), New York (+20%), Maryland (+18%), and a dozen others. Locked-down states should have had far fewer total lives lost than those open, and they did not. In many cases, they did worse.

State Comparisons

Overall Rank, as of April 6, 2021	State	Political Party of Governor	Deaths per Million, May 24, 2021	All-Cause Excess Deaths Feb. 2020 - April 2021	Percent of Schools Open for F2F Learning October 1, 2020	Percent of Schools Open for F2F Learning April 1, 2021	Number of Weeks COVID-`19 ICUs Exceeded 20% 2020 & 2021	Number of Weeks COVID-`19 Hospitalizations Exceeded 20% 2020 & 2021
1	Iowa	R	1,913	14.0%	36	100	10	0
2	Florida	R	1,698	14.2%	78	100	N/A	0
3	Wyoming	R	1,232	14.3%	100	100	N/A	0
4	South Dakota	R	2,262	17.0%	70	100	17	4
5	Texas	R	1,775	24.8%	57	84	25	4
6	Alaska	R	495	9.5%	28	65	N/A	0
7	South Carolina	R	1,881	17.5%	24	98	8	2
8	Oklahoma	R	1,748	19.8%	47	79	15	0
8	Mississippi	R	2,448	25.4%	71	64	18	0
10	Montana	R	1,501	11.8%	43	100	8	4
11	Idaho	R	1,164	14.7%	21	100	13	0
12	Missouri	R	1,568	17.7%	27	79	13	0
13	Arkansas	R	1,928	17.5%	94	96	26	0
14	Nebraska	R	1,162	15.9%	72	88	N/A	4
15	Arizona	R	2,412	24.3%	37	94	25	11
16	Tennessee	R	1,813	15.7%	61	96	14	0
17	North Dakota	R	1,978	13.1%	40	100	0	1
18	Utah	R	714	13.7%	68	88	13	0
19	Wisconsin	D	1,200	10.6%	11	60	7	0
20	West Virginia	R	1,547	5.4%	17	100	10	0
21	Alabama	R	2,266	23.2%	39	93	22	7
22	New Hampshire	R	988	9.9%	18	50	N/A	0
23	Indiana	R	2,013	6.0%	55	86	14	6

Overall Rank, as of April 6, 2021	State	Political Party of Governor	Deaths per Million, May 24, 2021	All-Cause Excess Deaths Feb. 2020 - April 2021	Percent of Schools Open for F2F Learning October 1, 2020	Percent of Schools Open for F2F Learning April 1, 2021	Number of Weeks COVID-'19 ICUs Exceeded 20% 2020 & 2021	Number of Weeks COVID-'19 Hospitalizations Exceeded 20% 2020 & 2021
24	Georgia	R	1,946	21.3%	53	87	N/A	6
25	Kansas	D	1,736	15.9%	40	96	10	0
26	Maryland	R	1,492	18.5%	0	13	22	0
27	Louisiana	D	2,263	20.7%	32	79	N/A	0
28	North Carolina	D	1,235	N/A	0	59	9	0
29	Ohio	R	1,686	16.7%	35	63	11	0
30	Nevada	D	1,803	18.8%	14	48	18	11
31	Kentucky	D	1,503	14.9%	5	73	11	0
32	Colorado	D	1,152	13.1%	35	89	N/A	4
33	New Mexico	D	1,162	24.6%	0	12	N/A	6
34	Illinois	D	1,973	16.5%	7	38	17	3
35	Oregon	D	622	8.7%	0	11	0	0
36	Pennsylvania	D	2,121	17.5%	25	56	14	0
37	Hawaii	D	350	2.3%	0	0	6	0
38	Massachusetts	R	2,586	14.0%	14	13	0	4
39	Michigan	D	2,017	15.6%	40	57	19	0
40	Minnesota	D	1,321	10.3%	0	66	5	0
41	New Jersey	D	2,937	27.0%	2	21	28	5
42	Rhode Island	D	2,552	15.6%	42	57	9	0
43	Maine	D	612	2.9%	17	17	4	0
43	Connecticut	D	2,303	17.4%	18	77	N/A	4
45	California	D	1,593	21.9%	3	6	19	6
46	New York	D	2,745	19.8%	6	39	24	4
46	Washington	D	757	8.4%	0	3	0	0
48	Virginia	D	1,301	13.8%	2	33	11	0
49	Delaware	D	1,704	18.2%	4	19	8	5
50	District of Columbia	D (mayor)	1,601	N/A	0	8	9	3
51	Vermont	R	409	13.9%	47	67	1	0

Sources: Wallethub; Covid Tracking Project; Burbio; Worldometers; USMortality.com

The states above are ranked by least stringent to most stringent restrictions as of April 6, 2021, according to *Wallethub*.[205] Factoring into these rankings are face mask requirements, restaurants and bars open, schools open for in-person learning, stay-at-home orders, and other restrictions. The obvious question is, did restrictions result in fewer COVID-19 deaths? That's the tradeoff. Lockdowns were costly personally and financially, but if the correlation worked, you can make an argument that they were a reasonable strategy. Below are key take-aways from the data chart above.

Politics

The seventeen least restricted states were Republican-led, as were 22 of the first 23 states. There is no doubt restrictions correlated more to the party of the state governor than anything else. Of the 26 most restricted states, 22 were Democrat-led. Of the four most restricted Republican-led states, Massachusetts, Vermont, and Maryland are strong Democrat-voting states. Five of the eight states with over 20% all-cause excess deaths were Republican-led, three Democrat-led.

Hospitalizations

ICU and overall hospitalizations are listed relative to state capacity. The data is directional only. A threshold of 20% is set for comparative purposes only. When communities were met with their COVID-19 surge, it's likely a handful of hospitals were at or near full ICU capacity of COVID-19 patients for three to four weeks. A hospital is supposed to run at near capacity, like a hotel, in order to sustain itself. During the pandemic, outside of a four-to-six-week surge, most ran closer to 70%; during the spring 2020 lockdown, nationally most were almost completely empty and going broke. Had the CARES Act not bailed them out, many would not have made it, nor would most smaller healthcare providers. The healthcare industry would have gone broke during a pandemic without government bailouts.

Only seven states out of fifty-one (including DC) ever had more than five weeks of hospital beds occupied with over 20% COVID-19 patients. None of those seven states were among the top twenty least stringent states except Arizona. Only California reached over 20% of the ten most stringent states.

Some states did not report ICU occupation of COVID-19 patients. Of those that did, 22 exceeded ten weeks with over 20%. 34 states exceeded 20% ICU occupancy greater than five weeks, and that does not include unreported states, of which six states surely did. That means forty states had surges reach their ICUs.

Below is a comparison of the five most and least restricted states throughout the pandemic and their hospital occupancy:

Least Restricted			Most Restricted		
State	Number of Weeks COVID-'19 ICUs Exceeded 20% 2020 & 2021	Number of Weeks COVID-'19 Hospitalizations Exceeded 20% 2020 & 2021	State	Number of Weeks COVID-'19 ICUs Exceeded 20% 2020 & 2021	Number of Weeks COVID-'19 Hospitalizations Exceeded 20% 2020 & 2021
Iowa	10	0	New Mexico		6
Florida		0	Illinois	17	3

South Dakota	17	4	Pennsylvania	14	0
Oklahoma	15	0	New Jersey	28	5
Arkansas	26	0	California	19	6
North Dakota	0	1	New York	24	4

The impact on the most restricted states docs include states that were hit very hard in the initial stage of the pandemic, including New Jersey and New York. They are much higher populated states. Two of the least restricted states, the Dakotas, both reached the top fifteen in deaths per capita and may well end up outside the top fifteen when this is over. Still, harder locked down states did not correlate to fewer hospitalizations. You could argue they resulted in more, but with the burden of proof on locked down states, they simply did not result in fewer people in ICUs and occupying fewer hospital beds.

25 x 25

Eric Thomas works as a software architect in the healthcare field, with an additional academic background in biomedical engineering and cardiovascular biomechanics. I connected with Eric through our joint work contributing analysis to Rational Ground. Throughout the pandemic, as a side-project, Eric researched the harms of lockdowns and compiled data on a variety of metrics regarding COVID-19 and the public health response. Eric compiled the chart below comparing hospitalizations per capita for the twenty-five most stringent and least stringent states in the fall and winter of 2020-2021. Can you find any correlation between improved results with tighter versus fewer restrictions?

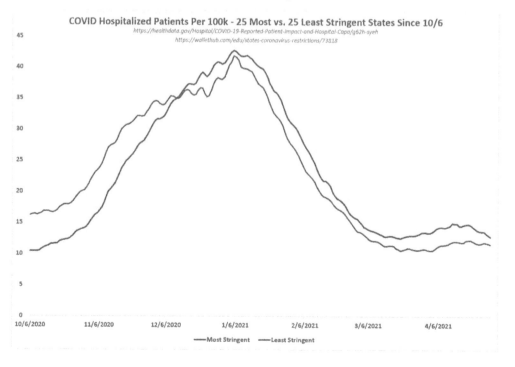

COVID-19 Deaths and Excess Deaths

Only five of the twenty highest COVID-19 deaths-per-capita results were from the top ten least restricted states. Fifteen of the twenty highest COVID-19 death states were also among the most restricted. This was consistent with previous stringency rankings from earlier in 2021 and back into 2020. The least restricted states did not dominate the highest death rates; it was the other way around.

Only five of the top ten least restricted states made the highest thirty in all-cause excess deaths, a huge lack of correlation between lockdowns and fewer deaths. This means excess deaths were more highly correlated to tighter lockdown states than to less restricted ones.

The average of the top 25 least stringent states in all-cause excess deaths was .2% less than the average of the 26 most stringent states (and DC). We can call that statistically insignificant. They were equal. Overall, tighter restrictions did not result in fewer deaths across the large sampling.

Fourteen months through the pandemic, the average COVID-19 deaths per million for the fourteen least stringent states was 1,580. The average COVID-19 deaths per million for the fourteen most stringent states was 1,640. The middle 23 states averaged 1,541. All were statistically about the same, within 5%.

The states bordering the southern border and gulf were among the most impacted in excess all-cause deaths in the country, except Florida. With varying degrees of lockdowns, tight in California and New Mexico, lighter in Arizona and Texas, gulf states all mask-mandated and largely remote schooling, every one was over +20% in excess all-cause deaths. All but one: the most open southern state, Florida.

New Jersey, New York, Rhode Island, and Massachusetts had the highest COVID-19 deaths per capita. Some of that was certainly due to hospital treatments in March and April 2020, something that improved markedly with time. Still, Massachusetts and Rhode Island had slipped out of the top spots for a while and regained high rankings in 2021, even with very tight restrictions and mask mandates.

Schools Open and Closed

Only two of the top ten highest deaths-per-capita states, Mississippi and South Dakota, had over half their schools open for face-to-face learning in the fall of 2020 and early 2021. This is relevant in that open schools did not correlate with high deaths per million.

Of the twenty states with 80% of their schools open for face-to-face learning in April 2021, their average COVID-19 deaths per capita were 1,654. Of the fifteen states with 50% or less face-to-face learning, their average COVID-19 deaths per capita were 1,539. The difference was insignificant. Smaller states with closed schools in Hawaii and Maine weighted that down, to where the average would have been near-identical.

There was no correlation between more in-person learning and more people getting sick in communities. Hard data shows that tight restrictions did not result in any better results than light restrictions. Closing schools didn't matter. Closing restaurants didn't matter. Wearing masks didn't matter. In the end, two mitigation tactics worked: those vulnerable isolating and social distancing, a form of isolation. The rest of the mitigations seem like they should have helped, but they just did not.

Grading the Governors

Not one governor performed perfectly during the pandemic and lockdowns. With media pressure, a desire to balance their constituents, and a desire to get reelected and move on to federal positions down the road, it was an enormously difficult job for all of them. For every single one, from Governors Newsom and Cuomo to Noem and DeSantis, it was the most challenging policy-making of their careers, and for any governor in perhaps American history. All grading below, like that for kids during their year-plus of remote learning, is on a curve. On that curve, here is how governors performed during the pandemic:

The A's

Governors Ron DeSantis (FL), Kristi Noem (SD), Pete Ricketts (NE), and Mark Gordon (WY). No governors faced more media pressure than Noem and DeSantis. Noem never locked down her state. She never state-mandated face masks. She held strong during a very difficult surge in November and December 2020. She leads a state populated comparably to a metro Dallas county and made more headlines for her stance than anyone not named DeSantis. Still, fewer than half the South Dakotan kids were forced out of class in 2020 and local governments were permitted to put up their own restrictions.

DeSantis led the third most populated state with a higher-than-average elderly population. Early on, he put in protections in long-term care facilities. He locked down last and reopened in May 2020. He removed state restrictions in September 2020, even as COVID-19 activity rose in the fall. He kept more classes open in Florida than any other large population state. And with that, Florida had no worse results than the national average. The burden was not on DeSantis and Noem to beat the street with their open states. The burden was on the lockdown states to have better results and that did not happen. You could not look at a blank chart of states' COVID-19 performance and pick out the tightly restricted versus looser states. For that, these bold governors get an A on the curve.

Mark Gordon kept schools open all 2020-2021, and for that, he deserves recognition. A brief state mask mandate and allowing Teton County to require masks and close restaurants when we went climbing there in 2020 was frustrating. Still, on the curve, Gordon gets an A. Ricketts does as well, staying under the national radar while making Nebraskans glad to be Nebraskans.

The B's

Governors Kim Reynolds (IA), Brian Kemp (GA), Doug Burgum (ND), Greg Abbott (TX), Kevin Stitt (OK), Henry McMaster (SC), Eric Holcomb (IN), Brad Little (ID), Mike Parson (MO), Asa Hutchinson (AR), Kate Ivey (AL), Gary Herbert (UT), and Tate Reeves (MS).

These governors all had state mandates at one point or another. Many of their kids missed school in 2020-2021 overall. Businesses were restricted and most had some mask mandates at one time or another. Still, we're grading on a curve. These governors presided over fewer restrictions and few of their states ever broke the top ten in deaths per capita. Governor Abbott would have been a C had he not completely opened everything in Texas up without restrictions nor face masks in March 2021, leading the way back. That was the A move of any of these governors. Asa Hutchinson kept more kids in class than any governor not named DeSantis or Gordon.

The C's

Governors Laura Kelly (KS), Bill Lee (TN), Steve Bullock (MT), Gina Raimondo (RI), and Doug Ducey (AZ). These governors at least allowed some kids to be in class throughout late 2020 and early 2021. Raimondo was surrounded by lockdown warriors keeping kids out of class and businesses closed, and she kept more kids in school than any state in the northeast or mid-Atlantic. Not enough kids, but we're on a curve.

The D's

Governors Jared Polis (CO), Ned Lamont (CT), Andy Beshear (KY), John Bel Edwards (LA), Mike Dunleavy (AK), Brad Little (ID), Mike DeWine (OH), and Jim Justice (WV). Few of these governors made headlines with their lockdown moves. None followed actual science. They went along with the pack and the polls. Their low grade is largely based on so few kids in class. Remember, science.

The F's

Governors John Carney (DE), David Ige (HI), Janet Mills (ME), Tim Waltz (MN), Steve Sisolak (NV), Michelle Lujan (NM), Roy Cooper (NC), Kate Brown (OR), Ralph Northam (VA), Jay Inslee (WA), Tony Evers (WI), Larry Hogan (MD), Charlie Baker (MA), Chris Sununu (NH) and Phil Scott (VT). Millions of their students were locked out of schools for over a year, thousands of businesses closed, and they were defiant in opening up when it was clear where the science stood. The only salvage for Ige, Mills, Brown, Scott, Sununu, and Inslee is that while they kept kids out of class and closed thousands of businesses, they did achieve low relative COVID-19 deaths and all-cause excess deaths. They likely would have anyway had they let kids get educated and let businesses function.

Complete Fails

Governors Andrew Cuomo (NJ), Phil Murphy (NJ), Gavin Newsom (CA), Gretchen Whitmer (MI), J.B. Pritzker (IL), and Tom Wolf (PA). There's a special place for governors that locked kids out of classrooms for a year and a half, ordered sick COVID-19 patients back into nursing homes, did not practice their own orders, shut down tens of thousands of businesses and still couldn't beat the U.S average in COVID-19 deaths or excess all-cause deaths.

CHAPTER 11
The Charts

Nothing tells the story of how well the non-pharmaceutical interventions worked than the graphs. No one knows this better than @ianmSC on Twitter. Ian began his journey of looking at the data like many of us, not because of politics or civil liberties, but because some things did not make sense. The apparent risks of COVID-19 as far back as March did not align with the sweeping lockdowns.

Ian began charting COVID-19 cases, hospitalizations, and deaths relative to lockdown measures all over the world to look for correlations. He once told me, "I'm not anti-mask or anti-closed-restaurants for no reason. The data led me there. They just didn't work." His chart tweets grew his following to tens of thousands as he stayed anonymous. A-listers retweeted his charts on many news outlets, governors, congressmen, and they found their way into the White House in the fall of 2020. Below are some charts he created for us to get a snapshot of how well lockdown measures worked.

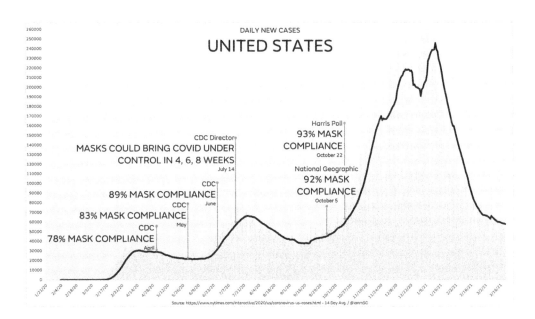

As a general baseline, mask-wearing in America was quite disciplined. In the few states that did not mandate them, many cities or counties did require them. The question to ask is, if masks work, why didn't masks work? The curve in the United States mirrored many countries with high mask adoption and those that did not, like Sweden. Sweden had a spring surge, mostly from long-term care facilities, and another winter 2020-2021 surge, and it mirrored the United States with no mask mandates or other restrictions.

We visited this chart and data in the CDC study section. In Kansas, some counties had mask mandates and some did not. The CDC study was measuring the increase in cases from a set date as we saw, but what about the absolute number of cases in these counties? If masks were effective at suppressing the spread of COVID-19, the counties with mask mandates should not have continued to have higher cases than those without. The numbers are fairly close and included the more populated Wyandotte (Kansas City) and Johnson counties. Still, the burden of proof is on the mask counties to demonstrate some trend that was better than the unmasked counties, and they did not.

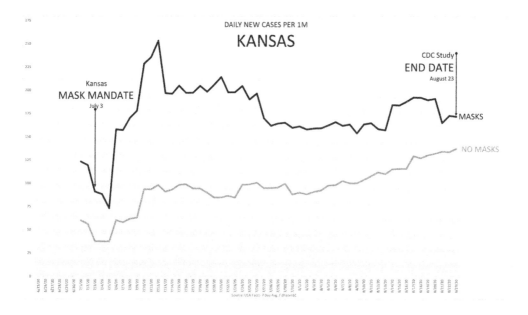

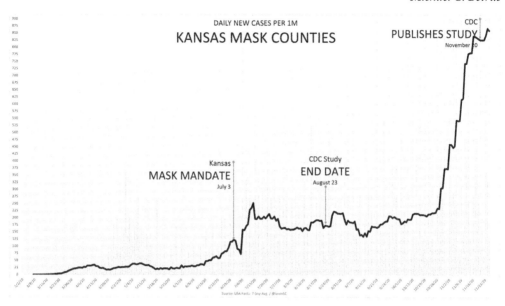

Revisiting Kansas, here are just the counties with mask mandates. The CDC cherry-picked data that showed some flat growth in cases and released it three months later, even when cases were surging. Masks did not stunt the case growth; it was seasonal. The case growth in Kansas in the fall looked like every state near it. It's data like this that led to questioning the efficacy of masks. It seems intuitive they would work, but for scientific reasons we saw in earlier chapters, they did not.

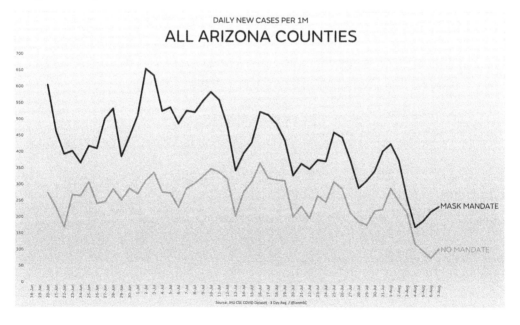

Governor Doug Ducey (AZ) never officially locked down his state, but counties were left to implement their restrictions. The fascinating part of this chart isn't that the mask mandate counties had a few more cases than the no-mask counties; the difference is insignificant. The telling part is that the curves are identical. When cases spiked, receded, and spiked again, it didn't matter the restrictions, schools closed, or gyms and restaurants closed. The virus did what it does regardless of government interventions.

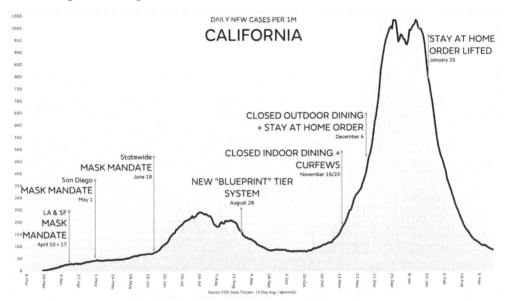

We could write an entire book analyzing the effects of California's lockdown measures. They tried so hard. First, mandating masks in major cities. Then the entire state. They closed indoor dining. They required people to stay home. In the end, these measures did nothing but cause huge collateral wreckage on kids missing their education, businesses closing, and people losing their jobs. We have to look at all these measures and ask, if wearing masks, closing restaurants, and ordering people to stay home worked, why didn't it work?

Diving deeper into Los Angeles, cases rose after the initial mask mandate. They rose after the outside mask mandate. They rose after indoor dining closed. They dipped like other states in that part of the country in August and rose in the fall. After mandating masks, closing restaurants, and issuing a curfew, cases rose sharply. After adding in a stay-at-home order, they still rose sharply. Finally, they peaked in very early January and dropped sharply. Activity in Los Angeles, and California as a whole, rose and fell independent of the lockdowns.

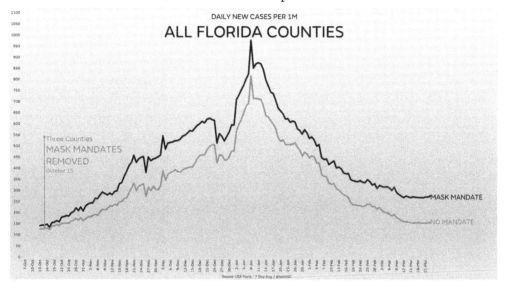

Florida as a state lifted restrictions at the end of September 2020. Some counties maintained capacity restrictions, kept schools closed, and required masks on people indoors, including the counties where Orlando, Miami, and Fort Lauderdale are located. Counties that did not require masks included Collier, where a predominantly elderly and more vulnerable population resided. The counties

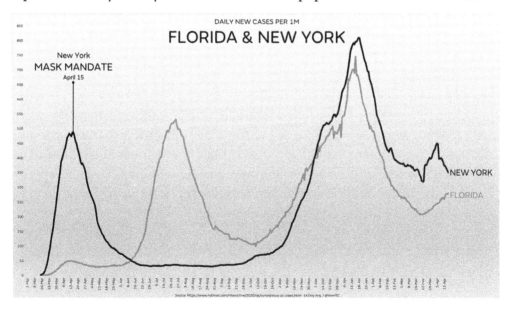

with and without masks followed the same curves. The numbers may be higher for the mask-mandated counties because they are larger in some cases, but the curves should not be identical if the mandates worked.

Florida and New York State have similar population sizes. They also had policies at opposite ends of the lockdown spectrum. New York was among the most restricted states for over a year, and Florida was among the least. Look how identical their cases counts were over a year. Both had a sharp first wave, just a couple of months apart. Both receded, and both spiked in the winter of 2020-2021 identically. Both states had nearly identical case numbers. After a year, New York had 18,000 more COVID-19 deaths than Florida. This was likely because Florida protected their nursing home patients while New York ordered COVID-19 patients into them, and the early treatments in New York were much worse than later treatments everywhere during the pandemic. Face masks, closed restaurants, closed schools, and other restrictions in New York resulted in many more deaths but no better case results than Florida.

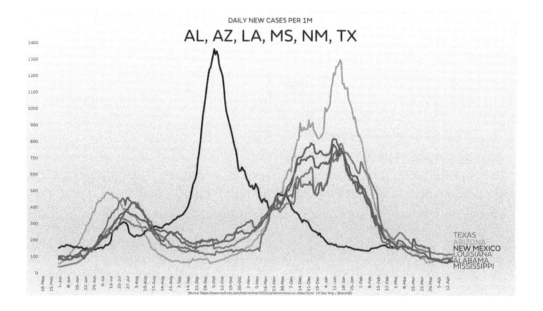

Above are the per capita case counts in all the southern states, from Arizona to Alabama. New Mexico peaked three months earlier than the cluster of the rest of the southern states. New Mexico had the tightest restrictions of any state on this board. It got so bad that they closed Walmarts, the only source of grocery goods in some communities. The strictest state in the south had the worst case results. With varying mask mandates, restaurants open or closed and schools open or closed, cases were identical in counts and timing from Texas to Alabama.

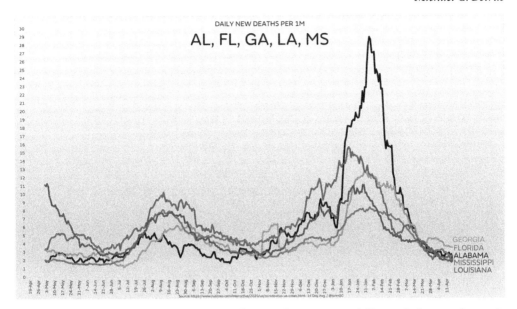

COVID-19 deaths per capita in the southern states followed identical trends in the summer of 2020 and winter of 2020-2021. Alabama had fewer kids in class during this period than every state listed except Louisiana, and Alabama had a statewide mask mandate. Alabama had the highest number of deaths per capita in the southeast. Overall, Alabama and Louisiana had more deaths per million by a wide margin than much less restricted Florida and Georgia. Florida was the least restricted state of these five states and had the fewest deaths per capita of them all. There was no correlation between tighter restrictions and fewer COVID-19 deaths.

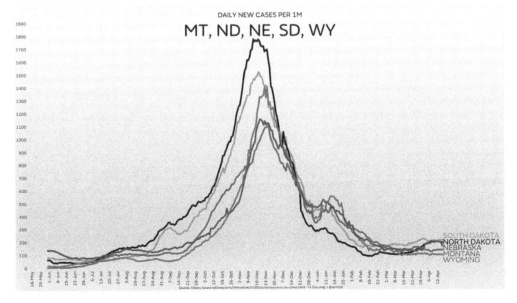

This chart includes states led by three governors awarded A's for their handling of the pandemic. November and December were difficult for the Dakotas, both reaching the top six in COVID-19 deaths per million for a few weeks in December. Both eventually fell out of the top ten in 2021, with some of the fewest restrictions at the state or local level. Cases, hospitalizations, and deaths were curved identically in these states, all with varying interventions. COVID-19 activity had much more to do with seasonality and regional timing than any government mandates. These states combined for the highest percentage of kids in class during 2020-2021 of any state grouping in the country.

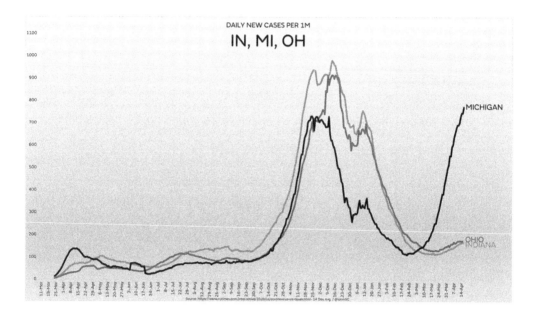

Michigan had much tighter restrictions than its two southern border neighbors Indiana and Ohio. Indiana had the fewest restrictions. Michigan kept the most kids out of class, closed the most gyms and restaurants, issued the tightest stay-at-home orders, restricted non-COVID-19 healthcare the most, and had the strictest mask mandates. What that got Michiganders was lower seroprevalence than their neighbors and an unusual asymmetrical spike in March-April 2021. In April 2021, Michigan's governor required those two years old and up to wear masks in public.

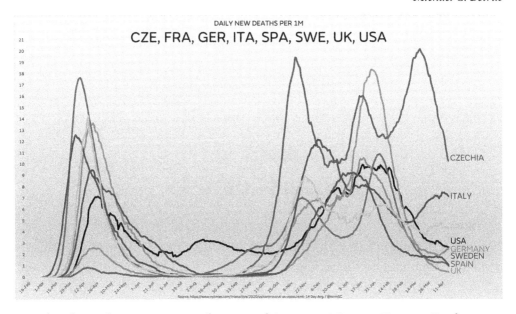

DAILY NEW DEATHS PER 1M
CZE, FRA, GER, ITA, SPA, SWE, UK, USA

The chart above compares the United States to Western Europe. In the summer of 2020, news outlets reported on how well Czechia (also known as the Czech Republic) suppressed COVID-19. In April 2021, they were ranked highest in the world in deaths per capita, after very strict mask mandates, dining restrictions, and remote learning. The media heralded Italy and France for their handling of the virus in the summer and fall of 2020 compared to the United States. Both ended up with about the same results as the United States. Germany was put up as the model of how to handle COVID-19, and then they got their turn in the winter of 2020-2021.

You can find hundreds of media articles criticizing American leaders and praising the leadership in these countries, take a look. The U.K. had one of the most disastrous lockdowns of the pandemic, locking down hard three times. What did it get them? Worse results than a couple hundred other countries and territories.[206] Sweden did very little in interventions and they fared better than every country on this board except Germany, with their kids getting properly educated. In the end, stricter lockdowns and mask mandates did not produce better results. What mattered most was how well the elderly were protected, what happened in their long-term care facilities, and obesity in the country. Little else mattered.

CHAPTER 12
Kids and COVID-19

Over the last few years, my son and I took up mountain climbing. We enjoyed the planning, the training, the connection under pressure. We've had some great adventures and were able to get deep into our national parks. In 2018, a movie came out that won an Academy Award for best documentary. We were very excited to see *Free Solo*, a documentary of Alex Honnold's climb up El Capitan's 3,000-foot vertical face by himself with no protection (rope). It's probably the greatest athletic achievement in history. If you doubt that, spend some time climbing in the mountains and let's regroup.

In watching dozens of interviews with Honnold about what happened during his climb, the inevitable questions he is always asked are, "Were you afraid of dying?" "Why take the risk?" and "Why do this if one little slip will be unrecoverable?" His answer is always about balancing risk and consequence. Honnold isn't a reckless daredevil. He's a very deep thinker and is very analytical. His response to those questions is always that while the consequence (of falling) is great, he feels the risk is low due to his preparation and understanding of the circumstances.

Governors, local leaders, and school leaders made enormous risk and consequence calculations when closing schools in 2020 and keeping them remote throughout 2021. What are the consequences of keeping kids out of classrooms, and what is the health risk if we don't? Most leaders and parents bet that the health risk was too great and worth the consequential collapse in education.

The problem is they misunderstood the risk in a way that Honnold understood his level of risk. The health risk was very low, lower than many other continued activities, and the consequences of those decisions impacted tens of millions of kids as education fell off the cliff without a rope.

If there is one blessing COVID-19 gave us, young people were mostly spared serious harm. The Spanish Flu ravaged very young kids and adults aged 20-40 before taking on the elderly—the CDC and WHO expected a pandemic influenza would impact kids as both primary spreaders and victims. Their playbooks largely revolved around that. That never played out for COVID-19. Before we get into the data and medical studies on kids and COVID-19, consider the commonsense questions. COVID-19 was the top story for a year and a half.

Were nursing homes hotbeds for COVID-19 activity? Yes. You don't have to be a student of the data to know this; it was broadcast on media outlets for months.

Were the elderly the most vulnerable group to COVID-19? Yes. Again, most knew this because it was on the news constantly. If you knew someone that got sick or died from COVID-19, the chances are high they were older and less healthy than others.

Were severely overweight people at a lot of extra risk to COVID-19? You may not have known this, but it was the number one underlying condition in COVID-19 victims under fifty.

Was it safe to fly during the pandemic? This one may be a little tougher. The answer was yes. How do you know, even without doing the research? Airlines flew passengers over thirty million times during the first year of the pandemic. That ends up over a billion people flying in airplanes and congregating in airports. You would know with that much activity because the media would be pouncing on any activity that was a hotbed for COVID-19. Being on an airplane was maybe the safest indoor place to be. A combination of healthy people traveling with excellent ventilation were the primary reasons flying was so safe.

Were kids at risk of COVID-19? Close your eyes and try to recall one news story, or personal story, where kids were victims of COVID-19. A few are out there, very few, and they were tragedies. I'm reflecting on a high school football player in Louisiana that had asthma and died with COVID-19, very sad for a parent to read. Still, kids made the headlines during the pandemic in one area: they were out of school.

Twenty times more kids lost their lives to a car accident, suicide, or drowning after a year of COVID-19. We had ten million kids in class in 2020-2021 (of the 50MM K-12 students in the U.S.). How many stories did you hear about people getting sick from that? None.

Even as Europe was hit with a significant winter wave, kids were in class. How many stories did you read about where they or their teachers had an outbreak and a bunch of people got sick? None. With all the drama going on as healthcare "experts" debated the safety of schools open, teachers unions resisting reopening schools, the CDC reviewing guidelines, and the Department of Education weighing fall 2021 plans, common sense left the room. If COVID-19 were risky to students and 90% of the teachers, why hadn't any groupings gotten sick from school anywhere in the world?

There Was No Pandemic For Young People

Below is a cause of death chart for the first eight months of the pandemic:

Table. Age-Specific Mortality Rates (per Million) for COVID-19 (March-October 2020) and Other Leading Causes of Death (March-October 2018)[a]

	Causes of death[b]				Unintentional injuries		Intentional injuries		Leading causes of infant deaths		
Age, y	COVID-19	Heart disease	Malignant neoplasms	Chronic lower respiratory disease	Transport accidents	Accidental drug overdoses	Suicide	Homicide	Birth defects	Short gestation	SUID
<1	7.4	51.6	8.6	2.9	15.5	1.6	0.0	46.7	773.7	682.2	603.4
1-4	1.0	4.8	13.1	2.0	17.5	0.3	0.0	15.6	15.9		
5-14	1.0	2.7	13.5	2.0	14.6	0.4	9.4	4.7	6.4		
15-24	9.9	13.8	20.9	2.8	108.3	66.1	97.0	72.1	5.5		
25-34	38.6	52.1	53.7	4.2	113.2	220.7	120.9	78.8	6.4		
35-44	109.9	169.1	172.0	10.1	93.8	234.0	128.1	54.7	7.2		
45-54	294.8	509.7	597.5	56.1	100.7	208.2	140.3	33.9	11.2		
55-64	683.3	1239.6	1802.4	285.8	105.0	161.2	139.8	23.7	17.8		
65-74	1574.6	2516.9	3702.0	809.9	99.2	50.8	114.1	15.7	13.4		
75-84	3832.4	6478.5	6845.7	2117.3	129.9	16.0	129.6	13.2	14.9		
≥85	10 699.7	24 530.2	10 442.4	4278.4	139.1	14.7	133.4	13.3	31.2		
Total	698.8	1287.7	1219.8	307.5	89.2	122.3	102.3	39.0	19.4		

Abbreviations: COVID-19, coronavirus disease 2019; SUID, sudden unexpected infant death (including sudden infant death syndrome).

[a] Table presents 8-month aggregate COVID-19 mortality rates during the period of March through October 2020[5] and mortality rates for other causes during the period of March through October 2018,[4] the most recent year for which detailed cause-of-death data are available.

[b] Causes of death are defined by *International Statistical Classification of Diseases and Related Health Problems* codes for heart disease (I00-I09, I11, I13, I20-I51), malignant neoplasms (C00-C9), chronic lower respiratory disease (J40-J47), transport accidents (injuries) (V01-V99, Y85), accidental drug overdoses (X40-X44), suicide (*U03, X60-X84, Y87.0), homicide (*U01-*U02, X85-Y09, Y87.1), birth defects (Q00-Q99), short gestation (P05-P08), and sudden unexpected infant death (R95, R99, W75).

Source: *https://jamanetwork.com/journals/jama/fullarticle/2774465*

As we review the data, applying critical thinking illuminates that young people were mostly unaffected by COVID-19.

In children ages 5-14, thirty times more kids died from a transportation-related accident, suicide, or homicide than from COVID-19. Thirty times more deaths.

- In children ages 5-14, thirteen times more kids died from cancer than from COVID-19. Thirteen times more deaths.
- In young people ages 15-24, high school and college-aged kids, eleven times more died in transportation-related accidents than from COVID-19.
- In those young people ages 15-24, six times more died by accidental overdoses than from COVID-19.
- In those young people ages 15-24, ten times more died by suicide than from COVID-19. That data often takes months to certify and get out, so it was probably more like fifteen times more.
- In those young people ages 15-24, seven times more died by homicide than from COVID-19.

We have to ask ourselves if COVID-19 was so dangerous to young people, shouldn't it have caused more deaths than one or two in a million? In the elderly over age 85, COVID-19 caused 500 times more deaths than transportation-related accidents and suicide. Even in the age group 45-54, more people died from accidental overdoses and suicide than from COVID-19. The data lags on this; it was likely 50% more from those self-inflicted causes.

Year in which death occurred ▼	Sex	Age Group	All Deaths involving COVID-19 [1]	Deaths from All Causes
2020/2021	All Sexes	0-17 years	226	37,537
2020/2021	All Sexes	18-29 years	1,866	71,479
2020/2021	All Sexes	30-39 years	5,485	101,822
2020/2021	All Sexes	40-49 years	14,792	153,493
2020/2021	All Sexes	50-64 years	77,215	648,381
2020/2021	All Sexes	65-74 years	113,198	795,802
2020/2021	All Sexes	75-84 years	144,064	969,808
2020/2021	All Sexes	85 years and over	160,729	1,189,298
2020/2021	All Sexes	All Ages	517,575	3,967,620

Source: CDC Weekly Updates by Select Demographic and Geographic Characteristics Provisional Death Counts for Coronavirus Disease 2019 (COVID-19)

For a cause of death to reach an "epidemic" level, a certain number of total deaths must contribute to the total. According to the National Center for Health Statistics Mortality Surveillance System, 7.3% is that threshold.[207] The CDC death totals one full year into pandemic were reported at 517,575. Nearly everyone following the data closely knows this was inflated. Dr. Birx from the White House task force called the CDC, reporting about 25% inflated. Reconciling reporting from Miami, North Dakota, and Iowa, where deaths *from* versus *with* were separated, inflation looks like 28-40%. A working number we will use here is 30% inflation, meaning 70% of reported COVID-19 deaths were likely *from* COVID-19, not coincidentally *with* it.

Of the 37,537 people seventeen and under that died from February 2020 through March 2021, 226 died with or from COVID-19. That is .6% of all deaths in young people with COVID-19. Reducing 30% for inflation, the percent is .37%. Further, in May 2021, two peer-reviewed studies reported that at least 40%

of the pediatric COVID-19 hospitalizations were overcounted.[208] This translated to a similar overcounting of pediatric deaths, which means that actual youth COVID-19 deaths were more like just over a hundred. That made COVID-19 several times less risky to kids than a seasonal flu. That analysis supports the approximately 30% inflation of all COVID-19 hospitalizations and deaths across all age groups.

Of the 71,479 people ages 18-29 that died from February 2020 through March 2021, 1,866 died with or from COVID-19. That was 2.6% of all deaths. Reducing 30% for inflation, the percent is 1.8%.

Of the 101,822 people ages 30-39 that died from February 2020 through March 2021, 5,485 died with or from COVID-19. That was 5.4% of all deaths. Reducing 30% for inflation, the percent is 3.4%.

Of the 153,493 people ages 40-49 that died from February 2020 through March 2021, 14,792 died with or from COVID-19. That was 9.6% of all deaths. Reducing 30% for inflation, the percent is 6.7%.

The COVID-19 impact jumps significantly in each age group over fifty. Inflation or not, COVID-19 was at epidemic levels for people over fifty, there is no doubt about that. However, it never neared epidemic levels in school-age children, young adults, and adults under forty. If we didn't know COVID-19 was a pandemic, people under sixty years old would have lived through it and never known it was a thing. Some people might have felt off, some may have lost their taste or smell, some with underlying conditions would have died, but nothing so grand it would have made a headline. For those over forty, it might have seemed like a tough flu year. For those under thirty, they would have felt like they dodged the flu for a season or two. Why? Because the flu disappeared around the world during COVID-19 after March 2020.

Below is a comparison of recent flu and COVID-19 deaths in recent years, according to data from the CDC. The 2019-2020 period was before COVID-19 hit in March 2020.

Flu Death Estimates	Age 0-4	Age 5-17	Age 0-17
2019 - 2020	254	180	434
2018 - 2019	266	211	477
2017 - 2018	115	528	643
2016 - 2017	126	125	251
2015 - 2016	180	88	268
2014 - 2015	396	407	803
2012 - 2013	291	870	1161
COVID-10 Death Estimates			
2019 – 2020	53	104	157
2020 - 2021	47	73	120

The CDC went on to describe that 35% of the pediatric COVID-19 deaths had "no plausible chain-of-event" with COVID-19 as an actual cause, which means about 65% of those pediatric deaths may have been caused by the virus.[209] There were soundbites throughout the pandemic that COVID-19 was basically the flu. That was never true. For older people, or those with certain underlying conditions, COVID-19 was more dangerous. For children, it was also not true. The flu was more dangerous to children.

Those supporting school closures might have said:
- Kids can get sick and die from COVID-19.
- Kids can transmit SARS-CoV-2 at schools and then transmit it to others, like they do the flu.
- Kids live with vulnerable people and the risk of going to school is there-fore too high.
- Teachers can catch the virus from the kids, or vice-versa, and then die.

In an absolute sense, that was true. Kids could get sick and die from COVID-19. It is also true more kids die every year from the flu than they did from COVID-19. As we saw earlier, kids have lost their lives from other things at far higher rates than they did COVID-19. Do we set a sweeping policy for one in a million odds? Those were the population fatality rates for school-age kids.

Children proved to be ineffective transmitters of SARS-CoV-2. Schools closed around the world expecting children would be a critical link in the virus transmission. We knew that was not the case by the summer of 2020, with no data supporting otherwise. No study has concluded why; we just know it is true because the data are overwhelming. There are some theories.

SARS-CoV-2 enters host cells through the angiotensin-converting enzyme 2 (ACE2) receptor. The ACE2 protein has a receptor to which the SARS-CoV-2 spike proteins (the red protrusions you've seen in images of the virus) attach. A theory is that the presence of the ACE2 proteins in the nasopharynx increases with age.[210] The nasopharynx is the upper part of the throat behind the nose. An opening on each side of the nasopharynx leads into the ear. If there is less concentration of ACE2 receptors in a child, the theory is they have less chance opportunity to catch it.

It does get more complicated. While that may be true, children with CO-VID-19 seemed to carry viral loads similar to infected adults. This all means that maybe kids have less ability to catch it, but when they do, they seem to carry similar viral loads to adults. What is also not yet understood is why kids don't transmit or get sick like adults from COVID-19. Into 2021 we do not know why; we just know because of all the circumstantial data points surrounding pediatric infections.

We know from medical studies kids are less affected directly by COVID-19 and ineffective transmitters. We know that kids are at extremely low, really no, measurable risk themselves from hard data on symptoms, hospitalizations, and deaths. This data is interpreted to determine if schools should be open and with what protocols (social distancing, face masks, pods, partitions) or no protocols.

Another argument we heard against schools being open is that kids can catch COVID-19 and bring it home and infect their elderly relatives living in their household. This is predicated on several things:

1. Kids have elderly people living in the household
2. Kids are average transmitters
3. Kids are more likely to catch COVID-19 at school versus anywhere else they may go. This last point is critical.

We have about 56 million kids going to school between kindergarten and grade twelve.[211] Of that, four million have an elderly person living with them. That equates to 7%. The spectrum across all states varies wildly. Hawaii leads the nation with 15% of seniors living with kids, followed by California at 11%. Texas is third at 9%, and then it drops off. However, many states are 4% or lower, including the Dakotas, Michigan, Iowa, Wyoming, Minnesota, Pennsylvania, Ohio, and others.

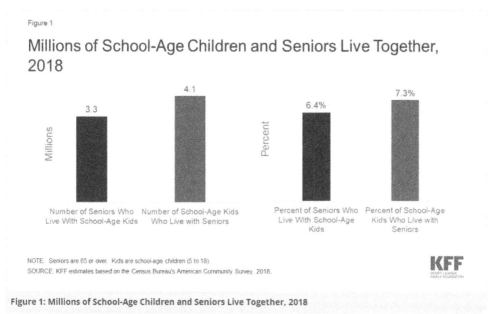

Figure 1

Millions of School-Age Children and Seniors Live Together, 2018

NOTE: Seniors are 65 or over. Kids are school-age children (5 to 18)
SOURCE: KFF estimates based on the Census Bureau's American Community Survey, 2018.

KFF

Figure 1: Millions of School-Age Children and Seniors Live Together, 2018

For a high majority of states, fewer than 5% of kids live with the elderly. Is it appropriate to factor in this metric when it applies to so few? It's debatable, but it seems like considering a policy affecting 56 million when it may apply to four million is disproportionate. And even with the four million, data showed the chances of someone in the household catching COVID-19 from a child is significantly lower than them catching the flu from them.

Was School Riskier for Kids Than Anywhere Else?

This was one of the most frustrating parts of the CDC and the federal and state governments. We had maybe 10-15 million kids in class face to face throughout the 2020-2021 school year. While hardly any lived in California, many did live in Texas, Wyoming, Georgia, Florida, Oklahoma, Iowa, the Dakotas, and many other states. Why did only one study take place in this hugely critical part of the pandemic?

The CDC conducted a study in Wisconsin on this very topic between August 31 and November 29, 2020, called "COVID-19 Cases and Transmission in 17 K–12 Schools — Wood County, Wisconsin, August 31–November 29, 2020."[212] Below are their key findings:

The net takeaway is that being in school resulted in less spread than not being in school. School was safer for kids and teachers than doing whatever everyone else in those communities was doing. Still, this study had no real impact on prompting more schools to open.

Utah

The CDC did a study on childcare facilities in Salt Lake City from April to July.[213] They followed three care facilities that included 74 adults and 110 children. 31 COVID-19 cases (12 children) were uncovered of the 184 people, with a "likely" probability those cases were sourced from one of the facilities or camps. They suggested that 54% of the cases were sourced from children. Knowing how this spreads, community seroprevalence, and how people circulate, the confidence level in this conclusion is low.

Some of the 31 people were symptomatic and no one was hospitalized.

Summer Camps

Daniel Horowitz from the *Blaze* did extensive reporting on COVID-19 and the lockdowns. He reported that Emily Oster, an economics professor at Brown University, and Galit Alter, a professor of medicine at Harvard Medical School, created a database of COVID-19 cases from selectively reporting child-care facilities and summer camps at their website, Covid Explained.[214]

Oster and Alter uncovered 1,426 summer camps and childcare centers in the summer of 2020.[215] 102,461 kids attended these camps and care centers. 32,682 staff supported the children. The people and facilities providing data volunteered and therefore was not a random sampling. As Horowitz points out, it is directionally informative. Sixteen kids and 42 staff members tested positive from these facilities. No one got "sick."

The CDC released a study in August 2020 called "SARS-CoV-2 Transmission and Infection Among Attendees of an Overnight Camp — Georgia, June 2020."[216] This study reported a stark difference from the study above. The CDC cited that from a June overnight camp there was an outbreak. The camp began with counselor orientation for three nights and was followed by a full camp for six nights.

597 people in total were at the camps. 85% were camp guests under seventeen years old, and most of the counselors were age 18-21. By the time the camp concluded, 44% of the counselors and guests tested positive. A quarter had no symptoms and the remainder had symptoms like fever, headache, or sore throat. None were hospitalized. The study did support that young people could catch and spread SARS-CoV-2 and statistically have no serious illness. That is anecdotally supported by the dozens of people I know under 22 years old that got it but had no symptoms worse than a seasonal flu.

CNN ran this headline after the CDC released their report: "A Georgia sleepaway camp's coronavirus outbreak is a warning for what could happen when schools reopen, CDC says."[217] Suppose the media ran a headline like this: "CDC study on Georgia summer camp shows kids that catch COVID-19 don't suffer worse than the flu, supporting schools reopening." Same data, different interpretation, outcome the same.

BMJ Analysis

In May 2020, the *BMJ* published "Children are not COVID-19 super spreaders: time to go back to school."[218] The analysis cited several studies (directly quoted below) from early in the pandemic from around the world:

- A case study of a cluster in the French Alps included a child with COVID-19 who failed to transmit it to any other person, despite exposure to more than a hundred children in different schools and a ski resort.

- In a school study from New South Wales, Australia, a proportion of 863 close contacts of nine children and nine teachers were traced for exposure. No evidence of children infecting teachers was found.
- In the Netherlands, separate data from primary care and household studies suggest SARS-CoV-2 is mainly spread between adults and from adult family members to children.

The majority of pediatric hospitalizations were associated with underlying conditions (77%), and those absolute numbers were extremely low. Their conclusion was that "governments worldwide should allow all children back to school regardless of comorbidities."

Separate from this *BMJ* conclusion, the *International Journal of Infectious Diseases* looked at COVID-19 spread in several countries and did a deep dive into what happened in Japan. COVID-19 lightly impacted Japan for reasons unclear. Two hypotheses are that though they have an elderly population, there is very little obesity there and in neighboring Far East countries. The other is that people in the Far East may have a more natural immunity to SARS-CoV-2 due to their proximity to coronaviruses, and this one is traced mostly to a horseshoe bat. The IJID study in Japan found that the "intervention of school closure did not appear to decrease the incidence of coronavirus infection."[219]

On February 3, 2021, the *BMJ* published "Closing schools is not evidence-based and harms children," written by four epidemiology and public health professors.[220] The authors called out the consequences of kids being locked down and out of the classroom, including:

- Loss of a safe haven away from a dangerous or chaotic home life
- Learning loss
- Reduced social interaction
- Isolation
- Reduced physical activity
- Increased mental health problems
- Potential for increased abuse, exploitation, and neglect
- Reduced future income and life expectancy
- Children with special educational needs or who are already disadvantaged are at increased risk of harm.
- 2.3 million children in England were living in unsafe home environments with domestic violence, drug or alcohol abuse, or severe mental problems among parents.

They largely drew conclusions based on a study of 12 million people from England. NHS England commissioned a study[221] published in November 2020 (which makes you wonder why schools closed thereafter that) on the risks of COVID-19 associated with living with kids. The conclusion was it was no risker to get COVID-19 living with kids, and even a little less risky to die of COVID-19 if you lived with kids. This is likely because most people that died from CO-VID-19 were older and had underlying conditions, characteristics uncommon with adults living with kids.

The *BMJ's* concluding statements from the study: "For adults living with children, there is no evidence of an increased risk of severe COVID-19 outcomes. These findings have implications for determining the benefit-harm balance of children attending school in the COVID-19 pandemic."

Ontario, Canada Study

On March 31, 2020, a study called "Simulation-Based Estimation of SARS-CoV-2 Infections Associated With School Closures and Community-Based Nonpharmaceutical Interventions in Ontario, Canada" was published in the *JAMA Network*.[222] This was a modeling simulation study based on a million Canadians from May to October 2020. The authors compared school closings to other NPIs (non-pharmaceutical interventions).

They found that "most COVID-19 cases in schools were due to acquisition in the community rather than transmission within schools and that the changes in COVID-19 case numbers associated with school reopenings were relatively small compared with the changes associated with community-based nonpharmaceutical interventions." They traced and found more COVID-19 incidents associated with large gatherings, workplace interactions, and general person-to-person contact in places other than schools. Their conclusion was that "school closure be considered the last resort in the face of a resurgence of COVID-19."

Norway

Norway conducted a study in the fall of 2020 on schools in their two most active COVID-19 counties.[223] Norway, in general, was not impacted by many COVID-19 deaths compared to neighboring Sweden. One theory is that in the prior two years, Norway had more excess flu deaths than Sweden and more all-cause deaths relative to expectations. Fewer prior year's deaths gave Sweden more "dry timber," thus enabling COVID-19 to catch them up to what would be normal. Sweden also has a less homogenous population makeup, like many EU countries or the United States.

Norway tracked teachers and students for COVID-19 activity. Teachers wore masks, students did not. Social distancing was one meter (two for those outside their own groups, which really means one meter). It's likely there was little social distancing. 234 students were tracked during the study period. Two kids tested positive and one adult associated with them. No one got sick. If masks and social distancing were required for schools to open, why did it not matter in Norway? Why didn't the kids, teachers, and student's families experience an outbreak? Because like everywhere, kids were not super-spreaders. They were barely-spreaders, and when infected, rarely affected.

Sweden

Sweden offered the soundest data supporting schools opening with normal protocols: no masks nor capacity limitations. A pool of doctors and scientists contributed to "Open Schools, Covid-19, and Child and Teacher Morbidity in Sweden" in the *New England Journal of Medicine* in February 2021.[224] This is probably the best solid data supporting open schools when only twelve million of America's fifty-six million kids were in class face-to-face.

Sweden kept schools open for up-to-16-year-olds with in-person learning and without face masks. Going into the pandemic, there were 1,951,905 children ages 0-16 in Sweden. For the four months preceding the pandemic, 65 of those children died from any cause. For the first four months of the pandemic, 69 more of those children died from any cause, almost exactly the same. During that latter four-month period with 66 school days, fifteen children were admitted to an ICU with COVID-19. Four of those had underlying chronic conditions. Of the entire eight-month study, the highest monthly death total was in January, before COVID-19 arrived. None of those fifteen children died. One in 130,000 was hospitalized.

Of the 103,596 teachers, about thirty (they deliberately did not release exact teacher data) ended up in an ICU with COVID-19. One died. Compared to other occupations (not including healthcare workers), they found preschool teachers at 10% more risk than the average non-healthcare job. School teachers were at over 50% *less risk* than the average job not in healthcare. This is similar to what we saw in Wisconsin: going to school was no risker than staying home and doing whatever other community interactions teachers and students did outside the classroom.

Perhaps Dr. Sunetra Gupta from Oxford said it best, stating that "thinking along the lines of eliminating coronavirus, without giving heed to the consequences on the disadvantaged young and globally, is a dereliction of our duties as global citizens."[225] More directly, keeping kids out of class for a year and a half with the known risks was a human rights crime.

Key Takeaways:
- Kids K-12 were at about one in a million at risk of dying of COVID-19. Being in a car was 15 times more likely to be a cause of death than COVID-19.
- There was not a single example in the world supporting the fear that going to school was riskier than staying home. Still, so many high schoolers spent more hours in 2020 and 2021 working at fast-food restaurants and other jobs than they did in a classroom.
- Studies from Norway and Sweden showed kids in class without masks had no higher average COVID-19 incidence than the community.

CHAPTER 13
We Don't Need No Education

Chapter 13

We Don't Need No Education

On April 29, 2020, I was texting with one of my friends about school in the wake of the lockdowns and how kids were sent home to learn remotely. Her son was a bright young man at the Air Force Academy studying engineering. I asked her how it was going for him, and she texted me a real-time video of her son asleep in bed next to his laptop, which was running an online class at the same time. It's a funny story and the video is hilarious, but how did kids cope with distance learning?

In America, we have the following breakdown of kids in public school by segment, as well as the number of teachers:
- Pre-K to eighth grade: 35 million
- Ninth grade to twelfth grade: 15.3 million
- Private school, all grades: 5.6 million
- College: 20 million
- All-in, about 76 million kids were in school in 2020
- Teachers: 3.2 million in public schools, .5 million in private schools

Below is enrollment in the top ten independent school districts in the United States:

Rank	District Name	State	Enrollment
1	New York City	NY	984,462
2	Los Angeles	CA	633,621
3	Chicago	IL	378,199
4	Miami-Dade	FL	357,249
5	Clark County	NV	326,953

6	Broward County	FL	271,852
7	Houston	TX	216,106
8	Orange County	FL	214,386
9	Hillsborough County	FL	200,674
10	Palm Beach County	FL	192,721

When Schools Closed

In mid-March 2020, seventy-five million kids and young adults went from structured, instructor-led teaching to remote learning: Zoom deliveries, and in some cases, pure distance learning, not instructor-led. Worldwide, 1.5 billion kids were out of school due to a virus that had no measurable effect on kids. Dr. Jennifer Nuzzo is a senior scholar at the Johns Hopkins Center for Health Security and, on March 10, 2020, wrote an op-ed in the *New York Times* called "We Don't Need to Close Schools to Fight the Coronavirus."[226]

Considering she must have written that piece the first week of March, she made some laser-accurate observations that held up a year later. She called out kids at very low risk of getting sick or of spreading COVID-19, though we are not sure why. She said if schools close, it will be difficult to determine when they should reopen before the pandemic is completely over, and this played out to be true. She also listed out the harms of missing education when it will be difficult to determine if school closings ever had an effect on mitigating it all. Still, within one week, every school in America shut its doors.

It tested parents and students alike. For pre-K to late middle school, parents had to take the lead on helping with lessons while enduring the stress of their lost job, or working from home, and isolation. It had all the makings of a new Calgon commercial.

Tutoring was hugely compromised for those who could afford it since lockdowns prevented that. With my son home from college, he placed an advertisement to tutor, something he did his last couple of years in high school. He got only one response, an inquiry for a FaceTime session in algebra. We were stunned, thinking he'd be inundated with requests until we realized the lockdowns and fear of the virus prevented people from seeking tutorial help. When school resumed in August 2020, mostly online and remote, Nextdoor saw an explosion of people asking for tutor referrals.

Families were cooped up like never before. Work-from-home responsibilities competed for quiet space and reliable Internet connectivity for many. Many parents are not well-equipped to bridge the teaching gap. It takes time, patience, and the intellect to do so. Kids with any kind of learning disability or lack of motivation suffered.

The Los Angeles Unified School District is the second-largest school system in the U.S. Into late April 2020, a quarter of all high school students had not logged into online classes at all. It was worse for elementary students. In Baltimore, only a quarter of students had their own laptops. Imagine the crunch of a lower-income family sharing a laptop or not having one, being out of work and faced with an extra $500 expenditure.[227] In August and September, nearly half had not logged into classes in Seattle, another example.

Atlanta had an estimated 6,000 students without computers. More than half of Louisiana's school districts said that half their students didn't have internet connectivity at home, let alone a computer. Marginalized communities suffered the most. It was Darwinism in action. COVID-19 preyed on the physically frail, and the lockdowns preyed on the socially and economically frail.

For all the time cable news and major newspaper reporting debated President Trump's comment about disinfectants at the height of all this, we never saw a story on education challenges covered. Had there been media pressure to reopen schools, no doubt schools would have resumed in the fall everywhere. Maybe even in May in most places.

Fall 2020 Reopening

Few schools opened on time in the late summer of 2020. Many private schools did, but public schools were very limited. Those that did mostly did so in a hybrid format. Because of the six-foot social distancing guideline, there was not enough space to accommodate full classes. Open schools 1) allowed any students that so desired to go full remote and 2) of the ones that opted for in-person learning, they went alternate days, like Monday and Wednesday, and the others Tuesday and Thursday. Nearly all schools were fully remote one day a week.

Burbio is a data aggregation and analysis company and put together the most centralized tracker of public school opening data in the country. They tracked each state for the amount of in-person learning *available* full-time, hybrid, and then full-time remote learning. We typically saw that of the available in-person learning, about half opted in and half remained remote. Then, due to social distancing rules, those opting in were in about two days a week.

Schools were scheduled to begin in August or September. By September 10, 6,936,524 of the possible 50,496,458 public school students had the chance to be in class face-to-face full time. That's 14% of all students. Less than half of those were actually in class. Wyoming was 100%, Nebraska and Arkansas were almost 100%. Texas, Mississippi, Indiana, and Iowa were quite high. Florida and Montana had no state restrictions on reopening, but they lagged other states because many ISDs did not reopen on schedule. All the states with sizeable numbers were Republican-led. The correlation remained throughout the 2020-2021 school year more closely tied to a political party than COVID-19 data.

Most schools opted not to try to teach new material. Fall semesters in high school began with a few weeks of previous year review in classes where the material of one year builds on the previous. By October 15, the number of kids that could be in full-time class in-person jumped to 9,381,567, up to 19%. Still, fewer than four million were actually in class. Two months later, almost identical numbers. Also, in December, two million more kids were learning in a hybrid setup, which means 39 million kids were completely remote the entire fall through the beginning of 2021.

In February 2021, 10.5 million kids were in class full-time face-to-face, barely more than in the fall. Four million were participating in hybrid learning. Again, the states offering full-time face-to-face instruction were highly correlated to political party leadership, not COVID-19 activity. By April 1, 2021, hospitals were empty (~3% nationally) of COVID-19 patients in 45 states and overall activity cratered. Vaccinations took root and between that, seasonality and prior infection immunity, the pandemic as we knew it was over. COVID-19 will remain with us forever, but the pandemic level of crisis we saw in waves in each community was likely behind us. Mathematically it was behind us.

Still, in early April 2021, 17 million kids were in class full-time in-person and another four million were learning hybrid. Nearly thirty million kids were still in complete remote learning as the pandemic was cleared of hospitals in nearly all states except Michigan, New York, New Jersey. Interestingly, those three states were seeing an odd spike in late March and April. If restrictions work, why those states and not looser Connecticut, Ohio, Indiana, Maryland, and the others around them?

No COVID-19 "school-outbreaks" were uncovered anywhere in the world by year end-2020, where kids in class proved to be any riskier than being home. For example, in America, of the 41 million kids age 5-14, 31 died with SARS-CoV-2, while 4,000 died from other causes (as of September 2020). According to the CDC report in the previous chapter after one full year of the pandemic, we were at an average of two in a million. Meanwhile, the number of kids absent and not participating in any schooling in the 2020-2021 school year is equivalent to all the students enrolled in the top ten school districts listed above combined. That's about the population of metro areas like Boston or San Francisco.

Why were so many schools remote in the fall of 2020? The *New York Times* ran "Should Schools in Your County Be Open?" in August 2020[228] and it was clear. Zero COVID-10 was the objective. They based reporting on a Harvard study called "The Path to Zero and Schools,"[229] where even in the title, the objective is a level of cases down to about zero in a community. At this time, New York City hospitals were about 1% occupied with COVID-19 patients and would not open schools. Below is a map of the counties (shaded) the *Times* recommended all schools be open in the fall:

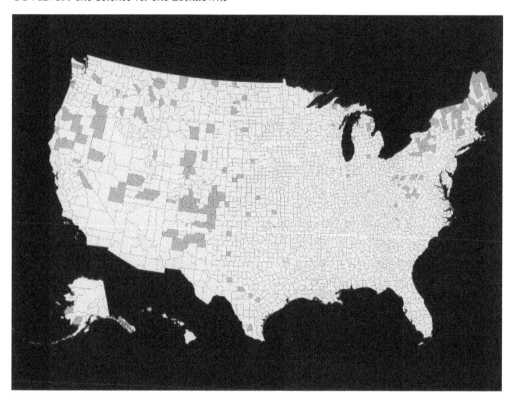

This was based in part on Harvard's zero-COVID approach. Much stemmed from the social distancing requirements and a philosophy that schools should not open until COVID-19 case rates were down to almost zero. Both were impractical metrics to guide openings based on common-sense data: schools were not spreader environments anywhere, and kids were at less health risk than the flu, as were 90% of the teachers.

Social Distancing and Schools

Schools that were open for in-person learning were still limited. Most went alternate days, where some students attended two days a week and the rest two days a week. Only about half the students that could attend in-person did so. We had a quarter of all students attending classes on any given day in the few schools that would allow it.

David Zweig writes for the *New York Times*, *Wired*, and *New York Magazine* and lives in a New York City suburb. Zweig told me while he considers himself liberal on most issues, he was completely departed from progressives on school reopenings. He wrote some of the most powerful pieces on why kids should be in school and how damaging remote learning is, as well as how many of the requirements to get kids back in class were overkill.

Zweig wrote a piece called "44 Square Feet: A School-Reopening Detective Story," published in *Wired* in September 2020.[230] It is one of the best pieces on social distancing and schools that you will find. Zweig uncovered that schools were operating under capacity objectives to give each student 44 square feet of space, which bore no connection to six feet of social distancing. If students were allotted six feet of social distancing, simple math dictates that each student needs a three-foot radius around them. The next student has their three feet and together, that totals six feet. Ignore for a moment that schools in Europe weren't doing this and that the CDC pulled back on the six-foot recommendation and reduced it to three feet.

Schools were giving students three feet of personal space and then six feet of distancing, which could be explained if the number were 81 square feet, but it wasn't. The guidelines came from a report in Education Week from August 2020.[231] The core problem with all schools' calculation was that they modeled a six-foot box in all directions around each student rather than three. This meant there was twelve feet between students, in which case capacity in a 700 square foot classroom could be sixteen plus a teacher. Had they calculated it correctly, that same class could have accommodated a more normal twenty-five students plus a teacher. These were the people leading teaching and math for our kids.

When you figure that half the kids weren't attending class out of fear, the ones opting in could have gone five days a week. Further, for younger kids in smaller classes, they all could have gone back to normal.

How Was Remote Learning Going?

Disastrous. Allen High School is located in a Dallas suburb and home to nearly 7,000 students, the largest in Texas. It boasts the largest high school football stadium in the country. Allen High School offered students the option to attend in-person or learn remotely by mid-September. Many did attend in-person. I asked some students what that looks like. One student told me, "The high achieving kids are there. It makes it easier because the ones attending want to be there and learn." The lower-achieving kids? Most were online. Maybe. In school districts like New York City, Los Angeles, Seattle, and others, the absentee rate hovered between 20-37%. Before school went in-person, I had lunch with those students in late August. While enjoying a late lunch at On The Border, one was attending class via zoom on her phone. Looked like quality learning.

The kids got a reprieve, though. Colleges all over stopped requiring ACT or SAT scores for admission. Schools are doing what states and the federal government did in the wake of the lockdowns: offer benefits to offset policies preventing people from working and going to school. Can't work? We'll give you better unemployment benefits. Can't go to school? No problem, we'll give you pass/fail grades, not hold you accountable for attendance and even get colleges to not count the inevitably lower SAT/ACT scores you'll get this year.

The most moving piece written about the blight of remote learning was written in both the *New Yorker* and *ProPublica*.[232] The story was about Shemar, a 12-year-old boy in Baltimore. Some excerpts:

> *Remote learning started in earnest on April 6. For Shemar, that meant just four hours per week of live online instruction — an hour for each of the four main subjects once a week, with nothing on Fridays. Shemar had an Xbox but no computer, so the pastor at our church, Rob Hoch, said that it would reimburse me for buying Shemar a laptop.*
>
> *It soon became clear that, even with the computer, this form of schooling wasn't going to work for Shemar. He had a wireless connection at his grandmother's house, but he spent some of his days at a row house, a mile to the southwest, that his mother had moved into, in one of her repeated efforts to establish a home for them.*
>
> *The Remind app was another problem. Shemar downloaded it on his phone, which had no cellular service but could be used with Wi-Fi. But, when his mother lost or broke her phone, she borrowed Shemar's. He often missed the reminders about his daily classes or the links to access them, which might change from week to week.*
>
> *Ryan Hooper, who teaches social studies at Joseph C. Briscoe Academy, a middle and high school for high-needs kids, told me that, of his typical class of between five and ten students, only one or two generally logged on for his sessions. Often, no one showed up. With the shift to remote instruction, he felt a "loss of purpose," he said. "All the gratifying, purpose-driven reward benefits of being a teacher were stripped."*

In Detroit, the following headline ran on September 14, 2020: "School report: This is furthering the divide between the haves and have nots."[233] Below are some parent comments about remote learning:

> *Awful. My 10th grader has been in tears 2 out of the 5 days they have had school. Power outages, internet issues, and Google Meets dropping all while the teacher continues to 'teach' to a screen. My senior is sad to be missing all of the milestones she worked so hard for. Up until 2:00 am trying to complete homework and self-teach topics she doesn't understand due to minimal availability of teachers. My 8th grader is also feeling stress and doesn't understand why he is spending all this screen time when he used to get in trouble for being on his electronics. People are paying for private tutors and teachers -- this is furthering the divide between the haves and have nots.*
>
> *Online schooling at the elementary age is a complete nightmare. My 2nd grader hates it and lasts maybe 15-20mins at a time. Both parents*

work outside the home. We have now had to cut our hours (and pay) to somehow navigate this! I don't see how the kids are supposed to concentrate and listen to their parents. Bring these kids back to school. The district has options but chose this, completely disregarding the parents' survey they sent out. Our family is now looking into private schools to transfer to.

I have been a part of assisting my 12-year-old nephew with online school while working from home simultaneously. To hear the teacher threaten to remove him from the class because she can hear voices in the background is very upsetting. These children are not living alone. Life is still going on in their homes. While we try to control the activity around him while still being able to monitor and assist him as he navigates through a system that still has many kinks, it is not easy. Many of the teachers take their frustrations out on the students, rather than admitting their connection may be poor, they don't know how to do things properly, the children have not been trained, and the various other intangibles that are occurring.

This is my daughter's first year in school and this is not how any of us imagined it. She is a kindergartner and we decided virtual would work better because it was supposed to be self-paced and user-friendly. The program our school district is using is NOT at all user-friendly. She was placed in a keyboarding class, and some of the work was typing sentences, doing a journal, and so on. She can't read or spell. How can she do this? I chose this week to pull my child out of our school district because as a parent we advocate for our children. Many others have also pulled children out. In our district, it's the elementary students that are suffering the most. We have started an online program so I can teach her until these kids can go back safely. I took a stand for my child and I feel 100 times better.

Texas

The Houston ISD is home to over 200,000 students. When they launched their remote learning in late summer 2020, it went off on a rocky start.[234] On the first day of school, the hosting site crashed. Over 12,000 students did not have a device on which to take classes. Anything other than a laptop or desktop is not a reasonable device for remote learning, so that number was likely a lot higher. 68,000 students did not log in that first week. 35% of all students did not even log into classes. A teacher I won't even name here was quoted as saying he'd give attendance and enrollment a B+. What's a C? Half the kids not enrolling?

In Abilene, Texas, nearly 50% of the students were failing at least one class.[235] That is normally about 13%. The Dallas ISD is home to just over 150,000 students. Remote learning was going so bad in the fall of 2020 that they decided to lower their grading standards.[236] The Dallas ISD found that 30% of students lost learning in reading and 50% of students lost learning in math. Texas has an academic readiness exam called the STAAR, where the goal is to have 44% of the students meet standards on the math portion. The Dallas ISD recommended lowering that goal to 26%. We were speechless. Without speech. Whom does lowering the readiness standards help?

Students skipped classes, missed assignments, and fell behind at alarming rates, likely not a surprise to parents reading this. Late in the fall semester, over three million Texas students were unable to attend class out of over five million total. Imagine that compared to all of California's six million students locked out of schools. That's ten million students out of school in just two states.

Judson Independent School District in Texas instructed principals to "grant any exceptions" and "extend grace" to students for missed assignments or poor grades. Cathryn Mitchell, principal of Austin ISD's Gorzycki Middle School, sent an email in early October, obtained by The Texas Tribune, alerting all staff to a "campus-wide dilemma."[237] The message that came from ISDs to hundreds of school districts around the country was to pass kids at almost any length for the good of the kids or the reputation of the school districts. Meanwhile, they locked kids out of class.

For much of 2020, this was not all the fault of school districts. Governors ordered public schools closed. Teachers were not prepared for online learning. The mechanisms for delivery and overall processes just weren't refined for this. It was a stopgap. To help with dismal engagement, some teacher teams in San Antonio visited their absentee students at their homes to talk to them and motivate them and their engagement.[238] This was one of the most inspirational teacher stories coming out of the 2021 school year. Still, why weren't kids in class at this point? Fear, social distancing, governor orders, and in many cases, militant resistance from teachers' unions.

California

Into the fall of 2020, up to a million of the six million public school students lacked connectivity for distance learning. No wonder Governor Newsom pulled his kids out of public school and put them in private school, offering face-to-face learning. You have to ask if he thought that was safe for his kids, why not open classes for all kids? According to a poll of Californians in September 2020, two-thirds supported distance learning versus face-to-face remote learning.[239] Polling like this is why there was so little pressure to reopen.

The same poll showed overwhelming concern for the learning loss for vulnerable children and the lack of social interactions. Nearly fifty questions were asked and answered about distance learning, challenges, support of this, or that. Pause and guess which questions were not asked. Do you think these may have been relevant?

- At how much risk of COVID-19 illness do you think your kids would be by attending class face-to-face?
- How many kids do you think have been hospitalized from COVID-19 compared to other causes?

- Do you feel the health risk of going to school outweighs the lost learning for your child?

The answers would have been overwhelmingly something like "high risk," "tens of thousands," and "yes with high certainty." This is why schools remained closed and politicians were under no pressure to reopen. The media did a poor job of informing the public on what was actually happening. Across all school districts, failing grades increased a good thirty percent. Los Angeles Unified continued spring's no-fail policy, where they would work with students for a few weeks to get students passing before report cards came out. If that teacher's union hadn't acted so poorly throughout 2021, you'd find some redemption in their motivation. Los Angeles Unified lacked integrity throughout the reopening process, a list with very stiff competition.

In December 2020, a group of families sued California for a widening gap of education for minority families.[240] Good for them, their general merits were warranted. Lower-income communities were hit harder than upper-income communities in all facets of the lockdowns. Reminder: Governor Newsom pulled his kids out of remote public school in 2020. In perhaps the most heartless, hypocritical action by the state, the state offered in-person learning for a convention center full of migrants in San Diego without legal authorization to be in America while legal California kids were locked out of classes. This isn't a political immigration position; it shows California did not actually believe in-person learning was risky. California leadership was perhaps the most egregious in how they handled the pandemic. That's not a political statement, many Democrat-led states did much better, and many Republican-led states weren't perfect. California, Michigan, Illinois, New Jersey, and New York were the worst states at balancing the risk and consequence of COVID-19 and government interventions.

New York

Students from the largest school district in America suffered from one of the strictest school lockouts in the country. New York locked its students out when COVID-19 hospitalizations were about 1% of capacity in the fall. As they trickled open in the first quarter, less than a million of their 2.6 million kids could see the inside of a classroom if they wanted; they were locked out. By summer 2021, New York never saw even half its students in class for nearly a year and a half.

Nearly ten percent of students in New York City failed every class in the spring of 2020. In the fall, schools were scrambling to convert NX grades, or those denoted as "courses in progress" into passing grades.[241] What do you do? It was a no-win situation. City Council Education Committee Chair Mark Treyger said, "No child in New York City should be assigned a failing grade for something they bear no responsibility for. Government failed them. That's who gets a failing grade, not our children." He was right. But then, passing a student isn't a great option either if you believe actual learning and understanding of course material matters. Do you pass students and allow them to progress if they didn't learn the material, even if through little fault of their own? Tens of millions of students were awarded just that.

Later, it was decided that no New York City students would fail in 2020-2021. Rather, the lowest grade achieved was a mark of "needs improvement" or "course in progress." The grading policy was a response to the "flexibility" families need during the pandemic, said DOE spokesperson Danielle Filson.[242] Flexibility? Would I appreciate a school passing my child when he failed because of remote learning as a parent myself? Maybe. It would keep doors open and not penalize his progression. What happens in the next grade when you are in algebra two and didn't really learn algebra one? The problem with all of this is that at one point in life, no one can give you freebies. It may stop in high school. It may stop in college. It definitely stops when you are in the workforce.

What you read about in Texas, California, Michigan, New York…that happened all over. That happened in open South Dakota, in rural Iowa, in 100% open-school Florida. It was such a disaster that was so poorly covered by the media, managed by the state and local leaders, resisted by teacher unions and ignored by the policy influencers we discussed. All get a failing grade for the pandemic school policies.

Student and Parent Experience

Students and parents coped with how kids could work at fast-food restaurants, retail, and grocery stores and yet were unable to go to school. Parents in Chicago marveled at how kids in Florida were playing fall football while theirs were sitting home on Friday nights. Families in California wondered how Disney World was packed with vacationers, but Disney Land was closed for months.

1.7 million teens work in fast-food restaurants and continued to do so, which means that's 1.7 million more teens working in fast-food restaurants than in class in the spring of 2020. Fast food restaurants remained open during the lockdowns. 1.3 million teens work in retail, which means we can add that to the fast-food workers and conclude the three million kids working was very close to the number of kids in class. Someone needs to answer to this with science (science BC) behind it.

Rebecca Bodenheimer wrote one of the most powerful pieces about schools closed. Her opinion piece was titled "A progressive parent's rant about the politics surrounding school reopening."[243] The sad part of the school reopenings is that it was so political. This is why this piece was so important. It wasn't a conservative clamoring for schools to reopen. It was a self-proclaimed progressive, not unlike David Zweig, who considers himself liberal, screaming off the page for leaders to allow kids back in class.

Below are some of Bodenheimer's comments, which are most impacting as direct excerpts:

> *The harms of prolonged school closure vastly outnumber the risk of COVID. It's not only learning loss among public school kids (mostly in urban areas), though that will, of course, have long-term implications, especially for teenagers who need to get decent grades to be able to get into college but who are flunking classes at astronomical rates. Remember they'll have to compete against private school kids, who are having a much more normal school year.*
>
> *It's our kids' mental health that's the real emergency. The rise in student suicides in Las Vegas and got the superintendent to open schools. All over the country, mental health emergencies and hospital visits by kids are skyrocketing.*
>
> *The politicization of this issue is what's really fucked up. Schools are largely open in red states and closed in blue ones. It's very difficult for me to understand the simplistic thinking that says: Trump said open schools, so we must keep them closed at all costs. I have never felt so alienated from the people I usually align myself with politically. I will never understand how the left in this country has decided that advocating for putting kids first is somehow right-wing.*
>
> *It's so clear to us that teachers' unions are dead wrong on this issue and that their interests are diametrically opposed to what's best for our kids. Your own kid might be doing okay in remote learning, but kids aren't doing well by and large. Mine sure isn't.*
>
> *Other things that have made me flip my lid about this situation: teachers' unions are demanding vaccinations before going back to school — last month, some here in SF and Oakland were even saying vaccinations wouldn't be enough to get them back to the classroom! No other essential worker has had the privilege to demand this — and this has been a real slap in the face to all the essential workers (like my spouse) who have been going to their workplace for 11 months with no vaccine and who aren't being prioritized like teachers are.*

Bodenheimer wrote a brilliant column that no doubt spoke for millions of conservatives, liberals, and progressives. When did Republicans become the party of children? In 2020.

At the time, Bodenheimer spoke her mind in February 2021. This is what school openings looked like by state. The numbers are the percentage of kids able to attend in-person if they chose:

Burbio tracker percent of schools open by state. (Hybrid counts as half.)

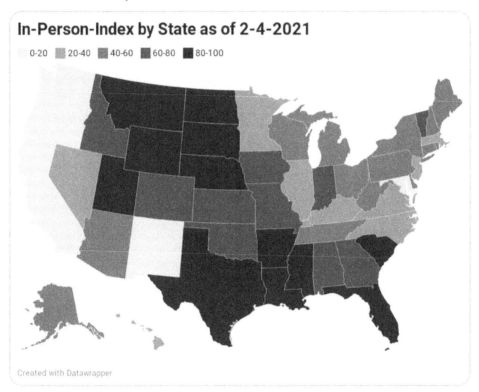

Does this look highly correlated to state leadership by party? The dark ones are all Republican-led states. Every single one. Other than Colorado, the two darkest shades look just like an election map. The lightest ones? All are led by Democrat governors. Every single one.

When Bodenheimer wrote her opinion piece in February 2021, this is what the seven largest Democrat and Republican-led states, and others, offered for in-person schooling. Only about half the students that could go to school in-person did attend in-person. This means barely any kids were in public schools in Democrat-led states.

Democrat-Led State	% of Schools Open for F2F Learning	Republican-Led State	% of Schools Open for F2F Learning
California	4%	Texas	79%
New York	26%	Florida	100%

Illinois	7%	Ohio	30%
Pennsylvania	19%	Georgia	69%
Michigan	39%	North Carolina	15%
New Jersey	2%	Arizona	49%
Virginia	8%	Tennessee	44%
Oregon	4%	Iowa	56%
Washington	2%	Indiana	55%
Massachusetts	4%	Louisiana	62%
Minnesota	13%	Mississippi	64%
New Mexico	5%	North Dakota	74%
Nevada	13%	Nebraska	70%
Wisconsin	27%	Oklahoma	51%
Hawaii	0%	South Carolina	76%
Maine	0%	Wyoming	100%

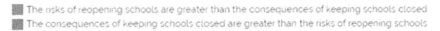

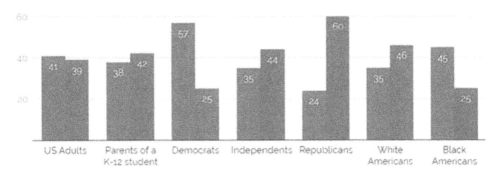

That same period in of February 2021, YouGov conducted a poll comparing the benefits of reopening all classrooms versus the health risk of COVID-19:

How sad is it that parents of K-12 students favored keeping schools closed? I wish in polls like this; they also asked questions about the associated risk of COVID-19. I would bet my house the majority of the respondents in favor of closed schools would not have passed a test on COVID-19 risk. Black Americans supported schools open by a large margin, as did Republicans and independents. Democrats supported school closings overwhelmingly. As you will see in chapter eighteen, nearly all media supported lockdowns, driving polls like this among Democrat voters. It wasn't the science. It was the result of the best ad campaign in history.

Uju Anya is a university professor in California and a mother to a nine-year-old fourth grader. On April 6, 2021, she tweeted: "My child got sent to Zoom detention for not paying attention in Zoom 4th grade. Email said here's the link to access the room to serve detention. I swear I'm trying so hard to take this life seriously." I read through Anya's tweets for a period to gain some insight and took away a few things: she leans liberal, is obviously bright, is even-tempered and likely calls it out with clarity. I'm wondering if Zoom detention was easier than actual detention from my school days. At least the kids didn't have to mop floors or clean chalkboards.

One Final Bit of Craziness

Baseball was our home life for ten years. I coached for several years and my son went on to play for a top twenty nationally ranked team while in high school, and then play for a Big-12 school. A half dozen of his former teammates are now playing for major league teams. Tournaments filled up twenty of our weekends a year all over the country for years. It was an exciting decade for us. Imagine the shock when this came out in April 2021:

STATEMENT RELEASED TODAY

Dreams Park Requires Vaccinating 12-Year-Olds, Upsetting Some Parents

Cooperstown Dreams Park is host to one of the major regional world series baseball tournaments every summer. The hosts there decided in 2021 that all players needed to be vaccinated to participate. There are several things completely wrong about this:

- All the COVID-19 vaccines were under EUA, emergency use authorization, they were not fully approved by the FDA as other vaccines for children are approved.
- There was a lot of legitimate questioning on the effects of the vaccines on kids long-term.
- Vaccine side effects were measurably worse for kids than getting COVID-19; we saw this as the Pfizer vaccine was granted EUA for kids 12 and older.
- Kids were at a one-in-a-million risk of losing their life to COVID-19. That number would jump to one in many millions of healthy athletic kids.
- Kids were known to be ineffective vectors of transmission for COVID-19 to adults.

The park statement did qualify that if vaccines were not approved for people twelve and older, they would reschedule the event. It raised two questions: one, did they understand the science as it relates to kids at all, and two, why vaccine mandates at all? A question that pounded away all of 2021 as vaccine passports grabbed headlines around the world reminded me of the final scene in the movie *A Few Good Men*. If you believe the vaccines work, and you've been vaccinated, why are you so passionate that everyone must be? The COVID-19 hysteria around kids felt so surreal; it was like living in the twilight zone.

Teachers and the Unions

In August 2020, CDC Director Robert Redfield said schools should be open and kids should get back in class. Most large districts held off, while many smaller ones in states that did not prohibit fully reopened. Small school districts in Florida, Ohio, Texas, Iowa, Nebraska, and hundreds went back to a sort of normal. Nearly all kids wore face masks, but there was some normalcy to catch up from an absent spring.

In the fall when that happened, we did not see teachers revolt much and unions weren't taking a stand against it. There were outright teacher "strikes," not official union stances when schools tried to open in some communities. In Milwaukee, nearly 300 Kenosha teachers reported absent on Monday, September 22, 2020, forcing seven schools to transition to online learning. The absences came as a surprise to where the school had to announce to parents they were switching to online at 10:00 pm the night before. It was like a snow-day announcement.

In Maryland, one county was ready to go hybrid in October 2020, but on the eve of that happening, 300 teachers walked out. Why? Because the ISD informed the teachers to expect 14-hour days, eight hours of in-person teaching and added to that planning and virtual teaching. Can you blame them? Parents had voted at a rate of 85% to get their children back in class five days a week. I spoke with two first-grade teachers that teach at opposite ends of Maryland. Both were teaching virtually in the fall of 2020. First, they said there was almost complete consensus among their peer group of teachers that normal, in-person teaching is far more effective than virtual, no surprise.

They also said they felt that a high majority of teachers desired to teach normal (as well as their principals), but the unions, boards, and superintendents were not supportive of that. The teachers they felt did not want to return were more about not wanting to deal with kids or because it was a lot more work and required more planning time than teaching remote. They said it's easier to "mute" a student on Zoom than to do so in class.

In April 2021, it was revealed that The American Federation of Teachers lobbied the CDC on school reopening guidelines in January 2021.[244] Emails uncovered that the teachers union lobbying preceded the CDC putting the brakes on a full reopening recommendation of in-person learning. Perhaps that is a normal course of action. Perhaps Goodyear and Michelin weigh in on state and local speed limits. Perhaps pot growers weigh in on marijuana legalization in states. That may be normal, but the CDC does not then get to say they are "following the science" when the unions influenced them.

CDC Director Walensky said at the time, "If you're in middle school or high school, we would advocate for virtual learning for that group … We don't want to bring community disease into the classroom. We also know that mask breaching is among the reasons we have transmission within schools when it happens. Somewhere around 60% of students are reliably masking. That has to be universal. So we have work to do." No, there was not a shred of science to support that statement or recommendation. Not. One. Shred. Of. Science.

Chicago

In early January 2021, thousands of Chicago Public School (CPS) teachers were ordered to return to class to prepare for school beginning January 11. Half stayed home because the Chicago Teachers Union (CTU) told them it was unsafe.[245] CPS ordered the teachers back, they resisted, and schools did not open in January. The guise was that it was too dangerous. Mayor Lightfoot threatened to sue the teachers union, but the whole thing was a farce, according to a union member that opened up to me about it. At the time, the federal government stimulus package was still in limbo, and it was all a bargaining chip to get more money, resources, and power for the union, and the kids were pawns in it all.

The CTU messaged that white, privileged parents were the ones seeking the reopening. The reality was that most of the kids that returned when they could in the southern Illinois area were black and brown kids. It so misses the point. White privileged families, or any privileged families, had the resources to bridge this learning gap. The ones screwed were the very constituents of the city: under-resourced minorities.

Carolina Barrera Tobon is Latino, a faculty member at DePaul University, and a mom in Chicago. In January 2021, she voiced concerns on a Zoom call shared by Karen Vaites on Twitter about the racial lines drawn regarding reopening Chicago schools. She said: "I've seen voices of Black and Latinx children & families coopted to support the union's and district's arguments. The union has capitalized on our and our teachers' fears to deny science for their agenda. Frankly, I'm tired of a predominantly white union and predominantly white administration telling me what minority children need. They exploited fears to spread misinformation and lies." She cited "grossly dishonest" use of statistics, noting that 69% of students planning to return to schools were Black or Latino.

Miami had opened. New York had sort of reopened. Houston was open. Dallas was open. Eight of the top ten districts were open. No COVID-19 outbreaks were occurring. They were taking a page right out of the federal government and their own stimulus. The government held off on a nearly two trillion dollar "stimulus" package to bake in as much as they could. The longer they held out, the longer all sides would cave to just get it approved. We saw this play out no place better than in Los Angeles.

California

California was the most stringent state in many areas, none more than locking kids out of classes in 2020 and 2021. Los Angeles Unified (LAU) is the teachers union over the second-largest school district in the country. In September 2020, a group of mostly minority parents filed a class-action lawsuit against LAU over substandard education.[246] Why? Other than remote learning being ineffective, their rules only required ninety minutes of live instruction per day. The rest of the "school day" was independent learning or watching pre-recorded lessons. Maybe the parents were overreacting. Elementary kids are known to be great at learning on their own, navigating Zoom calls, and finding answers to their questions on their own.

On September 9, 2020, audio surfaced of Los Angeles County Public Health Director Barbara Ferrer saying that K-12 schools in America's largest county likely would not open until after the November election.[247] Did you know the virus was going to go away after it voted? Me either.

The United Teachers Los Angeles released this statement on March 1, 2021, regarding reopening schools[248]:

> *Educators are unfairly targeted by wealthier and healthier people who are not experiencing this disease the same way as students and families in our communities. If this were a rich person's disease, we would have seen a very different response. We would not have the high rate of infections and deaths.*
>
> *If you condition funding on the reopening of schools, that money will only go to white and wealthier and healthier school communities that do not have the transmission rates that low-income Black and Brown communities do," said UTLA President Cecily Myart-Cruz. "This is a recipe for propagating structural racism and it is deeply unfair to the students we serve."*

The crazy thing about this statement is that 1) minority kids were very affected by remote learning, as well as all lower-income households, and 2) most other major school districts opened without incidence providing data that open schools were not any more harmful than going to the store.

In March, someone posted this on the UTLA Facebook page:

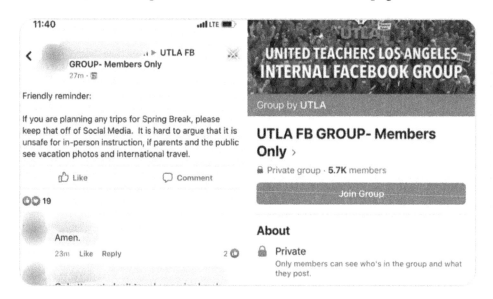

You can't blame that logic. That any teachers felt going on a spring break vacation was acceptable, but teaching was not is more than a little incongruent. We did see a leader in Chicago's teachers' union take a vacation to Puerto Rico at a time their schools were locking students out. Sarah Chambers from Chicago spent her holidays poolside and out of the contiguous 48 states while saying schools were unsafe to return.[249] The upside is that the UTLA demonstrated learning, avoiding the Chambers incident while they were negotiating.

In April 2020, the UTLA held students hostage again while demanding educators with young children may continue working from home until the district can provide them subsidized childcare and a proper child care program for teachers by the fall.[250] You have to give it to them for taking advantage of a crisis and holding kids hostage to get all their demands. Other essential workers like those in healthcare, retail, people working for UPS and FedEx, food processing plants, and so many others never made these demands, nor teachers outside California.

The March 2021 federal stimulus package allocated about $128 billion toward helping K-12 schools reopen from virus-induced shutdowns. However, at the time of passing, about $60 billion was unspent from previous stimulus packages. Just $6 billion of that March stimulus was earmarked for spending before October 2021, while about $32 billion per year was appropriated for 2022 and 2023. The remaining $60 billion would be spent through 2028.[251] If any readers can see how this fits with a COVID-19 plan to get schools open sooner, please reach out.

Teacher's unusual demands in California weren't limited to Los Angeles. As San Francisco talked about reopening, their teacher's union negotiated with the district over the number of hours and days students would return to school for live instruction. Options stipulated students only returning two partial days per week. Meanwhile, teachers were working normal hours in hundreds of school districts around the country. Schools in the Bay Area did squeeze one day of in-person "school" before the end of the school year so they could claim meeting a requirement to get a $12 million grant from the state.

@ReopenCASchools on Twitter did some great reporting on California's re-opening. When California was dead-last in both new infections per capita and in open classrooms, teachers' unions were contemplating taking federal stimulus money to bonus teachers from $2,500 to $6,000 each, and in one case giving each teacher a paid vacation to Hawaii after the semester. Teachers in Florida, Nebraska, Georgia and Oklahoma must have felt like suckers for doing their jobs all along and not holding kids hostage for a piece of the stimulus package. Or maybe they felt called to keep their students on track as best they could through a traumatic year.

Further north in California, some teachers got together from the Oakley Unified Elementary School District Board of Trustees on a zoom call to prepare for a public meeting. Their meeting immediately preceded a meeting with parents. A few teachers went on a rant during the pre-call meeting, and a parent recorded it and uploaded it to YouTube.[252] If this link gets removed, you'll be able to find it somewhere.

One board member said something about a critical comment someone made about her on social media. "Are we alone?" she asked. Once assured they were alone, she said, "Bitch, if you're going to call me out, I'm going to fuck you up. Sorry, that's just me." Another board member followed that up with the suggestion that parents were upset because "they wanted their babysitter back." Parents were outraged. Everyone on the board resigned. It was a disgraceful display. The one question that never came up was, how effective were any of them teaching via Zoom if they couldn't even work it right for their own call?

No political party has done a great job of handling the pandemic and balancing the risk and consequence. I'm not taking a political position here, but rather a risk and consequence one. Governors like Ron DeSantis, Kristi Noem, and a handful of others did the best job within political and media constraints. There was a high correlation that Democrat-led states and communities presided over the worst blows to the education of disadvantaged Americans in history, or at least since desegregation. It was the most disgraceful public policy in generations and history should never forget this.

Much of this section was spent sharing teacher resistance to going back to class. These stories are interesting, and they should trigger an overhaul in leadership in these areas. However, it's not representative of all teachers, principals, or even superintendents. I spoke to many around the country. Thousands of these professionals do see their careers as educational servants. They see the shortcomings in remote learning. They wanted to go back to work. They cared deeply about their students. They do not feel that they are babysitters. To those teachers, it's a shame you may be branded by examples like this when you do incredible work. Thank you for that.

While policy leaders and influencers touted Europe as the gold standard in COVID-19 management, most countries had no better results than America. Ten EU countries had worse COVID-19 deaths per million than the United States. Critics were right about one thing. Europe far outperformed the United States in putting kids back in class, as did the rest of the world. According to UNESCO[253], the U.S. had over fifty weeks with kids out of class, one of the worst in the world. Of course, there are variables to how this was counted all over, but assuming they used the same standards unilaterally, it's a fair comparison. Still, it's staggering when you see how many weeks so many countries kept kids out of class.

Over the past year, America's children have <u>missed more classroom learning</u> than children in any other high-income country.

Source: <u>UNESCO COVID-19 Education Response</u>

The Netherlands got it right. A school there tweeted out a lovely picture of children in class like normal. No masks, working on projects, close interactions, smiling faces, looking like a slumber party. Their Twitter account has 229 followers and that tweet got over 40,000 views around the world. They tweeted a follow-up that pretty much sums it all up. It makes me think the federal stimulus should have given grants for private tutoring for every under-achieving student and leapfrog the school grants.

Merkelbachschool
@bsmerkelbach

Replying to @bsmerkelbach

Young children in the Netherlands do not need to keep distance from each other. They do have to keep their distance from adults. We do not mix the groups. A mouth mask is not compulsory. After long school closure, we aim to offer the children a pleasant school climate again. 2/2

10:22 AM · Mar 11, 2021 · Twitter Web App

Key Takeaways:

- Few schools reopened for full face-to-face teaching in the fall of 2020. When they did, less than half the kids attended. States that led face-face-face learning were all Republican-led states.

- Kids were failing at alarming rates in 2020-2021, and most schools abandoned grading, or failing grading, thus maintaining their funding and preventing many kids from having to repeat their grade.

- Children of lower-income families were falling behind those families with more resources, widening the education gap.

- Teacher's unions in California and Chicago were lone hold-outs of the largest school districts in going back to teaching face-to-face. As 2021 unfolded, it was clear the holdout was a negotiating ploy to capitalize on receiving more federal government funding, with their students as pawns in the game.

- The United States was worst in getting kids in class of all western nations.

CHAPTER 14
College and COVID-19

The damages associated with colleges going remote in the spring of 2020 and the 2020-2021 school year were far less impacting than on pre-college students. Still, college kids were targets of the media, university leaders, and politicians for violating lockdown measures. In the spring 2020 semester, most colleges gave students the option for an earned grade or simply a pass/fail grade, and they got to decide that after their earned grades were released. That seemed like a reasonable compromise—also, preventive litigation. If learning delivery was compromised, a good argument could be made about the schools' participation if students' grades suffered.

I talked to a roundtable of college students about this. The bright ones disagreed and said it's just a matter of how much you wanted it, self-motivation. However, it's easy to say that when you're a gifted student. Most students benefit greatly from the structure school provides. Dozens of schools were sued by the summer of 2020 for not giving a tuition break due for moving delivery from live instructor-led to online.

In the fall of 2020, all we read about were "Outbreaks!" at colleges and universities. The United States has about twenty million students at colleges and universities. In April 2020, Olympia LePoint wrote "COVID-19: Thousands of Deaths Expected at U.S. Colleges this Fall."[254] This type of reporting and analysis drove fear and remote learning at universities and over reporting of "cases." The author calculated a range of 23,540 up to 117,700 people on college campuses could die from COVID-19. Someone never looked at the age stratification of COVID-19 deaths from the cruise ships, Italy, or New York at the time of that writing. Someone needed to go back to college rather than write about it.

At the time of this writing, it's impossible to find exactly how many college kids died of COVID-19 on college campuses. Anecdotally, be assured if it were measurable, it would have been all over the news. One year through the pandemic, about six hundred college-aged people lost their lives to the virus. About 25,000 of that age group lost their lives to all causes. So, of the thirty million or so people of college age, .08% died of all causes, and .002% died of COVID-19.

Thirty-three times more people that age died from either a transportation accident, suicide, overdose, or homicide. Thirty-three times.

College "Cases" Explode in the Fall 2020

The *New York Times* started a tracker in the summer of 2020, identifying "cases" at each college and university. It grew rapidly. No wonder. COVID-19 spread was concentrated in three areas, the only three of any statistical significance. The first was nosocomial, spread within healthcare facilities. The second and related was within long-term care facilities. The third was in the home and connected to dense housing. The higher the density per dwelling, the greater the spread. We saw that in New York City, and a reason Brooklyn and Queens were hit harder than Staten Island and Manhattan: those boroughs had higher densities per dwelling and even per room (2.2). That is how college kids live. I know this firsthand. In February 2020, one of my son's roommates got COVID-19, and within three days, all five got it. All were mildly symptomatic.

The reporting about college "cases" always focused on positive tests. You never saw reporting on how many of those kids were hospitalized or died. That's because hardly any were. COVID-19 was less dangerous on a college campus than a dozen other things that happen every day, and it was never reported. Critical thinking left college campuses and the kids were put through awful circumstances for no scientific reason.

Schools tested like crazy. By the end of October, well over 200,000 college students tested positive for SARS-CoV-2. Outbreak!, right? University of Alabama, Florida, Auburn, Florida State, Indiana University, Texas Tech, University of Wisconsin, Ohio State, University of Georgia, and many others were considered hot spots. What happened? A dozen or more were hospitalized and a handful died. While not minimizing that, more college kids will die in a normal year from alcohol or drugs, or driving, than from COVID-19.

At most colleges and universities, nearly all classes were delivered online. Freshmen and sophomore classes were online more than senior and graduate-level classes. Imagine what going away to college as a freshman during a lockdown was like. You go away to college often not knowing many people, including your roommate. Your classes are online. Your dorm may serve food but requires social distancing while you eat. If not, the students had to get food elsewhere, without cooking facilities. They most likely didn't have a car if they lived in the dorms, so it's delivery only. It wasn't solitary confinement, but considering they did nothing wrong, it felt like it to them. Don't laugh; that happened all over.

Most couldn't congregate outdoors, and if they did, it was wearing a mask. Pick up football games, throwing a Frisbee; those activities may be prohibited. You give up and decide to finish up at home. Oh, and that's without a cost break. Many schools did not announce they were going online until after registration, a true bait and switch.

University of Colorado

In September 2020, I wrote an op-ed for the *Washington Times* called "Colleges COVID-19 Quarantines and the Chaos They Cause."[255] College leadership did what most states did during the pandemic: they locked down everyone equally, rather than promoting safety and insulation for the at-risk segments of the population and freeing everyone else up. One size did not fit all. If one had extreme obesity, severe diabetes, severe hypertension, or a serious respiratory condition, they should exercise precautions and be very careful. If one is over 65, they too should exercise caution. College students? They should have been free to be college students.

Colorado saw about five daily average COVID-19 fatalities for months. In response to this very positive data, what did Boulder, Colorado do? Selectively lock down only the least vulnerable. In Boulder County, adults age 18-22 were prohibited from: any gatherings of any size; they could only leave their living space for essential travel; public transportation was banned; in living arrangements of four or more, people could not congregate in common areas and had to wear a face-covering in all common areas, and social distance. University of Colorado students that tested positive even if asymptomatic had to self-quarantine, isolate from others, use a separate bathroom (or disinfect a common one – that was in the rule), not travel - basically experience solitary confinement. Thank goodness they didn't take the kids' laptops or phones away.

This was probably the first time a 21-year-old would have paid for a fake ID to be a 17-year-old. College students were singled out by administrators and the media as being reckless for doing what they should have been able to do all along: live normally.

College Cases

The *New York Times* maintained a COVID-19 college case tracker[256] in both 2020 and into 2021. They stopped the tracker in March 2020, much like the COVID Tracking Project ceased their work in March. The pandemic crisis had changed with the advent of vaccines and so many naturally recovered infections; governors, policy influencers, the media, and many school administrators just didn't see it.

About twenty million young people attend college in the United States. After a year of COVID-19, about 535,000 students were "cases" from 1,800 schools. It's such a low number that it doesn't make population sense. That would make total infections 2.7% of all students. Population-wide at that time, the U.S. was over 8% officially and probably 55% unofficially. Taylor and Francis published a study from December 2020 called "Are college campuses superspreaders? A data-driven modeling study."[257] They tracked activity by school and specifically thirty schools for this study:

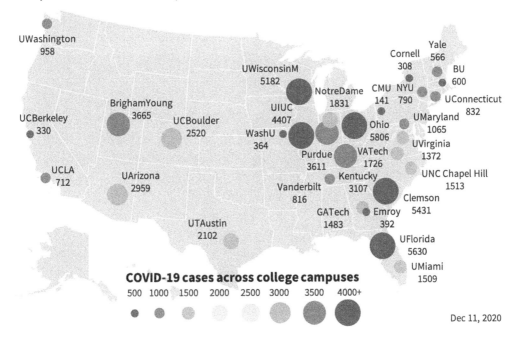

This study, and reporting in nearly all major media outlets, proclaimed campuses super-spreaders. To a degree, that could be true. Close living quarters do equate to more community spread. The media was highly critical of students for any kind of "normal" behavior. After 500,000 "cases" on campus, what happened? Maybe a couple of dozen hospitalizations and fewer than ten students that died from COVID-19. The data is inclusive, but it's very low. Media headlines suggested higher death numbers on campus, still under one hundred, but in the fine print, it wasn't students as much as on-campus employees.

Is it a super-spreader if no one gets sick, or no one gets sicker than they do from the flu? That's for you to decide. The actual serious illness rates on campus were not even measurable they were so low, and yet college kids paying between $15,000 and $80,000 a year for school were locked down or living at home, learning from a laptop. My son had an economics class delivered online from scripted PowerPoint slides. He never had a single live interaction with his professor.

Student Experiences

If you started college in the fall of 2020, it's likely you had no idea what normal college life was supposed to be like. Where a new campus experience would be full of life, new independence, and growth, it was a big dud for most students, and for many, worse than being at home. That at a higher cost than the previous normal year at most schools.

Students walking around campus freely without masks, walking and biking to classes, eating all over campus: gone. Student unions packed with kids eating, studying, and hanging out: gone. Free food at different places around campus: gone. Libraries and gyms packed with students: gone. Packed classes where you struggle to find a seat: gone. Ease of making friends through classes, activities, and within the dorm: gone. Below are some direct comments college students shared about life and education on campus during the lockdowns and remote learning:

"College was WORTH it pre covid. There were things to do on campus besides getting tested. The fees you paid actually went towards events/activities you could participate in. Going to class was a hassle sometimes, but it was a lot easier to learn and way less work. Plus, campus felt like home. It's just sad now- no people, no events, nothing."

"For some reason walking to class, sitting in a classroom made the learning easier. Socializing was so easy. I lost my job due to COVID and I realized how much going to work (though mundane) really impacted my mood. My mental health since the beginning of college was so bad and it just got worse for a number of reasons."

"I just miss the whole energy/vibe of college. It's not really easier in person, in many ways, it's much harder in my opinion. In online classes, you can use notes and stuff. I miss going to class, talking to new people, walking around campus and a chilly fall evening and seeing what everyone's up to, hanging out in coffee shops or libraries studying, etc. It's hard to describe, but I just love the whole feeling of being at college and I think that it makes studying less terrible and dare I say, even a bit fun at times. I just can't wait to go back to normal and be able to meet new people and stuff."

"Pretty much nobody is allowed on campus right now. I'm taking all my classes and seeing everybody through an old computer screen. My strict parents won't let me out of the house because they think I will get the corona and spread it around. This year has been ridiculously messed up - I and COUNTLESS others worked so hard, only to have every reward taken away from us. What's the point of working so hard if we knew this was going to happen? I'm so pissed to the point where I'm just considering dropping out as my hopes for an in-person school year vanish, we're not getting the senior years and freshman years of our dreams, like those in the movies. I really don't know what to do with my life anymore and am seriously considering dropping out. That's why I'm reaching out to this community for support."

"I'm more depressed than I've ever been. School's just so stressful online and it's so hard to attend classes online with strangers and the zooms are awkward AF, and as a freshman, I don't understand how the system works, which makes everything so much more stressful. I dreamed of going to college and meeting new people, but none of that is possible."

"Once upon a time, you could go to a study room and work with peers and readily consult TAs when you got stuck. Now every time you have a question, you have to send an email, join an online waitlist, or ask it publicly in an already crowded and [likely] poorly organized Zoom meeting. It's really not conducive to learning, so I think a lot of people give up and follow the path of least resistance (i.e., cheating)."

"I don't condone cheating at all, but I feel like it's been harder to learn the material in the first place online, and I mean so much harder (at least for me). And then, if you don't do it, the feeling of seeing all your peers ace it because they cheated and you getting a worse grade because you didn't is just not a good one at all. But it's definitely more rewarding to learn the material."

"Cheating is just so easy. I'm not used to cheating at all, and I was studying super hard at the beginning of the semester, but then I saw everyone getting better grades than me, and they all cheat, so I just started doing it too. I'm worried that next semester is going to be in person because I really don't know how to study anymore. I can't imagine myself memorizing all the formulas (and all the information in biology too). I'm really hoping it's online." What a sad state of school affairs.

The Professor

A Canadian economics professor wrote me in April 2021 about the fails of remote learning on campus. I'm sure his words speak for hundreds of professors too of being canceled to voice their opinion:

I write to you regarding the effects lockdowns have had on my students. Currently, all of our economics classes are online, and I haven't seen the inside of my office since October. This has had a deleterious impact on my students; during virtual office hours, many confess to me how angry they are, and a number seem visibly depressed and lonely; one of my students was particularly vocal, telling me of his inability to visit his grandma in a care home, and of his cousin, who has been laid off and spends his entire day playing video games. My heart particularly goes out to those who live in cramped condominiums.

Despite these problems, the students still pay full tuition, without the benefit of on-campus life: including networking opportunities.

This is incredibly frustrating and makes my profession into a joke. My colleagues seem satisfied being at home, but I feel that there is nothing honorable about squeezing our students for money while we continue to make six-figure salaries, sitting on our butts in front of a computer screen. I have repeatedly expressed this frustration to my wife, but am fearful of expressing this to my university's administration. The effect of COVID-19 has been to further chill and restrict free speech.

I admit I was afraid of COVID-19 early last year; I even wrote articles in newspapers, calling on the Canadian government to restrict travel from China, like Trump had done in the U.S. (I don't like Trump, but he did sensible things early on during the pandemic). Now that we have more data about COVID-19, however, it makes no sense to support lockdowns or mask mandates.

Grades

OneClass is an education technology company that provides virtual access to study materials. They surveyed over 14,000 college students from 232 schools about their fall 2020 experience. About 85% of respondents said the pandemic had a negative effect on their performance.[258]

Based on several small and not completely comprehensive studies, as well as talking to many college students, it seemed that students other than freshmen in 2020-2021 weathered the online classes and mental health better than any other students of any age. Their grades appeared stable, as well as their mental health. They had a familiarity with college-level courses, knew their way around college life and had a group of friends and faculty relationships from their previous years.

Freshmen struggled the most. Average GPAs fell for college freshmen compared to the same semester in 2019, and the number of them earning F's or withdrawing from courses rose. At the University of California at Santa Cruz, a student survey in the fall of 2020 found 70% of them struggled with motivation.[259] Motivation seemed to be the biggest barrier to high performance.

In the spring of 2020, nearly all colleges enabled students to have pass/fail grades only, and that after their finals. Wayne State University in Detroit allowed students to convert F's and D's to a "pass/no credit" option instead. Indiana University at Bloomington allowed students to withdraw from classes right up until final exams. The University of Michigan allowed students to "cover" grades they did not want to be reflected in their GPAs. (About 30 percent of grades were covered.) This was all reported by *The Chronicle of Higher Education*, a liberal-leaning publication.

Quarantining

Students that tested positive for COVID-19 were usually quarantined on campus, which drove many to not get tested or report it. That may explain why college campus "cases" were lower than the general population numbers, something that after a year defied logic.

One student shared this quarantine story: "I tested negative for COVID-19 but was exposed to someone who tested positive. We were both quarantined and given a blanket, trash bags, a brown banana, 4 packs of cookies, 2 water bottles, and a granola bar. That's it. I called the office to ask for soap and toothpaste, but they only had toothpaste and offered a deodorant bar in place of soap. A quarantine hall doesn't have soap? This literally felt like prison. RA's drop off food or supplies outside your door, they POUND on your door and it gives me anxiety attacks. Good to know that my school cares about both mental and physical health!"

This type of situation happened at hundreds of colleges and universities in the United States and Europe, mostly in the U.K. They treated positive, or maybe positive, student "cases" as if they were....do you remember the 1959 classic *Ben-Hur*? They treated these people as if they were the lepers at that leper colony.

According to one student at the University of Michigan, students were required to use empty apartments that the school turned into quarantine zones for those who test positive for the virus. "We were given almost no supplies -- no food, no masks, no gloves, no microwave, and no bedsheets," the student said. "No soap, no cleaning supplies, nothing -- except we were given one roll of toilet paper, single ply."[260] This was amidst student graduate teachers on strike in protest that students were on campus at all.

Governor Kristi Noem's open-state stance during the pandemic did not extend to South Dakota State University. The *South Dakota State University Collegian* wrote one of the best recaps of what happened during one of these crazy quarantines.[261] A student was possibly exposed to a COVID-19 positive person and was immediately required to quarantine on campus. The student spent fourteen days in quarantine and isolation.

- The student had to leave her dorm immediately once the school learned she may have been exposed. She didn't have two weeks' worth of clothes to take with her. The school would not give her time to wash her clothes. They suggested she leave it on the street for friends to wash and deliver.
- Student: "I got there Friday, and we didn't get more food again 'til Monday," Johnson said. "For the whole weekend, we got three of those styrofoam boxes." For those three days were three meals and no ability to warm the food, plus cereal and granola bars. Complaints got them more food and microwavable containers.
- Student: "We just got what we got. I'm not a picky person, but the people there with me had dietary restrictions, and those were not respected at all. One of the people staying with me had a dairy allergy, and they got dairy in every single one of their meals, so they just did not eat most of their meals."
- They were charged for those meals, all day-old leftover boxed meals from a local restaurant.
- Student: "For the first three days, we didn't even have shower curtains. Luckily I knew some of the girls on my floor so I could text them, 'Hey, I'm going to shower. Please don't come in because I'm gonna be frickin' naked in the shower.'"

- The quarantined students were not provided bedding and ran out of toilet paper at one point.
- The school did not provide COVID-19 tests. If the test was positive, it was free per the CARES Act, but if not, the student went out of pocket $140.
- The student was then told daily counseling would be provided at no charge. That was on a Friday and she received her first call the following Wednesday night.

The story goes on, but in the race to treat people the worst through lockdowns, it was a race between students, patients at long-term care facilities, and then the airline passengers.

Cracking the Whip

The University of Virginia made a myriad of requirements for students, including social distancing, masks outside their living area, hand washing, disinfecting anything they touched (science!), and a handful of other requirements. "Failure to adhere to these initiatives may result in immediate removal from University housing, Interim Suspension, and/or disciplinary proceedings."[262]

Northeastern University in Boston expelled eleven students in September 2020 for not observing social distancing at a Boston hotel that was serving as a makeshift dormitory. 800 students were staying in the hotel. After expelling the students, the school kept their $36,500 tuition.[263] No one got sick as a fallout from this "violation."

The State University of New York at Oswego paused all in-person classes and athletics, Greek life, in-person dining, and residence hall visitation in September when "cases" spiked. Students in the dorm had to figure out how to eat without going off-campus and with no cooking facilities in their rooms.[264] No one got sick throughout this lockdown.

Providence College in Rhode Island issued a stay-at-home order for students and switched to remote learning after about eighty students tested positive, and police were inspecting off-campus housing for compliance. Students could not leave campus for fourteen days and were not attending classes.[265] No one got sick at Providence College.

The University of Wisconsin locked two dorms of students down in early September 2020 because they had a brief period where over 20% of the students tested were positive.[266] Students feared the quarantine and food limitations and rushed to beat the clock, gathering food and other essential items before the doors closed. Classes went remote all over campus. No one was hospitalized.

The University of Maryland at College Park placed an entire residence hall on lockdown, instructing students to not leave the building for fourteen days. Students were not permitted to go to class or to dining halls and were asked to wear masks in the bathrooms.[267]

Bates College is a private liberal arts college in Maine and home to about 1,800 students. Maine was ranked 48th in the country in COVID-19 deaths per capita and had about one official death per day to COVID-19 for several weeks when they locked students down. On April 2, 2021, the college locked students to their rooms for at least a week in fear of an outbreak.[268] Students could not leave campus or their residential rooms except to get food from the dining hall or a delivery driver, use the restroom, go to the doctor, or a few other options, including required testing. It's nice they were allowed to use the restroom. None of the kids were sick.

Three University of Massachusetts-Amherst students were suspended in May 2021 for not wearing masks off-campus at a party.[269] The students posed for a picture and posted it on Instagram. Another student that didn't like it sent the picture to the school administration. The school suspended the students and gave them nine hours to get off campus, rendering them effectively homeless. They were unable to complete finals, which made their semester a waste, along with no refund of their $16,000 semester fees. At the time, Massachusetts had less than 5% of their hospital beds and ICUs occupied with COVID-19 patients.

Students at Columbia University and the University of Chicago went on tuition strikes during the lockdowns. One Columbia student said while "the problem" of rising tuition existed before COVID-19, the pandemic "has really exacerbated this problem for students and students see that they are paying $80,000 to attend online Zoom classes and their frustration kind of boiled over. And you recognize even further how detached this high price of higher education is and how detached it is from the actual quality of education students are receiving."[270] The students' list of demands included several social justice issues, but remote learning put it over the edge.

This could go on and on. In the United States and in Europe, students were penalized for something happening on their turf that was happening everywhere because a virus does what a virus does. Overall, college compliance was very good. If you read Reddit, 247, and college boards, or simply walked around college campuses, you saw very high face mask compliance, social distancing, and respect for guidelines. I visited my son several times at the Big-12 school he attended and was amazed at how all the students even wore masks walking around campus by themselves. It was pointless, but most students were pretty good rule-followers. And they didn't get sick (statistically) from COVID-19. Still, the schools played power cards and did not understand the science.

As K-12 and colleges closed, then opened, then closed again, governors, local leaders, and university and college leaders were trigger-happy with school closings. Imagine an episode of the *Family Feud*. Governors Whitmer and Newsom are at the podium. Steve Harvey says, "What do you do when cases reach 5% positivity?"

Governor Whitmer slams the button and yells, "Close restaurants! No, wait! Mask two-year-olds!" Survey says – number two! Newsom rolls his eyes and says, "Steve, you always close all schools." The top answer. Whitmer slumps back to her team and the other governors scold her, "Don't you know the first thing we do is close schools?!"

CHAPTER 15
The Policy Makers

The pandemic brought Americans stay-at-home orders that were unimaginable to anyone, including the CDC and WHO, prior to 2020. Observing Wuhan lock down, and then Italy, made the policies not just palatable but even reasonable to Americans. Freedoms were thrown out the window for hundreds of millions of Americans. In the summer of 2020, a poll showed a median of respondents thought 9% of Americans had already died of COVID-19. That's about thirty million people. If COVID-19 were that lethal, you can make a great case that implementing policies in an attempt to mitigate the spread was a reasonable tactic worthy of superseding freedoms Americans enjoyed for centuries.

As the United States locked down in March 2020 and restrictions continued for more than a year, policies varied wildly from state to state. Like with anything, it was the outliers that stood out. Some governors mandated almost no restrictions. Some mandated incredibly tight restrictions. The extremes on both sides drove controversy and passion from followers on each side. They also provided us with data-based comparisons of what worked and what did not.

Beyond the governors, there were some key influencers that provided direction, data, and opinions that drove both policy and public perception. Some were doctors, some were journalists, and some were data-crunchers. These were the key players from the COVID-19 pandemic and lockdowns.

The Policy Makers

Governor Andrew Cuomo

It's hard not to lead with the highest-profile governor of the pandemic. New York City was the hardest hit area of the pandemic in America. It hit hard and fast in March and April 2020. New York was likely hit so hard for several reasons. One, many points of entry from so much international travel influx. Two, very tight living conditions in the city's outer boroughs, mostly in Brooklyn, Queens, and the Bronx. Three, so much close proximity in housing and transportation, working and socializing.

Cuomo reached a new level of approval and celebrity with daily briefings on television. While New York suffered the worst COVID-19 results in the country, many hailed Cuomo as the gold standard of pandemic leadership. His approval rating soared. He was awarded an Emmy for his briefings. He wrote a book called *American Crisis: Leadership Lessons from the COVID-19 Pandemic.* It may have been the first time the losingest coach in sports wrote a book about coaching. To be fair to Cuomo, New York (and New Jersey) dealt with a crisis no other state really did in the pandemic. A lot of March and April decisions are forgivable for any of the leaders. Still, writing a book about leadership and the pandemic when the pandemic hadn't even peaked yet?

New York locked down on March 22 under Cuomo's directive. On March 25, Cuomo ordered that nursing homes could not refuse admission of COVID-19 positive patients:

NEW YORK STATE OF OPPORTUNITY. | **Department of Health**

ANDREW M. CUOMO
Governor

HOWARD A. ZUCKER, M.D., J.D.
Commissioner

SALLY DRESLIN, M.S., R.N.
Executive Deputy Commissioner

DATE: March 25, 2020
TO: Nursing Home Administrators, Directors of Nursing, and Hospital Discharge Planners
FROM: New York State Department of Health

Advisory: Hospital Discharges and Admissions to Nursing Homes

Please distribute immediately to:
Nursing Home Administrators, Directors of Nursing, Directors of Social Work, Hospital Discharge Planners

---

COVID-19 has been detected in multiple communities throughout New York State. There is an urgent need to expand hospital capacity in New York State to be able to meet the demand for patients with COVID-19 requiring acute care. As a result, this directive is being issued to clarify expectations for nursing homes (NHs) receiving residents returning from hospitalization and for NHs accepting new admissions.

Hospital discharge planning staff and NHs should carefully review this guidance with all staff directly involved in resident admission, transfer, and discharges.

During this global health emergency, all NHs must comply with the expedited receipt of residents returning from hospitals to NHs. Residents are deemed appropriate for return to a NH upon a determination by the hospital physician or designee that the resident is medically stable for return.

Hospital discharge planners **must** confirm to the NH, by telephone, that the resident is medically stable for discharge. Comprehensive discharge instructions must be provided by the hospital prior to the transport of a resident to the NH.

No resident shall be denied re-admission or admission to the NH solely based on a confirmed or suspected diagnosis of COVID-19. NHs are prohibited from requiring a hospitalized resident who is determined medically stable to be tested for COVID-19 prior to admission or readmission.

Information for healthcare providers on COVID-19 is readily available on the New York State Department of Health public website at https://coronavirus.health.ny.gov/information-healthcare-providers. As always, standard precautions must be maintained, and environmental cleaning made a priority, during this public health emergency.

Critical personal protective equipment (PPE) needs should be immediately communicated to your local Office of Emergency Management, with the appropriate information provided at the time of request. Requests **MUST** include:

 o Type and quantity of PPE by size;
 o Point of contact at the requesting facility or system;
 o Delivery location;
 o Date request is needed to be filled by; AND
 o Record of pending orders.

Thank you for your ongoing support and cooperation in responding to COVID-19. General questions or comments about this advisory can be sent to covidnursinghomeinfo@health.ny.gov.

Empire State Plaza, Corning Tower, Albany, NY 12237 | health.ny.gov

Cuomo further indemnified nursing homes from liability from COVID-19, signed on April 3. The language was slipped into the New York state budget on page 347: long term care facilities "shall have immunity from any liability, civil or criminal, for any harm or damages alleged to have been sustained as a result of an act or omission in the course of arranging for or providing healthcare services."[271] Cuomo ordered patients be admitted because he feared, based largely on the IHME model we saw, that hospitals would be overrun with COVID-19 patients. Never mind that New York had created 1,700 extra capacity beds at the Javits Center and the federal government sent the U.S.N.S. Comfort to provide another 1,000 beds. And never mind that of the 20,000 hospital beds in New York City and 53,000 in New York state, 11,000 were occupied at peak with COVID-19 patients.

Many New York City area hospitals were definitely stretched in April 2020. Treatments were also barbaric at times. Many healthcare workers would not serve the COVID-19 patients, and many others did serve from all over the country, and huge recognition to them for stepping up. The crisis was documented in a riveting book called *COVID-19 Frontliners: Against All Odds*. The book was written by several nurses serving in Brooklyn and Queens. It's a raw, unvarnished look at what happened in New York. There were times in those hospitals that floors ran out of oxygen for patients. Nurses were wearing the same N95 masks for a week at a time while cases were found unopened in storage rooms. Food ran short because there was no cafeteria nor food workers. Patients went hungry at times. Often electronic charting wasn't available, and in many situations, there wasn't time to do so anyway.

There are things you can control and things you cannot. The strongest pandemic leader could not control the virus. A great leader could control the strategy and the tactics. A great leader would have ensured that healthcare workers and COVID-19 patients in New York had the proper resources. It was a great failure – and so was the rush to ventilate. This was complemented by the disastrous nursing home policy. The risks may not have been intuitive to Cuomo and other governors with the same nursing home policies like Whitmer (Michigan), Newsom (California), Murphy (New Jersey), and Wolf (Pennsylvania). This isn't playing politics, but there is something to the five that implemented this policy all being from the same party.

The nursing home policy should have absolutely been intuitive to the CDC, Dr. Anthony Fauci, Dr. Deborah Birx, and state HHS secretaries. We knew this from the cruise ship data and what was already coming out of Italy. Nursing homes were ravaged in Italy. By March 20, anyone that did not realize the elderly were by far the group at risk proved they could not process simple data and critical thinking, or chose not to do so.

The pandemic disappeared from New York by June 2020. Hospitals were emptied of COVID-19 patients and from other patients as well that either could not get in or were afraid. Spring 2020 data on COVID-19 deaths from nursing homes showed some states had very high percentages. Connecticut, Rhode Island, New Hampshire, Minnesota, New Mexico, Massachusetts, Washington, and Maine all had over 50% and up to 79% of all COVID-19 deaths sourced from nursing homes. They were the highest. All Democrat-led. Again, not taking a political side; it's what the data was.

Meanwhile, in the summer of 2020, New York led COVID-19 per capita deaths in the country. The median age was nearly 80. Victims had an average of three comorbidities. Those are largely people in care facilities. In the second quarter of 2020, New York reported nursing home deaths were 20% of their total. By third quarter that rose to 29%. No one following the data believed that. The consensus was it had to be 55-60%. We could not figure New York out. No doubt the reporting was incorrect, or misleading in that a nursing home patient sick with COVID-19 went to a hospital and then was not counted if they did not die in the nursing home. Was reporting lower nursing home counts deliberate? Nursing homes were already indemnified, so what was the endgame?

On January 28, 2021, New York State Attorney General Letitia James released a report that suggested the state undercounted nursing home deaths by perhaps 50%. It was probably a much higher percent than that, likely closer to a doubling than a 50% increase. The bloom was off Cuomo's pandemic leadership rose, and reputation for likely the remainder of his career.

Governor Gavin Newsom

Governor Newsom was the first governor to lock down a state in California on March 20, 2020. When the news hit, it sent shockwaves across the country. Unlike the New York area, California had no real COVID-19 activity early in 2020 to prompt the lockdown. It was preventative. The largest state in the country, about forty million people, was closed. Schools were closed and remained so well after a year, one of the longest with the fewest classrooms open in the country.

All indoor dining was closed. Zoos, museums, non-essential retailers, gyms, hair salons, and many other businesses were forced to close. California opened some indoor dining in early summer, then closed them in July when they got their southern California wave. They later reopened in some places and closed again when they got their final winter wave. Schools were closed the entire year. California ranked dead last in the number of classrooms offering face-to-face learning, according to Burbio's K-12 School Opening Tracker. School opening was a directive of the governor.

Governor Newson had four kids age 4-11 in 2020. Newsom pulled his kids out of public school and into a private school offering face-to-face learning in October 2020.[272] If Newsom believed, really believed, that kids going to school was unsafe, would he have sent his own kids? In the winter of 2020, indoor dining was closed all over California. Before it was even closed, Newsom tweeted that anyone eating out should wear a face mask between bites of food. He also tweeted that families getting together for Thanksgiving were required to eat outdoors and be six feet apart at all times. It seemed reasonable; everyone has outdoor tables and seating to accommodate six feet between family members. Then outdoor dining closed in California while people were packing restaurants indoors in Florida.

On November 6, 2020, Newsom and many friends gathered for an indoor dinner (forbidden at the time within the state) for a lobbyist.[273] The group was over a dozen people sitting as close as they would have before COVID-19. No masks were seen. Many at the dinner were healthcare executives. The French Laundry restaurant in Napa Valley served up $450/person meals and a wine bill estimated at another $12,000. Again, if Newsom believed, really believed, indoor dining was unsafe, would he have participated? What on earth could Newsom have been thinking by sending his kids to an open school and eating at a super expensive restaurant while he prevented Californians from doing the same?

Newsom was subject to a recall over his handling of the pandemic. It was the sixth attempt in his two-plus years in office, but this one had the votes to make it. By nearly any measure, California and New York needed fresh leadership in the wake of their lockdowns.

Governor J.B. Pritzker

Governor Pritzker led Illinois to the second state lockdown, just after California announced. Pritzker led Illinois to one of the tightest lockdowns in the country, once ranked in the top five along with California and New York. Pritzker's miscues weren't as bad as Cuomo or Newsom's, but he managed to make headlines nevertheless a few times.

On May 5, 2020, Pritzker released "Restore Illinois," a detailed plan specifying the criteria for a phase 1-5 restoration:
- At or under a 20% positivity rate and increasing no more than 10 percentage points over a 14-day period
- No overall increase (i.e., stability or decrease) in hospital admissions for COVID-19-like illness for 28 days
- Available surge capacity of at least 14% of ICU beds, medical and surgical beds, and ventilators
- Testing available in region regardless of symptoms or risk factors
- Tracing: Begin contact tracing and monitoring within 24 hours of diagnosis for more than 90% of cases in the region.

When nonessential businesses could resume, the preceding metrics ALL had to be achieved to reach phase three. Even with these metrics met, gyms and indoor dining would still be banned. Social distancing and face masks would still be required. At this time, Illinois hospitals were practically empty. Still, meeting every one of these criteria at the same time without population immunity would be nearly impossible to achieve anytime soon.

Anytime we heard a politician talking about contact tracing, it was evident they did not know what they were talking about. Contact tracing something so widely spread and contagious, was like some beavers trying to dam up the Niagara River. Illinoisans were in for a long summer. And fall. And winter. And spring. Well, not all Illinois residents. During the stay-at-home order, the governor's wife flew to Florida to spend her time at their $12MM home in a state with few restrictions.

The governor's daughter was able to compete in her athletics, just in other states, while those in Illinois could not. While schools were closed for over a year as well as athletics, the first daughter got to continue her activities out of state. Once again, if Pritzker believed, really believed, youth sports were unsafe, why would he allow his daughter to compete? One more example of a governor tightly restricting their residents but not abiding by it themselves.

Governor Gretchen Whitmer

Governor Whitmer took center stage as one of the faces of lockdown leaders. As mentioned in chapter six, Whitmer enacted some of the tightest restrictions of any state and maintained them for over a year. She fought to maintain her state of emergency orders and kept schools closed even when COVID-19 activity dropped down to almost nothing in the summer of 2020.

Whitmer's biggest hypocrisy was when her husband tried to leverage her power to get their boat launched on Memorial Day weekend in 2020 when it was against the state order. Still, she set a new bar with these unique restrictions:

- No traveling between one's own residences during the lockdown
- No yard/lawn services could perform work
- Big box retailers like Home Depot couldn't sell paint or plants; those were roped off from customers. Again, she was following the science. Remember all the medical journal studies and directives from the CDC and WHO highlighting the dangers of buying do-it-yourself stuff for your home?

In March 2021, Whitmer took a trip from Michigan to Florida to see her father, whom she said was ill. There was nothing wrong with that, other than: she kept the trip secret; flew on a private jet while paying under $1,000 for the flight and did not disclose it as a gift; stayed longer than she originally disclosed; her father was later seen shopping in Michigan; the flight information was later blocked from public view. Traveling to see an ill family member is a noble action in any situation, but why would Whitmer keep it a secret rather than be upfront about it? She was encouraging Michiganders not to travel, so if there was nothing to hide, she should have been well in front of this trip disclosing it to her constituents.

On May 22, 2021, with a mask mandate and dining restrictions still in place, Whitmer ate out, in close proximity and without social distancing with a large group, and without face masks, at the Landshark in East Lansing, Michigan.[274] When I was in college at Michigan State University, the Landshark had just opened and we played pool several times a week there. We watched the Hagler-Leonard fight there; it was a great college bar. It was closed for much of Michigan's lockdown. When pictures of Whitmer at the Landshark surfaced on Facebook (again, more social media…), she apologized and said, "Because we were all vaccinated, we didn't stop to think about it. In retrospect, I should have thought about it. I am human. I made a mistake, and I apologize."

Governor Greg Abbott

Texas was one of the first states to reopen, on May 1, 2020, after the initial lockdown. Critics pounced on him and Governor Brian Kemp from Georgia. Texas had very little COVID-19 activity until July 2020, a wave that was predominately in the south: Houston and the border towns. The summer wave lasted about a month, and the second wave was a little larger, peaking in January 2021 and also lasting about a month. COVID-19 hospital occupancy broke 20% during this second wave.

Texas implemented a statewide mask mandate in early July 2020. Other than that, it felt fairly normal living in Texas. Many schools were open, though less than half the students attended. Dining indoors at restaurants felt normal, though clearly fewer people were going out. Gyms were open. Retailers were open. In speaking with friends and colleagues in Michigan, California, New York, and Louisiana, Texans had it better than most. Austin was probably the only tight-feeling place in the state.

On March 2, 2021, Governor Abbott announced the removal of all pandemic restrictions. He not only lifted the state mask mandate, but he also prevented cities and counties from doing their own. Private businesses could still require them. Costco did, as did Walmart (but didn't enforce it). Most retailers either did not or were lax about it. Most restaurants did not. It was interesting visiting LA Fitness after the order took effect. With no mask requirement, over half the members still wore masks while working out for several weeks.

The only caveat to Abbott's order was if COVID-19 hospitalizations exceeded 15%. Texas was leading the way to normalcy. Mississippi joined Texas in their announcement. Austin, Texas, and its county, Travis, said they would not abide and would require masks. Attorney General Ken Paxton then sued the city and county for compliance. Sigh.

The media crucified the governor, as did the president. Some headlines following Governor Abbott's announcement:

"Texas Mask Mandate Lifted 'Too Soon' As U.K. COVID Variant Spreads in Houston (*Newsweek*)."[275] The interesting thing about the U.K. variant is that COVID-19 activity in the U.K. mirrored the United States and plummeted. How dangerous could the U.K. variant be here if it wasn't there?

- "Texas ends mask requirement at critical moment in pandemic" (*Washington Post*)[276]
- "'A recipe for disaster': Health care workers react to dropped mask mandates and lifted COVID-19 restrictions" (*ABC News*)[277]
- "Maskless Spring Break Visitors Descend on Texas Beaches After COVID Curbs Lifted" (*Newsweek*)[278]

Texas never saw a bump in COVID-19 activity following the governor's order. COVID-19 wards in hospitals all over Texas closed. The governor's order led the way back, with the CDC following his lead two months later.

Governor Ron DeSantis

Throughout the lockdowns, two governors were the face of reality. It's not that they had the lightest restrictions anywhere, though Governor Kristi Noem's South Dakota had ranked least stringent at one time. Florida and South Dakota were both low restricted and led by charismatic governors. They made good television. Lockdown advocates who saw COVID-19 as an apocalypse had nothing but contempt for Noem and DeSantis.

Unlike the other governors mentioned above, DeSantis prevented infected individuals from admission to long-term care facilities. Florida had a stay-at-home order briefly in April. By June, most businesses were open to serve customers indoors with capacity restrictions. Florida had three COVID-19 waves in August 2020, January 2021, and August 2021, though the latter resulted in fewer deaths than the first two, even with more hospitalizations. Schools did not reopen face-to-face in the large school districts in late summer as scheduled. Like in most places, lawsuits and challenges delayed the return to the classroom. Most classrooms were open for face-to-face learning by the end of October.

On September 25, DeSantis ordered all businesses may be open at full capacity. Cities and counties may still require masks to be worn in public, and major ones did. Headlines and news pieces criticized the governor, and many expected Florida to be ravaged by the virus. In November 2020, DeSantis passed an order preventing local governments from restricting a business that could put people out of work or close down a business.

By any objective measure, DeSantis did not act recklessly or issue unsafe policies. In the context of what other states were doing and the media pressure, DeSantis was one of the bold and balanced governors. The criticism of him throughout became so unbalanced it was comical. Apocalyptic predictions never realized, and criticism turned to Florida's vaccine rollout.

At its core, DeSantis prioritized patients in long-term care facilities and the elderly for the COVID-19 vaccines. Media reports in several large print, online, and cable news were critical of this. Media criticism became completely abandoned journalism. *USA Today* ran this headline on December 29, 2020: "Long lines, crashing websites, conflicting information confound COVID-19 vaccine rollout to Florida seniors."[279] *USA Today* reporting, which was mirrored on telecasts on *CNN* and *MSNBC*, claimed DeSantis "ignored Centers for Disease Control and Prevention guidance for COVID-19 vaccine priority and allowed people 65 and older to jump ahead of essential workers, even as many health care employees in Florida wait for their shot."

This may have been the sickest reporting of the pandemic. Reporting that the elderly were "jumping the line" ahead of essential workers was perhaps the worst reported line of the pandemic. It demonstrated the CDC and many reporters still didn't understand the pandemic after nearly a year. The median age of COVID-19 deaths was about 78. Nursing homes were contributing half the COVID-19 deaths. Most essential workers were at very low measurable risk. The race should always have been on to get the elderly protected as soon as possible. Essential workers that were not high risk (elderly, severely obese, or suffering from diabetes or hypertension, or a respiratory condition) should never have been prioritized by a single state ahead of the elderly. That the CDC recommended that was just one more example of the CDC guiding absent science.

Governor Kristi Noem

No governor ignited more controversy than Kristi Noem in 2020. Noem refused to lock her state down during the entire pandemic. The criticism of Noem began and ended with the zero-COVID approach: only COVID-19 metrics matter, and if you aren't doing everything possible to suppress every last infection, your policies are reckless. Noem recognized two things early on: you can't stop the virus spread, you can perhaps slow it down and you can't issue orders affecting people's livelihoods, psychology, and education in an effort to stop something that can't be stopped.

South Dakota had very little COVID-19 activity when the pandemic began, not even measurable until October 2020. Schools did close in March. No businesses closed, though some restrictions were in place. Noem never mandated face masks state-wide, but some cities did for a period, like Brookings and Sioux Falls. Noem encouraged an Independence Day celebration on July 4, 2020, at Mount Rushmore. South Dakota hosted the Sturgis Bike Rally in August as normal, with about 500,000 attendees. Media giants reported wildly on the recklessness. Do a search on media coverage at the time. None of these incidents impacted their COVID-19 activity. It wasn't until the cool weather set in that that region of the country got its first wave.

Noem was criticized as South Dakota cases, hospitalizations, and deaths rose in November and December 2020. About a quarter of nursing home residents got COVID-19, which is really what propelled South Dakota to temporarily reach the top five in deaths per capita.[280] Still, she kept her state restriction-free from any state-issued mandate. Below are a few examples of what was reported on Kristi Noem as and after South Dakota's COVID-19 wave:

- "The Covid Queen of South Dakota: Gov. Kristi Noem's state has been ravaged by her Trumpian response to the pandemic — but that hasn't paused her national ambitions."[281] (*Rolling Stone*)
- "South Dakota gripped by pandemic amid Kristi Noem's no-mask approach."[282]
- "South Dakota's Noem scrambles to defend pandemic failures; South Dakota Governor Kristi Noem (R) wants to put a positive spin on her state's experiences with the pandemic. It's not going especially well."[283]
- "Kristi Noem hails South Dakota as a coronavirus success story — using badly cherry-picked numbers."[284]
- "South Dakota's covid-19 numbers have been terrible, but the governor says that's the wrong metric."[285]

Noem demonstrated great resolve amidst the media pressure. No state sparked more controversy on social media. No governor ignited more passion on either side of the lockdown policy. When cases and hospitalizations peaked in early December 2020, prominent media figures called Noem out on every turn. By the tone and case built in this book, you can surmise support for Kristi Noem's policies. The Dakotas were both top five states in deaths per capita when their wave came. They both eventually fell out of the top ten. They were average in excess deaths throughout the pandemic. States that surpassed them and climbed ahead with mandates included: Rhode Island, Massachusetts, Alabama, Arizona, Louisiana, Connecticut, New York, and New Jersey.

The questions to ask are:
- If closing businesses worked, why did so many other states surpass the Dakotas (North Dakota had similar policies) in deaths per capita?
- If face masks worked, why did cases and hospitalizations peak identically in every state bordering the Dakotas, many requiring masks?
- If South Dakota's policies were reckless, why weren't they by far the worst-performing state in COVID-19 or excess deaths?
- Is zero-COVID-19 a reasonable approach, or is exercising some balance better?

Governors exercised enormous power during the pandemic. Some followed the science, and some made up the science (see Governor Whitmer). When the sun sets on COVID-19 as a pandemic and shrinks to another influenza-like contagion, state legislatures need to tighten up the emergency powers of each governor. Pennsylvania did just that in May 2021. Voters signaled their disgust for overreach and voted to amend their constitution, permanently preventing Tom Wolf and any future Pennsylvania governor from repeating emergency powers for as long as a governor chose to do so.[286]

CHAPTER 16
The Policy Influencers – Team Reality

While there were many more policy influencers driving continued lockdowns, school closures for over a year, double mask-wearing even after recovering from COVID-19 or receiving a vaccination, there was a small key group that became the source for nearly all data supporting a return to normalcy. Much of the arguments you saw in support of reopening can be traced back to these people. Some were doctors and scientists, and many were average, non-attention-seeking people without a background in this. I got to meet many of these people. They felt called to speak out about this, and many of them even hid behind a pseudonym so they would not feel a cancel firestorm.

Alex Berenson

It's hard not to begin the Team Reality list without the man that coined the phrase. Alex Berenson is a journalist and author. He spent a decade reporting for the *New York Times* and left in 2010 to become a full-time author. He wrote several best-selling novels and, in 2019, a nonfiction work called "Tell Your Children" about the dangers of cannabis. In January and February 2020, Berenson tweeted to his 7,000 followers that COVID-19 was looking bad for America and shared some dire outlooks on the pandemic.

In March 2020, Berenson looked at the data out of Italy and noticed deaths were predominately the elderly, mostly in care facilities, and with several underlying conditions. By mid-March 2020, as lockdowns began and hospitalizations were not meeting model predictions, he was tweeting out that governors had made a big mistake locking down so severely. His Twitter following grew to 40,000 in a month and a year later, he had hundreds of thousands of followers. He appeared on *Fox News* and One America News often.

In June, he self-published a book called *Unreported Truths*, which became a number one Amazon Kindle seller. In that book, he predicted 450,000 to 600,000 lives lost to COVID-19. His prediction dated May 2020 is as close to any model forecast that existed. It's not that COVID-19 wasn't real, according to Berenson; it's that there was little we could do to stop it and with huge consequential harms of locking down.

Berenson took hard data and waxed it into providing more information than any single source early in the pandemic. He named the group supporting hard lockdowns and closed schools Team Apocalypse, and those believing the non-pharmaceutical interventions were an overreach and ineffective as Team Reality. No one triggered the ire of those believing in the lockdowns more than Berenson. In April 2020, Alex was a guest on Sean Hannity's evening show on *Fox News*. During the interview, Berenson stated that people under thirty were at practically no risk to COVID-19. Hannity dismissed him as off base and the next couple of days, many in the media ripped on Berenson's interview. I was watching it in real-time that evening. I knew then that Alex was right. Why? Because when tens of thousands of people had already died from COVID-19, fewer than a hundred young people died with it, and nearly all those with underlying conditions. He was looking at the data. When the United States had a hundred thousand COVID-19 deaths and over 3,000 all-cause deaths to those under 30 in 2020, 31 young people had died of COVID-19.

Berenson tweeted about and wrote booklets about the ineffectiveness of lockdowns, wearing masks, and how the data was being manipulated. He appeared several times a week on *Fox News* for over a year and appeared on Joe Rogan and Megyn Kelly's podcasts. The information Berenson shared was then taken by hundreds of writers, radio and podcast hosts, and television anchors to share a contrarian view that lockdowns were ineffective.

Berenson tweeted this on August 28, 2021: "Don't think of it as a vaccine. Think of it – at best – as a therapeutic with a limited window of efficacy and terrible side effect profile that must be dosed IN ADVANCE OF ILLNESS." Twitter permanently suspended Berenson's account for misinformation as he reached 350,000 followers and was adding about one thousand per day. Prior to COVID-19, the CDC defined a vaccine as "a product that stimulates a person's immune system to produce immunity to a specific disease, protecting that person from the disease." On September 1, 2021, the CDC changed their definition of a vaccine to "a preparation that is used to stimulate the body's immune response against diseases."

Berenson's tweet was worded closer to accurate than inaccurate. The COVID-19 vaccines did have more side effects than any vaccine in a generation. That doesn't mean they were not an effective option for those at risk; they were. That the CDC modified its definition of a vaccine to accommodate the COVID-19 vaccines rather than the vaccines conform to the standard we are used to is suspect and one more example of the CDC jumping the shark. This is not an anti-vaccine comment; I took the Janssen vaccine and have encouraged those at risk to do so. It does speak to the media censorship and lack of integrity by the CDC throughout COVID-19. It would be perfectly fine to label the mRNA or Janssen shots as "vaccine-like" or immunity stimulants." Who cares? There was measurable efficacy from the shots, and transparency was and is always the better approach for the long run.

Dr. Scott Atlas

Dr. Scott Atlas is a radiologist, a senior fellow at Stanford University's Hoover Institution and was a professor and chief of neuroradiology at the Stanford University Medical Center. Atlas joined President Trump's COVID-19 task force in August 2020. Atlas was steadfast from the beginning that the lockdowns were an inappropriate response to the pandemic, consistent with CDC and WHO work prior to COVID-19.

On March 26, 2020, Atlas wrote a piece for the *Washington Times* called "Widespread isolation and stopping all human interaction will not eradicate COVID-19."[287] Atlas highlighted the high infection fatality rates of 3.4% by the WHO (March 2020) were impossible and cited examples including, you guessed it, the cruise ships. He called out then that 99% of the cases have mild to no symptoms. A year into the pandemic, we had a million total COVID-19 hospitalizations (including about a third *with* it and not *from* it). Estimates by even the CDC suggested that in the first quarter of 2021, well over one hundred million Americans had been infected. That translates to about 1:175, even milder than Atlas's 99%. Atlas promoted isolation and quarantining for those sick and protection for the elderly at most risk, but against one-size-fits-all population lockdowns.

In April 2020, Atlas continued lobbying in public for reopening schools and businesses, highlighting that people healthy and under 30 were at practically no risk. He gave television, podcast, and other media interviews, in addition to writing op-eds on the subject. He called out that herd immunity was the only way through this, which is historically and biologically true. The question is how you get there. Atlas never stopped highlighting the damage associated with closing up healthcare facilities to non-COVID-19 patients. This, along with school closings, was the most egregious and damaging of any of the lockdown measures, both proving unwarranted with tragic long-term effects.

When Atlas joined the president's advisory team reporting like this from *CNN* was a daily headline: "Trump adds coronavirus adviser who echoes his unscientific claims."[288] Atlas saw things very differently than advisory members Dr. Birx and Dr. Fauci. The difference in their perception was apparent to anyone following the story. Atlas saw huge consequences to the lockdowns: huge long-term life years lost in excess of the COVID-19 life years lost, with no proven benefit of the lockdowns. Team Apocalypse hated Atlas, and no one was subject to more public criticism in the second half of 2020 than he.

YouTube pulled interviews with Atlas[289] and dozens of print and online media pieces persecuted his views. Television news programs on *CNN* and *MSNBC* criticized him of ignoring the science daily. Atlas argued this:

- COVID-19 is measurably harmless to young people. Herd immunity is the only way out of any pandemic. If enough young, healthy people get through it, the virus will have too few people to spread through to reach the vulnerable. Our best option is to insulate the elderly and those at risk with great discipline and allow the rest to practice personal responsibility.
- He was the only one in public health to call out the consequences of the lockdowns: 46% of six most common cancers didn't get diagnosed; half the 650,000 cancer patients didn't get treatments during the lockdowns; half the child immunizations didn't get done; 85% of living organ transplants didn't get done; 200,000+ cases of child abuse during the spring lockdown; 25% of college-age adults thought of suicide in June 2020. Fifty million kids were getting fractured education for a year.

This wasn't political but became political. Most liberal-leaning people supported the lockdowns, while traditional liberal voters were the most harmed by the lockdowns and by COVID-19 in general. Conservatives latched on to Atlas and his balanced approach. If you happen to think Atlas was off-base and reckless, ask yourself this: how much did you ever hear about lockdown deaths, ignored medical casualties of the lockdowns, or the harms of closed schools from anyone else in an official public health role in 2020?

The Great Barrington Declaration

Doctor's Sunetra Gupta (Oxford), Jay Bhattacharya (Stanford) and Martin Kulldorff (Harvard) released The Great Barrington Declaration on October 4, 2020, along with dozens of other medical experts denouncing lockdowns as a mitigation tactic, highlighting "lower childhood vaccination rates, worsening cardiovascular disease outcomes, fewer cancer screenings and deteriorating mental health – leading to greater excess mortality in years to come, with the working class and younger members of society carrying the heaviest burden. Keeping students out of school is a grave injustice."[290]

Recall that Gupta was behind the Oxford study in March 2020, condemning the assumptions in the Imperial College model that triggered the initial lockdowns. Bhattacharya wrote in March 2020 that the model assumptions were overstated and that the components of many lockdowns had severe costs to the people. Kulldorff was born in Sweden and is a professor at Harvard Medical School and Brigham and Women's Hospital. Kulldorff is a member of the Food and Drug Administration's scientific council for drug safety and risk management and a member of the Centre for Disease Control's scientific committee for evaluating side effects after a COVID-19 vaccination. Kulldorff spoke out repeatedly as well on the disproportionate and ineffectiveness of the lockdowns during the pandemic.

The Great Barrington Declaration has, at the time of this writing, nearly a million signatures, including over 50,000 science and medical professionals. Interestingly, more signatures per capita are from Germany and U.K. than any other country. Most people that don't follow the pandemic and lockdown coverage very closely don't know who these doctors are or what the declaration represents. If you don't, go to YouTube and search their names, including a roundtable Governor Ron DeSantis hosted on March 18, 2021, with the three doctors and Scott Atlas. Judge for yourself. You will find the arguments fact-based and, moreover, public-health balanced. Public health wasn't just minimizing COVID-19 deaths. Public health was so much more: mental health, all the untreated and undiagnosed ailments already discussed, education, and much more.

Kulldorff and Bhattacharya were both interviewed on Megyn Kelly's podcast on December 7, 2020. They stressed the harms of the lockdowns in ways that were not spoken of often during the pandemic and stressed that history will remember this as the worst public policy countries have ever deployed.

On March 13, 2021, Kulldorff tweeted a picture of his daughter at a ski hill. His comment: "My 5-year-old daughter was just kicked off Gunstock Ski Mountain, NH, for not wearing a mask. She had a virus in December, so immune and cannot infect others. Even other kids outdoors are not spreaders. When/why did we turn mean on children?" Enough said. Study the science of the Great Barrington Declaration doctors.

Senator Rand Paul

No one in Congress took a stronger stand against Science-AC than Senator Rand Paul. Perhaps it's because he's a doctor by trade, an ophthalmologist. Perhaps it's because he got COVID-19 in March 2020. Perhaps it's because he's more libertarian than Republican, which by definition emphasizes freedom of choice and voluntary association. Perhaps it's because he just clearly saw the data and balanced the risk and consequence between COVID-19 and the lockdowns.

On June 30, 2020, Paul said this to Dr. Fauci during a Senate hearing on the lockdowns and the pandemic: "Dr. Fauci, every day we seem to hear from you things we can't do. But when you're asked, 'Can we go back to school?' I don't hear much certitude at all. 'Well, maybe.' 'It depends.' Guess what? It's rare for kids to transmit this. I don't hear that coming from you. All I hear is, 'We can't do this, we can't do that, we can't play baseball.'"[291] No one in Congress challenged the lockdowns and closed schools with more passion than Paul did.

Paul challenged Fauci again in a senate hearing on September 23, 2020, again on the efficacy of the lockdowns and government measures. On November 12,

2020, Paul said this: "We should tell [people who had COVID-19 and recovered] to celebrate. We should tell them to throw away their masks, go to restaurants, live again because these people are now immune."[292] Detractors said that was not true or not proven. Yet, for the perhaps billion people that were infected by then, fewer than fifty cases were ever shown to be reinfected.[293] If recovering from COVID-19 did not offer immunity, it would deviate from past virus infection and recovery traditions.

On March 18, 2021, Paul went after Fauci once again on face masks and immunity. "You've been vaccinated and you parade around in two masks for show. Do you want to get rid of vaccine hesitancy? Tell them they can quit wearing their masks after they get the vaccine."[294] They sparred on the efficacy of the vaccines and the need for face masks once vaccinated or once one has recovered from COVID-19. After over a year, neither Fauci nor the CDC would commit to circumstances that would end the need for face masks. Paul often accused the task force leader of it being theater, to which Fauci disagreed.

Rational Ground

Rationalground.com is a repository of data analysis by many contributors that provided information to support reopening schools, businesses, and a return to normal. The contributors have wildly varied backgrounds. Many have IT and data backgrounds; some are engineers, a few doctors, a few teachers, and many others have normal day jobs. They all felt a calling to analyze the data and saw the lockdowns were a gross overreach and ineffective at mitigating COVID-19. I got to know many of the contributors and wrote several pieces for them. Many were excerpts from my books on the lockdowns. The contributors understood COVID-19 well. Many got it; some were sick from it; some lost family members to it. There was a common bond that, as real as COVID-19 was, government policies went too far.

Contributors came together through Twitter. Most have never talked to each other, just shared data through tweets and group chats and the articles. They are from all over the world too. A flight attendant from Russia, a music industry professional from Los Angeles, a data guy from Croatia, a stay-at-home mom in Florida, a teacher from Chicago, a business executive from Puerto Rico. All varied backgrounds, all incredibly smart.

The analysis they produced permeated content for Team Reality in nearly all news sources and political arguments in the United States. @justin_hart started it and was frequently speaking on news programs throughout the pandemic. @ianmsc developed charts that found their way to the White House in 2020, and he contributed many charts in this book. @RMconservative writes for the *Blaze* and @SKMorefield writes for *Townhall* and the *Daily Caller*. @Kelleykga ran a website crunching Georgia data. @foogatwo, @ewoodhouse7, @jhaskincabrera, @hold2llc, @aginnt, @kylamb8 (Kyle Lamb became a DeSantis advisor on

COVID-19), @kerpen (Phil Kerpen, who was on *Fox News* weekly sharing reality data), @benmarten, @wyattsheepie, @IAmTheActualET (Eric Thomas), @ifihadastick (Josh Stevenson), and dozens more pumped out more quality analysis than any other collected source on the pandemic.

It may be intuitive for some to think they're a bunch of conservative CO-VID-19 deniers bashing liberals. They were not. The discussions and analysis were apolitical, and it was always about sharing data about COVID-19 risks and lockdown consequences. Any one of these members would have embarrassed Dr. Fauci or the CDC directors in an open debate simply by sharing the reality that while COVID-19 was a pandemic to be reckoned with, the government policies were disproportionately destructive and largely ineffective.

CHAPTER 17
The Policy Influencers – Team Apocalypse

There was a tight group of influencers of COVID-19 policies in 2020 and 2021. Some were government health leaders, or former ones, and some were doctors and journalists and everyday non-political Americans crunching data and offering their opinions on what the science was telling us. Government health leaders made recommendations that many of the governors implemented. Other doctors and scientists weighed in. Most impressively, some Americans of whom we never heard before stepped up to a calling and began their analysis of the response measures and feeding it to policymakers. It was there that some of the most important science was uncovered.

Dr. Anthony Fauci

It's hard not to begin with the face of the lockdowns and the pandemic response, Dr. Anthony Fauci. Fauci is an immunologist leading the U.S. National Institute of Allergy and Infectious Diseases (NIAID) and is the chief medical advisor to the president. Fauci advised every president since Ronald Reagan. When rumblings of COVID-19 began in early 2020, Fauci gave countless interviews. He was not concerned about COVID-19 for America in January or February and was even less aggressive in recommending mitigations than the CDC in early March. That changed in late March.

An entire book could be written about Fauci's perspective, recommendations, and flip-flops during the pandemic. No one was more visible speaking about the pandemic than Fauci. Those opposing lockdowns and non-pharmaceutical interventions held him in contempt. Those in favor of lockdowns? Well, as *MSNBC* host Nicole Wallace said many times on her television show, they viewed Fauci as a "national treasure."

Fauci had good intentions with respect to COVID-19 suppression. He led Team Zero COVID-19. That is the single reason Fauci failed as a public health care influencer. Wander back to the third week of September 2001. President Bush is meeting with a room full of generals discussing options to eradicate al-Qaeda and their host, the Taliban. Some toss out very surgical approaches like sending in special tactics squads, the Marine Raiders, or even Navy Seals.

General Tony Fauci raises his hand. Eyes turn to him. "We should drop a dozen gravity nuclear bombs that will wipe them out." Silence in the room.

Generals Jay Bhattacharya and Martin Kulldorff speak up and say, "Won't that cause a lot of unnecessary destruction?" General Scott Atlas says, "What about the nuclear fallout on surrounding areas? And Americans over there?" Fauci replies, "Our mission is to get rid of the enemy. It's the only thing that matters." The other generals make a final plea: "But the science says that we won't get them all anyway. A surgical approach makes much more sense for the long run." General Fauci waves them off, dismissing the concern for collateral damage.

That's essentially how Fauci approached the pandemic. Of the thousands of interviews he did, there was not one where his key message was to get the fifty million kids in America back to class. There was not one where he considered masks might not be working. There was not one where he could answer why states with few restrictions didn't do any worse than the harsh lockdown states of New York, New Jersey, Michigan, California.

In 1987 Dr. Fauci was interviewed on the transmission of HIV, the human immunodeficiency virus that leads to AIDS acquired immunodeficiency syndrome.[295] In this interview, Fauci gave real, fact and science-based analysis of how HIV is transmitted. Without going into details here, do check it out. Fauci was confident in his assessment of specific acts that are highly likely versus unlikely to transmit HIV from one person to another. His comments then have played out to be accurate. 1987-Fauci served as a public health servant, delivering analysis based on science. 2020-Fauci would have told people they should not hold hands without testing.

When COVID-19 first broke in 2020, Fauci was publicly not concerned it would be a big event in America, though in February on he did call out the possibility of reaching a pandemic. He said this in February 2020: "I think there's this misperception that wearing a mask, even if you were in an area where there was transmission, is going to absolutely protect you. A mask is more appropriate for someone who is infected to prevent them from infecting someone else."[296] There are two possible takeaways on this. One, COVID-19 had not really breached America yet, so why wear masks? Two, masks don't protect you from catching a virus like SARS-CoV-2, so why bother?

The Fauci Emails

A trove of emails involving Fauci were released in June 2021 through a Freedom Of Information Act request, over three thousand pages of them.[297] Some excerpts are below, showing that Fauci understood the science of masks much better than he portrayed in the public forum for a year and a half. Seeing these email comments and reconciling them with his public pronouncements that face masks were effective should forever encourage people to do independent research on controversial issues. What our leaders say may be very different from what they think:

February 5, 2020: "The typical mask you buy in the drug store is not really effective in keeping out the virus, which is small enough to pass through the fabric. It might, however, provide some slight benefit in keep out gross droplets if someone coughs or sneezes on you. I do not recommend that you wear a mask."

February 26, 2020: "Once a pandemic erupts, it is virtually impossible for any country to be free of cases. People need to understand that. You can mitigate the effects, but you cannot avoid having infections since you cannot shut off the country from the rest of the world. Also, you need to speak of the real and present danger of seasonal influenza every year. Do not let the fear of the unknown (i.e., a pandemic of a new infectious agent) distort your evaluation of the risk of the pandemic to you relative to the risks that you face every day. The only thing that we can do is to prepare as best as possible and do not yield to unreasonable fear."

To Fauci's credit, his emails were professional. When Wikileaks released the plethora of emails from John Podesta during the 2016 election, the most astounding thing was the lack of professionalism so many of the correspondents demonstrated. Many emails from powerful political players were so unprofessional they would never survive Fortune 500 intracompany communications. Fauci's tone and writing were professional, a relief to see from someone in such a high leadership role.

By the end of March 2020, Fauci was publicly considering masks for Americans. At the same time, Surgeon General Jerome Adams was largely dismissive of mask benefits. Fauci was all-in promoting face coverings and closed schools and non-essential businesses in April. Fair enough at this point. In April, New York was experiencing the truest surge of the entire pandemic in America. It was in May that lockdown measures appeared off the science rails.

The core problem with Fauci serving as the lead healthcare expert advising on COVID-19 was that science left the room and conjecture stepped in. One reason was an abundance of caution, and one was a fear of possibly getting it wrong on the one percent chance that the science and facts changed. 1987-Fauci would have advised this in the summer of 2020:

- Schools should open with normal protocols in the fall of 2020. COVID-19 has contributed to less than 1% of under-18 deaths. Deaths of infected people under 18 are statistically 0%, perhaps 1 in 200,000. Riding in a vehicle is 15 times more dangerous to young people than COVID-19. 90% of the teachers are not in an at-risk class either.
- Cloth and surgical masks are not a fail-safe. They probably help, but the data is not showing true suppression. If you have any symptoms of COVID-19 or have tested positive, you should stay home and wear a well-fitted (preferably N95) mask if you go out.

- When we see a rise in cases and hospitalizations in a given community, consider staying at home, limiting shopping, and going out. These surges typically last four to six weeks. In these instances, large gatherings should be canceled.
- If you are severely obese, you are at high risk of COVID-19. Keep a low profile and limit your interactions where possible, particularly with those outside your household.
- If you are elderly, or over 50 and suffer from hypertension, a respiratory condition, or severe diabetes, also keep a low profile and limit your interactions where possible, particularly with those outside your household.

This was the science, and 1987-Fauci would have reported this as he did on HIV. In 2021 Fauci continued to support lockdowns as hospitalizations were cratering. On March 22, 2021, Fauci gave an interview on the efficacy of lockdowns and said this:

I think the lockdown situation is really very complicated. Because there have been some states that said they locked down, and when you look at the actual tracking them on GPSs about how much they locked down, it isn't nearly as much as was claimed. In fact, they did a comparison of the European lockdown versus the United States lockdown, and they did it by GPS, how many people go to the stores, how many people go to the parks. And when Europe locked down, they locked down a heck of a [lot] more strictly than we did. [The lockdowns], it has efficacy in suppressing the outbreak, but it also, as you say, and I agree, has significant economic consequences.[298]

Someone should point out how many European countries performed at par or worse than the United States. If strict measures worked, why didn't they work?

This is why Fauci should not be viewed as a public health expert or advisor. The lockdowns did not statistically show suppression. Fauci never thought through the lens of the damage of schools closed or other health consequences. He saw things through a Zero-COVID-19 lens and would never concede the trade was not worth it and the worst public policy in 150 years.

CDC Directors

Director Robert Redfield led the Centers for Disease Control as COVID-19 began, and Director Rochelle Walensky took over with the Biden administration in 2021. The CDC had enormous influence over COVID-19 policies in 2020 and 2021, as they should. As we saw in chapter three, Dr. Redfield and his organization drifted from science-based recommendations into conjecture. This continued with Dr. Walensky.

CDC guidance is important to policy leaders for two reasons. A very real one is the guidance on healthcare risks, measures, and recommended behaviors to navigate the pandemic. The more real, but less important reason is risk. If a governor creates a policy because "the CDC said so," they're free of accountability. Doing what Governors Noem, DeSantis, and Abbott did took enormous courage. The CDC must report on facts and science without regard to politics or the media.

Walensky presided over the CDC when they released their report on the case and death risks of dining indoors and not wearing masks. That differential? About 1%. A rounding error. There was no real difference in their analysis between wearing masks or not and eating in or takeout. Further, Walensky was highly visible on cable news as soon as she took her appointment. She should. We were in a pandemic, and the voice of the director is a required one.

She repeated recommendations in March 2021 on television that people should not air travel as it is still unsafe. She went further, saying that gatherings would risk "the holiday surge we saw" in late 2020. Think about that first one for a moment. In 2020 and 2021, how many studies or stories have you read that identified planes and airports as hotspot spreaders? Do an internet search. How many do you find? Right, none. If the holidays prompted surges, why did the upper Midwest begin its winter trajectory in early November and it died off in mid-December? If Christmas travel and getting together triggered a surge, why did we peak in hospitalizations nationally on January 6, 2021, with a completely symmetrical growth from November 1, 2020?

Dr. Walensky pleaded with America in tears in March 2021 that there was doom ahead if people stopped wearing masks and began circulating more. People did and there was not. The pandemic was in clear recession when the calendar passed to spring. Walensky was anything but a calming voice following the science when he assumed her post.

Dr. Deborah Birx

Deborah Birx worked in public health service for most of her career, serving in the U.S. Army, then as a physician at Walter Reed Army Medical Center. Later, she led the HIV/AIDS division for the CDC, and then served under Presidents Obama and Trump in an HIV/AIDS world ambassador capacity. In the spring of 2020, she joined the COVID-19 task force in the White House.

Birx generally kept a low profile. She did comment in the spring that the CDC was overcounting COVID-19 deaths by about 25%. The *Washington Post* reported Birx went so far as saying that "there is nothing from the CDC that I can trust."[299] Birx reached national attention when she did what we see many leaders promoting lockdown strategies did: she violated her own orders.

In November 2020, COVID-19 activity was ramping up nationwide. In many interviews leading up to Thanksgiving, Birx repeatedly said that everyone should avoid family get-togethers and travel for the holiday. Then, in mid-December, news broke that Birx left Washington to visit her Delaware home the day after Thanksgiving, where three generations of family members gathered. Birx tried to dismiss the deviation from her policy rather than owning it. She retired days later, concluding her career in public service.

On March 28, 2021, Birx was interviewed for a *CNN* special on the pandemic doctors. In that interview, she said, "In my mind, for the first hundred thousand deaths, we have an excuse. There were about a hundred thousand deaths that came from that original surge. All the rest, in my mind, could have been mitigated or substantially decreased." The question is, how?

Birx did not intervene on the original policies of nursing homes taking in COVID-19-positive patients. Not a word was publicly uttered by her. Nursing homes continued to get ravaged into February 2021. By summer 2020, it's reasonable to assume that fifty million people had been infected. In many strict lockdown states, we saw continued 2021 COVID-19 activity, such as in California, Rhode Island, New Jersey, New York, and Michigan. Interviewer Dr. Sanjay Gupta never asked a follow-up question on how so many deaths could have been avoided or explain the math. For Birx to state 80% of all COVID-19 deaths could have been prevented or substantially decreased without specifics was reckless. It put a bookend to her career and showed she should never have been on the task force from the beginning.

Dr. Tom Frieden

Tom Frieden served most of his career in public healthcare service. He began with the CDC in New York City and grew to lead as the Commissioner of Health of the City of New York. President Obama appointed Frieden as the director of the CDC, and since then has headed up Resolve to Save Lives, an organization chartered to prevent epidemics and cardiovascular disease.

Frieden was very visible throughout the pandemic and, in the interest of continuity, was one more purveyor of lockdowns and NPIs as an effective means of suppressing the spread of COVID-19. As a former CDC director, Frieden had significant influence. Frieden was supportive of states locking down, remote schooling, and wearing face masks throughout 2020 and 2021. His interviews and tweets were consistently promoting restrictions, believing that locking down for what became over a year was the correct policy.

The problem with Frieden's commentaries is like those of many other policy influencers. He promoted a one-size-fits-all measure. Never did Friedan read the science that kids should be in school unequivocally, as the data clearly showed. Friedan's promotion of continued lockdowns only reinforced media support, which drove polls, which drove governor policies.

Frieden perceived public health like Fauci and the other CDC directors: zero-COVID-19. The reckless part of his messaging was that he did not promote kids returning to class. He did not promote families seeing each other for gatherings. When the pandemic crisis was receding by the end of March 2021, he messaged about the risk of the U.K variant with great panic when it had done nothing out of cycle and seasonality in the U.K. The delta variant that slammed the southern states in the summer of 2021 was sourced from India. When the science refuted that six feet was the right social distance, he still encouraged it. When the science told us anything other than locking down and wearing a mask were the right courses of action, Frieden ignored it in the media. Policy influencers like him were reinforcement of the governors' lockdowns.

Dr. Michael Osterholm

Michael Osterholm was a special kind of panic-purveyor throughout the pandemic and took that gift to national news programs weekly, at times daily, influencing those in the media, viewers, and policymakers. Osterholm is an epidemiologist and Director of the Center for Infectious Disease Research and Policy at the University of Minnesota. When President Biden became the president-elect, Osterholm joined his COVID-19 advisory team.

Osterholm became known for COVID-19 consistently observing "wait two more weeks" and "expect this to get really bad over the next six to fourteen weeks." These became canned statements repeated each month, and each month he warned against any reopening, kids in class, any return to normalcy. Osterholm had some quality observations in April 2020.[300] He felt that we would not get out of this until we reached about 60% herd immunity, a fair statement. He put a number of 800,000 deaths as a reasonable estimate, and his logic made some sense. He was off just over a half percent on the fatality rate, but his estimate was in April 2020. And, he predicted in April a wave or two before the pandemic winds down, also fair. It wasn't until late summer 2020 that his observations went off the rails.

On August 7, 2020, Osterholm and Neel Kashkari, president of the Federal Reserve Bank of Minneapolis, penned an op-ed in the *New York Times*.[301]

Opinion

Here's How to Crush the Virus Until Vaccines Arrive

To save lives, and save the economy, we need another lockdown.

By Michael T. Osterholm and Neel Kashkari
Dr. Osterholm is director of the Center for Infectious Disease Research and Policy at the University of Minnesota. Mr. Kashkari is president of the Federal Reserve Bank of Minneapolis.

Aug. 7, 2020

The pair wrote that the United States needed to go into an aggressive lockdown. Not the lockdowns like we experienced in April - something much more aggressive. Their idea was to drive cases down to 1:100,000 per day. Vermont, one of the lowest per-capita states in COVID-19 activity, did this for about a third of the first full year of the pandemic. Then the winter wave hit and they tripled in cases after a very slow August and September.

They recommended only "true" essential workers work for six weeks. Everyone else stay home except to get food or visit the doctor or pharmacy. That meant 39% of the people continue working. That translates to about half the number of people working as they did in April, with tens of millions of people still out there. They said that after that, contact tracing could nip any new cases before they transmit. They further asserted that medical needs (non-COVID-19) could continue because medical professionals have learned how to protect themselves and patients from spreading the virus. The opinion piece concluded with one paragraph on how to fund it through economic savings achieved by the lockdowns. They referenced the low COVID-19 activity in the summer of 2020 in Europe and Asia and Canada, as having successfully suppressed COVID-19.

This is the kind of analysis that drove continued NPIs and lockdowns and kept schools closed. The crazy thing is that this was authored by two highly educated, successful, accomplished men. It reminds me of one of the comments Bill Gates made about continued lockdowns: recommendations by really smart people that somehow missed the common sense of this pandemic. Taking this apart in pieces, here are the major flaws:

- Simply believing you can control a virus as contagious as this in a country as big as the United States. If you did this in just Hawaii and prevented any incoming visitors until everyone was vaccinated, you probably could quiet it down for an economic, educational, social, and psychological cost.
- The number one source spread of COVID-19 was nosocomial, having originated in a medical setting. There was no evidence that those environments had learned how to protect themselves or patients (not a criticism, just a reality), or even could.
- As we saw in Antarctica and with COVID-19 in other countries and communities in the United States, it can appear quite suppressed and then spread spontaneously.
- It's impossible to contact trace effectively when millions of people had caught the virus and in such a large geography.
- They referenced better results due to mitigations in Europe, which after their writing had a significant wave in the winter.
- Lockdowns simply had not worked in the western world. As we saw after a year and a half of the pandemic, each country got its turn. How hard they were hit was largely impacted by the age, obesity rate, and rate of comorbidities in that country.

Osterholm predicted in multiple interviews an explosion of COVID-19 activity associated with school reopenings, which never happened. One reason is that few opened. Another is that, and the data was out at that time, kids simply were not effective transmitters of SARS-CoV-2, nor were they susceptible. In October 2020, Osterholm predicted numerous times that "the next 6-12 weeks would be the darkest of the pandemic." He was somewhat correct on that. Winter seasonality (like the flu) was approaching. And, with so many people infected, the counts were higher because as long as someone tested positive, they were included whether they were sick with the virus or from COVID-19. Still, there is no doubt we experienced a winter spike.

Hospitalizations reached their all-time high on January 6, 2021. But he repeated the claim in February and March 2021, when all COVID-19 activity had dropped by 80% from two months prior.

In February, he warned of one more "the next 6-12 weeks would be the darkest of the pandemic" based on variants, specifically the U.K. variant. What no one could answer is, if the U.K. variant was so lethal, why hadn't it affected the U.K.? He predicted a "Category 5 hurricane brewing off the U.S. coast,"[302] when we'd never exceeded a category two and the pandemic was well in retreat.

These predictions went on in March and April 2021 when vaccines had taken root, hospitalizations had dropped to 3% nationally, and cases and deaths in long-term care facilities had dropped to almost nothing. Claims by Osterholm on dozens of media outlets only prevented kids from returning to school. Claims like that inhibited the reality context of what was happening to permeate the American psyche. In late March 2021, Osterholm was in the media advocating for vaccinating children: "We do want to vaccinate our kids. That will really be a very important part of trying to get them back into school safely."[303]

Later, on April 4, 2021, Osterholm and Friedan both went on the Sunday news talk show circuit with appearances on NBC and *Fox News*. Frieden said the variants were "spreading faster and kills more." Osterholm claimed that the U.K. B.1.1.7. variant would cause more a new wave and be a serious risk to children. The *Fox News* host made the comment that more kids were "getting sick." There was no data supporting any of these talking points. COVID-19 was spiking irregularly in Michigan at the time, but other states with greater variant prevalence like Florida were not spiking. Children were not getting sick anywhere at this time. It was reckless reporting. When you see these anecdotal reports on children that don't report on actual illnesses or hospitalizations, feel free to dismiss them.

Osterholm then called for new lockdowns while hospitalizations were under 4% nationally.

Xavier Becerra

Xavier Becerra was confirmed as the United States Secretary of Health and Human Services in the Biden administration. Before his confirmation, on January 24, 2020, he was on *CNN* talking about the pandemic. I was writing this at the time with *CNN* muted in the background. I looked up and saw this:

The caption made me do a double-take. Becerra said the COVID-19 plane was in a nose-dive. Two days before, I did a media release myself stating that "the pandemic as we knew it is over." I went on to comment about plunging hospitalizations, seasonality, recovered infections, and vaccines all contributing to us really just running out the clock. The pandemic as we knew it was over, though we saw subsequent waves in the south in the summer of 2021 and northern states a few months later when it cooled off. We weren't through it, but we were in no way in a nosedive. There was a lot of good news to discuss at the end of January. Meanwhile, policy-influencers had nothing but fearful things to share with America. This is how the panic cycle works: "expert" says how bad it is and doesn't share balance, context of good news → media runs with what they say → people get afraid → leaders keep locking down.

Andy Slavitt

Andy Slavitt began his public health career when his firm stepped in to help with the Affordable Care Act website and enrollment issues in 2013. He was later appointed as Principal Deputy Administrator of the Centers for Medicare and Medicaid Services in 2014. Slavitt is a graduate of both Wharton and Harvard. When COVID-19 broke out in 2020, Slavitt, in the private sector, was vehemently critical of the Trump Administration's approach. Slavitt joined President Biden's COVID-19 advisory team in late 2020. Throughout the pandemic, Slavitt was active as a policy influencer on Democrat governors and on Americans through thousands of tweets and national interviews.

On March 14, 2020, days before states locked down, Slavitt penned "CO-VID-19 March 14 Update: Without urgent action we will have tens of thousands more COVID-19 cases than we have beds, and we will have 1 ventilator for every 8 people who need one."[304] Below are some excerpts, you can see how governors that believed his projections would lock down.

- *Currently, experts expect over 1 million deaths in the U.S. since the virus was not contained and we cannot even test for it. This will be recorded as a major preventable public health disaster. The original sin is Trump's months-long denial and his dismantling of public health and response infrastructure.*
- *Hospitals must get rid of elective procedures.*
- *Nursing home infection control is terrible to begin with. And they are better than elder care or senior living facilities. The death rate among those older than 80 years old who contract COVID-19 is 18%.* [This prediction is worse than the 9% that *U.S. News and World Report* predicted. Slavitt here is predicting well over a million people over eighty would lose their lives. If 18% could be close, why did only 1:432 die on the cruise ships? Based on infection rate of about 30%, by his math, we should have lost 25 people over 80, and we lost one.]
- *And look, this is where we are regarding nursing home regulations: The Obama Administration implemented them before a pandemic. Trump eliminated them before the pandemic. And is trying to reinstate them now.*

In late April 2020, Slavitt partnered up with Dr. Scott Gottlieb to recommend the Contact Tracing Force.[305] They proposed to leaders in Congress that we build a workforce of 180,000 to test and trace COVID-19 cases to stop the spread. Before the pandemic, the WHO stated contact tracing was ineffective once you get a significant community spread. Recommending this much contact tracing, when it takes days to contract, you can spread it before symptoms appear, and tens of millions were carrying it was always a preposterous idea. They then proposed $4.5B to allow people positive with the virus to isolate in hotels.

In November 2020, Slavitt was heralding Europe's better handling of the virus and then went on to compare South Dakota and Vermont.[306] Whenever you hear an "expert" cherry-pick one hard-hit COVID-19 state and compare it to a lightly-impacted state across the country, know they are disingenuous. It takes a trend and similar geography to make a comparison, something explored in the Burden of Proof chapter.

Slavitt pitted the United States against Europe and cited Germany. Know what happened to Germany? After the article he wrote, Germany had a surge and locked down twice, in the winter of 2020-2021 and again in the spring of

2021. If they did so great, after a year, why did they have to keep locking down? Leaders took so long to learn that while COVID-19 is very real, lockdowns just weren't the answer.

On February 17, 2021, Slavitt, now on the Biden COVID-19 team, appeared on *MSNBC*.[307] *MSNBC* anchor Stephanie Ruhle asked Slavitt to comment on a great observation: California has basically been in constant lockdown compared to Florida and their numbers aren't that different. Slavitt stumbled and replied that "there's so much of this virus we think we can predict, we think we understand, that's just a little beyond our explanation...." Translation: We Got Nothing.[308] Here is how he should have answered that question:

> *That is correct, Stephanie. After a year of looking at this, we are seeing that lockdowns aren't working, and the least restricted states are not doing worse than locked down ones. We should open schools immediately. Those that are sick or positive with the virus should isolate for a week to ten days. We need to get our vulnerable population vaccinated quickly, and we should return to normal for everyone else, each person practicing personal responsibility.*

Policy influencers like Dr. Fauci, the CDC directors, Michael Osterholm, and Andy Slavitt continued to push for continued non-pharmaceutical interventions well after a year. They were interviewed on television constantly pushing for continued lockdown measures and could never answer the basic question: if lockdowns work, why didn't the states with lesser restrictions do a lot worse, or worse at all? The data clearly showed kids were less affected by COVID-19 than the flu. Their statements drove media narratives which drove polls that influenced state policies.

CHAPTER 18
How the Media Fueled the Lockdowns

After writing one of the first books on the pandemic, I was interviewed several hundred times on television, radio, and podcast news programs, all new to me in 2020. Among others, I became a regular on a show from Arizona, Wake Up Tucson, spending an hour every other week with host Chris DeSimone and his listeners. On one show, I asked Chris what the pandemic would look like without Twitter and social media. His initial thought was that social media-fueled panic and continued lockdown measures. For sure, that was accurate, but I wondered aloud about the other side of social media, a benefit. It's a complex circle.

Social media has become the primary news source for more Americans than any other medium. Imagine if COVID-19 struck in the 1980s before cable television. Primary news sources were 1) network news, 2) major newspapers like the *New York Times* and *Washington Post*, and 3) local newspapers. Those mediums covered COVID-19 in 2020 as if it were a category five pandemic and drove opinion that schools and restaurants should be closed and everyone should be masked, perhaps even at home and in the car. They constantly reported that hospitals were lined up over capacity with sick, dying patients. However, we'd be looking around our communities, not seeing much activity. We'd know it was out there, but we'd see hospitals were empty and few we knew were getting sick.

Remember, other than the four to six weeks when a community got hit, you wouldn't know COVID-19 was a pandemic. Outside those surge periods, doctors would have assumed it was a weird or strong flu or something. The symptoms were similar to the flu, just worse if you were vulnerable enough to be hospitalized. If COVID-19 struck communities, it was like a few-week hurricane and it left a vacuum of emptiness in hospitals. In my home of Dallas, some well-intentioned college kids visited Parkland Hospital downtown to take care packages to frontline workers when we were in tight lockdown in April 2020. The nurse at receiving thanked them and laughed. She told them they had no COVID-19 activity and with non-COVID-19 patients kept away, it was empty. She walked them down darkened halls free of patients, nurses, and doctors. Their voices echoed as they talked in the silence.

Nearly all major media outlets were absent any COVID-19 information suggesting the risk didn't support the lockdowns. *Fox News'* primetime shows often reported on it, that with three million viewers nightly, one percent of America, and likely the same one percent all the time. *Newsmax* and *One America News* did too, but their viewership was relatively low, less than a half-million viewers combined. That left 99% of America without a view from the mainstream media that maybe the lockdowns were a cure too far.

Nearly all data to counter lockdowns originated with Twitter users. It largely began with Alex Berenson's constant pouring of data to counter the models that triggered the lockdowns. Berenson began appearing on *Fox News* weekly in April 2020. Other Twitter users like The Ethical Skeptic (don't laugh, he stays anonymous, but the guy is a genius) and Justin Hart, and contributors to his Rational Ground, provided nearly all hardcore data. If Twitter did not exist, it's hard to imagine where data to support stopping lockdowns would have come from. Hold your thoughts on the mention of *Fox News* if you're not a conservative. We need open thought and debate on something as huge as worldwide lockdowns. It was a sad state of journalism that *Fox News* was the only major media company to offer this, though, by summer 2020, the *Wall Street Journal* did some quality analysis on the lockdowns. Most media outlets were very selective in their reporting on the lockdowns.

There are different kinds of media bias. One form is the omission of facts. You can provide some information but not all, just sharing the data that supports the "journalist" point of view. "Journalist" is in quotations because there are so few. If an actual journalist, the person has an obligation to facts, reporting accurate information to the reader or listener. That must be a little boring because there are so few high-profile ones out there.

Another kind of media bias is simply choosing what to report on. This is most prevalent today. Watch the network and cable news one day nonstop, flipping channels between *ABC/CBS/NBC* nightly news, and cable news on *CNN*, *Fox News*, *MSNBC*, *Newsmax*, and *One America News*. Most days, you will see different topics covered on the same news day. Nearly all cable news is opinion reporting, with few reporting objectively on the day's events. Few news shows are opinion-free. There isn't anything wrong with that, it can be great entertainment, particularly if it supports your point of view. It's just not journalism. The major network news shows, *CNN*, *MSNBC*... never had one of the data experts against the lockdowns on their shows to debate school closures or face masks.

Where We Get The News

ABC's World News Tonight leads network news with about nine million viewers nightly, followed by *NBC Nightly News's* seven million viewers and *CBS Evening News's* five million. *Fox News* typically gets about three million viewers, followed by *MSNBC's* 1.5 million and *CNN's* one million viewers. It's very fair to say of that, and there may be some overlap, that 23 million television news watchers were getting pro-lockdown, closed school, and face mask support from all programming except *Fox News* primetime.

Online news and media sites touch hundreds of millions of viewers. Below is Statista's breakdown of the most frequented online news sources based on unique monthly visitors[309]:

Yahoo News	175 million
Google News	150 million
Huffington Post	110 million
CNN	95 million
The *New York Times*	70 million
Fox News	65 million
NBC News	63 million
The *Washington Post*	47 million
The *Guardian*	42 million
The *Wall Street Journal*	40 million
ABC News	36 million
USA Today	34 million
LA Times	33 million

The *Atlantic* self-reported that they received ninety million unique online visitors in March 2020.

There is obvious overlap of the same unique visitors to many of these news outlets. Within this breakdown, for a solid year into the pandemic, the only major news sources that were offering coverage against the lockdowns were *Fox News* and the *Wall Street Journal* and the *New York Post*. The *Guardian* ran a few pieces on lockdown damage, mostly harm from school closings, as did the *New York Times*. While the *Times* pushed many lockdown measures, they did some excellent reporting on school closings. In general, there's a ratio of 845 million to 105 million, or better than 88% coverage driving continued lockdowns, school closings, and face mask mandates.

Social Media

An enormous and growing source of news Americans receive is through Facebook, Twitter, and YouTube. Pew Research identified that 36% of U.S. adults get their news from Facebook, ninety million people of the 170 million Facebook users. About sixty million adults get news from YouTube and fifty million from Twitter. Now, most of the news on these social media platforms often originates from the news sources above. However, just like large news organizations demonstrated bias in what they reported, the social media platforms demonstrated bias in what they allowed to circulate.

Facebook

Facebook has become a primary news resources for hundreds of millions of Americans and others worldwide. They did some good too. Facebook created a vaccine finder tool used by millions to help them secure vaccines more efficiently. They also became the arbiter of COVID-19 news and what they called misinformation. Facebook removed sixteen million pieces of information that they deemed inappropriate even if they did not violate their rules, like comments and articles discouraging wearing masks or getting vaccines. They removed the Great Barrington Declaration page. Do a quick search and find the GBD and read through it - it's short. It condemns the one-size-fits-all lockdown measures like closing schools and businesses and rather stresses the importance of those measurably at risk to be protected, whether in a long-term care facility or at home.

Are those crazy concepts that should not be open for discussion? Kang-Xing Jin was a college friend of Mark Zuckerberg and took the lead on COVID-19 information and misinformation for Facebook. KX has no medical background, but then neither do I; that's no showstopper to analyze data, risk, and consequence. The stickiness comes in when the giant tech companies that shape our lives can't draw the line between misinformation and healthy debate and discussion.

Facebook pages, messages, and posted articles that promoted that kids were at ~zero COVID-19 risk, that discouraged masks, and argued that no requirement should be made to wear masks were all at risk of censorship. They banned "misinformation" related to theories ranging from saying SARS-CoV-2 was manmade to posting that it's safer to get the disease rather than the vaccine. As for the latter, based on VAERS (vaccine adverse event reporting system), that may have been true for those under thirty years old and was definitely true for kids eighteen and under. At a minimum, debating the risk and benefit for an emergency use authorization vaccine is legitimate. Another banned opinion is that COVID-19 is no more dangerous than the flu. As discussed, for those older it was. For babies to at least college age, it just wasn't, and it wasn't close.

Facebook also banned anything stating that the vaccines kill or harm people. Well, based on the VAERS reporting, Facebook was flat out wrong. Vaccines did, in very small but measurable cases, kill people. They caused more side effects than all other vaccines over the past couple of decades combined. They absolutely made millions sick. The J&J vaccine I took made me very sick for two days. Having said that, if you were fifty or over or at risk, taking it was a no-brainer. For kids, the encouragement when they were at no risk was also a no-brainer; the vaccines should not have been pushed in 2021.

Other theories or lines of comments banned were unfounded theories. This included thinking that COVID-19 was a bioweapon or that hospitals kill people for the extra federal relief payments. Where does that line get drawn of banning?

Who gets to make it? Is it okay if they err on the side of caution? That argument might be stronger if they were taking the lead from agencies that were following the science.

YouTube

Very early on, YouTube took down videos that were critical of lockdowns or face mask mandates. YouTube took down a video interview with Dr. Jay Bhattacharya in the spring of 2020, as well as many others that discussed overcounting of COVID-19 deaths or lockdown harms. In March 2021, Florida Governor Ron DeSantis hosted a roundtable discussion with Dr. Scott Atlas and the Great Barrington Declaration doctors Jay Bhattacharya, Martin Kulldorff, and Sunetra Gupta. The triggering comment made was their condemnation of masking children. YouTube took down the video. Bhattacharya, who really is a gentleman, kindly made a comment that he'd love to debate the 24-year-old YouTube employee making that decision.

YouTube responded to taking down the roundtable discussion with the following statement: "We removed this video because it included content that contradicts the consensus of local and global health authorities regarding the efficacy of masks to prevent the spread of COVID-19. We allow videos that otherwise violate our policies to remain on the platform if they contain sufficient educational, documentary, scientific, or artistic context. Our policies apply to everyone and focus on content regardless of the speaker or channel."[310] The problem was the consensus of local and global health authorities not following the science. These were not public health officials, they were zero-COVID-19 officials.

If you've come this far, you've read how little risk COVID-19 posed to children and the ineffectiveness of masks. Let's say you don't agree with the science and data here. There is still a strong enough case made to warrant an open discussion about it. For sure, Google employees aren't qualified to make that determination. If they think they are, they should reach out. I'd love to have a live YouTube discussion with them on it.

Twitter

Nearly all original content and data in challenging school closings, hospital capacity, face mask efficacy, closed restaurants, and the rest of lockdown measures can be traced back to Twitter. Organized media, a good 90% of it, was driving fear through on-screen graphics and reporting. Very rarely did media outlets contextualize that 1) the models were wrong, 2) kids were at ~0 risk, 3) mask efficacy was very iffy based on pre-COVID-19 science and the data in the U.S., 4) closing businesses didn't do anything measurable and 5) not fully reopening schools in the fall of 2020 was insane. The data and critical thinking on these topics originated on Twitter.

Twitter was a fairly open platform on these arguments from the beginning of the pandemic. There was robust, fiery, and at times aggressive information exchange on Twitter. So many bright people brought data to light. Then it became time for Twitter to flex its muscle and did they ever. Their policy of misinformation included:[311]

- *In order for content related to COVID-19 to be labeled or removed under this policy, it must: advance a claim of fact, expressed in definitive terms; be demonstrably false or misleading, based on widely available, authoritative sources; and be likely to impact public safety or cause serious harm.*
- *We will label or remove false or misleading information about: the safety or efficacy of treatments or preventative measures that are not approved by health authorities; adverse impacts or effects of receiving vaccinations, where these claims have been widely debunked.*
- *We will label or remove false or misleading information about personal protective equipment (PPE) such as claims about the efficacy and safety of face masks to reduce viral spread; local or national advisories or mandates pertaining to curfews, lockdowns, travel restrictions, quarantine protocols; how vaccines are developed, tested and approved by official health agencies as well as information about government recommendations.*
- *We will label or remove false or misleading information about: the prevalence of the virus or the disease, such as information pertaining to test results, hospitalizations, or mortality rates; the capacity of the public health system to cope with the crisis, for example, false information about the availability of PPE, ventilators, or doctors, or about hospital capacity; research findings (such as misrepresentations of or unsubstantiated conclusions about statistical data) used to advance a specific narrative that diminishes the significance of the disease.*

Twitter began censoring like crazy after the November 2020 election. Note, after the election, when Republicans lost the White House and Senate after their watchdogs were out of power. Thousands of accounts were blocked, as were millions of tweets questioning mask efficacy, vaccine safety, and anything else not aligned with the CDC. Freedom of speech? Sort of, if it aligns with their ideology. The lockdowns, school closings, mask mandates, and vaccine passports were all the biggest issues anyone alive had ever encountered. They deserved a healthy debate. And they were often denied.

Here's what this means. The CDC director could tweet out something like, "Hospitals are overflowing in California. Please do not leave your house except when necessary." Someone could reply with, "Hospitals are not overflowing; ICUs are only at capacity at 30% of hospitals and half the hospitals don't have 20% COVID-19 occupancy." Bam. That tweet could be flagged or cause an account to be suspended.

This was a benign tweet someone made in April 2021: "A friend traveling around California contacted me to stay at my house for a few days. I asked her if she was vaccinated and she said no, so I said no. She said she already had COVID, but she still needs to be vaxed." Someone I know replied with this, "This is a virus with a 99.8%+ survival rate. Still, your vaccine protects you. My naturally acquired immunity protects me. Many people's good health protects them whether they are vaccinated or not. Wake up." That tweet was flagged as misleading. However, it was as close to fact as anything the CDC tweeted out.

That same person tweeted this in April 2021: "Of course, the CDC cares about cycle thresholds for Covid PCR when faith in vaccines is on the line. Why didn't they care when thousands of PCR tests well over cycle count of 30 were being reported as "cases" – used to count/attribute deaths to the virus." She then provided a link supporting that claim. Twitter suspended her account for that tweet. What she wrote was in bounds. We did set a PCR cycle threshold higher than other countries and well above what would identify a live virus. Setting higher cycle thresholds above a 30-cycle count did result in false positives, sometimes by up to 50% false positives. Then, if that person died with a positive test in their recent history (sometimes up to months), it's a COVID-19 death regardless of why they died. Again, this doesn't mean hundreds of thousands of people didn't die from COVID-19; it does expose a lack of integrity in the data. The question is, why would deciding bodies do that? Who at Twitter knew enough about the data to determine that it was misleading?

Martin Kulldorff is the Harvard professor and epidemiologist that co-authored the Great Barrington Declaration. Kulldorff tweeted this on May 14, 2021, the day after the CDC removed mask recommendations for vaccinated people: "Naively fooled to think that masks would protect them, some older, high-risk people did not socially distance properly, and some died of #COVID-19 because of it. Tragic. Public health officials/scientists must always be honest with the public."

That tweet got Kulldorff's Twitter account suspended for violating terms of providing misleading information. There was not a single part of that tweet that was false or inaccurate. Social distancing and self-isolation were the only interventions that were measurably effective. Either Twitter handlers were completely lacking knowledge about the pandemic, or they blindly censored alternative perspectives on data that didn't strictly follow CDC or WHO guidelines. It's the latter, of course, but how dangerous is that?

Let's suppose you think the social media companies should have suppressed lockdown criticisms. Go back to 2003. After the U.S. sent troops to Afghanistan, the U.S. decided to invade Iraq. The two justifications were an affiliation to al-Qaeda and weapons of mass destruction residing in Iraq. There was a near-unanimous consensus within Washington D.C. that it was the right move. "Experts" said it was the right move. In the moment, my dad and I sat around watching the news and shaking our heads. At his salty near-80 years of age and a veteran of Korea, he said, "Those bastards are going to send these kids to war and they'll get killed and for what? Iraq is no threat to America and there's no proof they were involved in 9-11." He never again considered himself a Republican and never looked back.

The Iraq War was a huge event in American history. Nearly every politician supported it and there was universal media support. Sound a little like the lockdowns? A huge public policy based on sketchy risk and consequence data. Now imagine if media companies banned criticism of the war – eliminating any healthy debate on something history proved to be a disaster. History will not remember the lockdowns as a proportionate response. This isn't about freedom of speech. It's about healthy debate on policies that have enormous consequences.

Puzzle Pieces Connected

This is why the media bias supporting mask mandates, school closings, closed restaurants, and the rest of the interventions was so devastating.

Media coverage promoting lockdowns

Drove polls supporting lockdowns

Which gave politicians the affirmation and support to lock down as hard as they wanted

COVID-19 was unlike other controversial political issues like gun control or climate change. Everyone had the same starting point, and information was on a level playing field. In this one instance more than any other, we saw how enormous the power of the media had on influencing people's opinions and the effect that had on policy. Media coverage out of the gate condemned any thinking that closed schools were a bad idea, that schools were not a risk. The idea that face masks did not work was condemned, and even things like criticizing closing indoor dining. There was no open debate.

Do you think politicians believed in these interventions? Some, but I know personally many did not but feared the media backlash. It was much safer to go with the media flow and polling. Regardless of how you feel about them, this is where Governors DeSantis and Noem showed extreme mettle in standing up to media pressure to follow actual science. There were a lot of things followed during the pandemic: polls, politics, public pressure, fear of being canceled. Science just wasn't one of them. History is showing the most damaging interventions did not improve COVID-19 results anywhere in the United States.

On May 12, 2021, California Governor Newsom announced that on June 15, 2021, he would remove all mask mandates (many states already had). Why June 15th? COVID-19 was not causing any crisis in California, and tens of millions of Americans were doing just fine without California's restrictions. Alex Berenson made a funny if not astute observation in a tweet comment below:

February/March 2020: YOU DON'T NEED A MASK
April-December 2020: YOU WILL DIE WITHOUT A MASK
January/February 2021: NO, TWO MASKS
March 2021-June 15, 2021: MAYBE ONE MASK IS OKAY
June 15, 2021 - ???: YOU DON'T NEED A MASK
It's science, see?
Governor White Teeth is following the science! And by science, I mean polls.

Maybe not quite science. Maybe it had something to do with the governor's fallen approval rating and his upcoming recall election. I received emails from readers in Australia, Italy, Ireland, Ontario, California, Michigan, and so many other tightly locked places whom I'd never met that knew I lived in Texas. They'd all ask, why are we locked down and required to wear masks when your state is not and it's not doing any worse than it is here? For Michigan residents, it was actually much worse there in the spring of 2021.

Media Coverage

It's still hard to understand why most media outlets were so motivated to drive panic. Many said it was over the November 2020 election. If they could convince voters President Trump did a poor job handling the pandemic, they might vote for a change. There was something to that and it probably worked, but it continued far beyond the election. Two months after the election, the CDC was promoting double masking. The first media break in the dike was a shift in February toward opening schools, and in-person learning did go up significantly in the spring of 2021, too little too late for the school year.

While Yahoo News and Google News were the largest online media sources, they were not material originators of content. You can trace media influences to large outlets like the *New York Times*, *Washington Post*, and to a lesser degree, the *Atlantic*, *Fox News*, *Huffington Post*, *The Guardian*, and others. Their content then cascaded down to larger mediums on Yahoo, Google, Facebook, and Twitter.

The New York Times

The *Times'* writers published thousands of articles on COVID-19 beginning in early 2020. The *Times*, and The *Washington Post*, set the narrative for news. They are foundational media sources because their writings cascade into other analyses from other writers, podcasts, and of course, posts on Twitter. The *Times* drove enormous panic porn in 2020, energizing lockdown policies. Below are some examples.

Tom Friedman

Tom Friedman is a writer for the *New York Times*; he's an A-lister. In 1989, Friedman wrote a very comprehensive and terrific book called *From Beirut to Jerusalem*. I read it in the moment as a college student and loved it. You should check it out even now. Friedman had nothing but disdain for President Trump. As an opinion writer, that's fine, healthy, and fair to offer his point of view. During the discussions of reopening the country, the opinion writer made some reckless commentary about the president and the associated risks of reopening. In an April 18, 2020 column in the *New York Times*, the headline read "Trump Is Asking Us to Play Russian Roulette With Our Lives."[312] In the piece, Friedman wrote:

> *'LIBERATE MINNESOTA!' 'LIBERATE MICHIGAN!' 'LIBERATE VIRGINIA.' With these three short tweets last week, President Trump attempted to kick off the post-lockdown phase of America's coronavirus crisis. It should be called: 'American Russian roulette: The Covid-19 version." What Trump was saying with those tweets was: Everybody just go back to work. From now on, each of us individually, and our society collectively, is going to play Russian roulette. We're going to bet that we can spin through our daily lives — work, shopping, school, travel — without the coronavirus landing on us. And if it does, we'll also bet that it won't kill us.*
>
> *Because it is clear that millions of Americans are going to stop sheltering in place — their own President is now urging them to liberate themselves — before we have proper testing, tracking, and tracing system set up. Until we have a vaccine, that kind of system is the only path to dramatically lowering the risk of infection while partially opening society — while also protecting the elderly and infirm — as Germany has demonstrated.*
>
> *'Liberate?' Think about the use of that word. We were not in jail! We were not doing something wrong! We were doing what our president, governor, mayor, and national epidemic experts told us to do: behave responsibly and shelter in place to break the transmission of this virus.*

The flaws in Friedman's argument are numerous. Russian roulette, strictly speaking, is when you load one bullet in a revolver, spin the chamber and pull the trigger, with a fully equal one in six chance of dying. There is a haunting scene depicting this in the classic film *The Deer Hunter*. Russian roulette gives everyone an equal probability of dying.

COVID-19 did not give everyone an equal probability of getting sick, much less dying. With the economy on fire, hospitalizations and deaths declining and knowing who was at risk, requiring vast testing and tracing was not a reasonable requirement for opening the country up. Washington Governor Jay Inslee required just that (on May 18, 2020) to open up Washington.

Friedman is a smart man and an accomplished journalist. Did he actually believe what he wrote, or was his dislike for President Trump motivating this? Friedman's next article was titled, "We Need Herd Immunity From Trump and the Coronavirus." The one after that was, "Is Sweden Doing It Right? The Swedes aren't battling the coronavirus with broad lockdowns." Perhaps Friedman was coming around. We never saw a retraction for heralding Germany as the standard for COVID-19 prevention either. In the winter of 2020-2021, Germany surged with cases and deaths with the same or more impact the U.S. saw in the same period.

This isn't about picking on Friedman; he was speaking metaphorically about Russian roulette. Messages like his were enormous influencers on social media, which drive public opinion. Public opinion was largely scared as states began reopening. When print, online, and television media promoted scary news like cases growing without context, it shaped public opinion and polls.

Apoorva Mandavilli

Apoorva Mandavilli is the medical and science journalist for the *New York Times*. She was one of two primary writers for the *Times* on the pandemic. Mandavilli (who does possess a great name) wrote hundreds of articles and opinion pieces for the *Times* and participated in many interviews on COVID-19 in 2020 and 2021. Her reporting erred on the side of pandemic pessimism and maintaining lockdowns throughout. Headlines of articles she wrote included:

- "Six Months of Coronavirus: Here's Some of What We've Learned."[313] on June 18, 2020. In this commentary, Mandavilli asserted two things that science and data just weren't showing: that masks work and that natural infection does not result in achieving herd immunity. Herd immunity became a toxic thing to talk about in 2020. Never mind that is exactly how every historic pandemic ended. In June, she also wrote that airborne transmission (versus through large droplets) isn't a significant thing, something common sense showed couldn't possibly be true knowing what we knew a few months into the pandemic.
- "Older Children Spread the Coronavirus Just as Much as Adults, Large Study Finds; The study of nearly 65,000 people in South Korea suggests that school reopenings will trigger more outbreaks."[314] on July 18, 2020.

Headlines like this drove media, politicians, and parents alike to resist reopening schools. The assertion was patently false. By the time this was written, data showed older kids were not equal spreaders, and practically none had become seriously ill from COVID-19. Summer camp data showed this, as discussed earlier.

- "Children may carry high levels of the coronavirus, up to 100 times as much as adults, new Lurie Children's Hospital study finds."[315] on July 31, 2020. Not even sure what to say about this one, other than this was never happening.

- "C.D.C. Calls on Schools to Reopen, Downplaying Health Risks"[316] On July 24, 2020, with Mandavilli contributing. The analysis suggested CDC Director Robert Redfield should not have said schools should reopen fully in the fall. The writers criticized President Trump for driving home that schools should reopen and said this line of thinking was putting kids and teachers at risk. That was just false; data at the moment made this obvious.

- "A Parent's Toughest Call: In-Person Schooling or Not?"[317] On September 1, 2020. The takeaway was to not send kids back to school without elaborate precautions and interventions. The focus was on cases rather than illnesses to kids and teachers that could be at-risk. Illnesses would have been statistically zero for kids and over half the teachers.

- "The coronavirus mostly spares younger children. Teens aren't so lucky."[318] on September 29, 2020. No headline in the fall was more reckless, misleading, or infuriating. Teens were incredibly lucky. Maybe it depends on how we define lucky.

- "The Price for Not Wearing Masks: Perhaps 130,000 Lives. The pandemic death toll could be lowered by next spring if more Americans wear masks, a new analysis finds"[319] on October 23, 2020. The journalist took a shot at Dr. Scott Atlas for saying masks don't work, as well as the president. You saw earlier the data comparing heavily masked areas and less masked areas. That data was obvious by summer, and suggesting masks could have such an impact was taking the lead from "experts" without any independent analysis. The data showed otherwise.

There were many more articles that Mandavilli wrote like these. There were also many articles that she wrote that were fair to the data at hand with a balanced outlook. With a trickle of panic-inducing articles resisting herd immunity as a thing and keeping kids masked and out of school, it rippled into other media and policymakers. Mandavilli displayed on Twitter many times that she preferred the lockdown culture.

Why on earth so many politicians and media figures in influential roles feel the need to vent on Twitter is a bigger mystery than COVID-19 ever was. On

Saturday, March 20, 2021, Madavilli, who lives in Brooklyn, tweeted this: "We were out of the house today for six hours, probably half of them in the car, and I am utterly spent. Reentry is going to be brutal." Perhaps there's a different perspective of what "utterly spent" means to someone that lost their job and had to bridge a learning gap with their kids that were cratering behind. Elites that kept their jobs had resources and got to work from home embraced the lockdowns.

Jeffrey Tucker leads the American Institute for Economic Research and wrote *Liberty or Lockdown* in the summer of 2020. He observed the media playbook that was true for over a year:[320]

- Attribute economic fallout not to the lockdowns but to the virus
- Deliberately confuse readers about the difference between tests, cases, and deaths
- Never focus on the incredibly obvious demographics of COVID-19 deaths
- Dismiss any alternative to lockdown as crazy, unscientific or cruel, while acting as if Dr. Fauci speaks for the entire scientific community
- Above all, promote panic over calm

Further south, the *Washington Post* published a similar flurry of pandemic reporting. On April 21, 2020, the *Washington Post* ran a column titled, "Georgia leads the race to become America's No. 1 Death Destination."[321] In it, writer Dana Milbank blasted Florida, South Carolina, and mostly Georgia for their plans to reopen. One of the blames was the lack of testing. He predicted the coronavirus would burn through the people of Georgia like a fireball after they reopened. Had he looked at the data? Milbank closed in his piece:

> *You and a guest are invited to LIBERATE GEORGIA! The Grand Reopening of the Petri State*
> *Grand Marshal: President Trump*
> *Dress: PPE optional.*
> *As a promotion, Georgia could offer ventilators to the first 100 hotel guests to register (room service would offer supplementary oxygen at no cost to all others). Atlanta's own Coca-Cola would sponsor festivities, using the new slogan 'Share a Coke with Covid-19.' The Atlanta Symphony Orchestra would perform a new variation on Berlioz, 'The Damnation of Fauci.' Trump and Kemp would lead a packed house at Atlanta's State Farm Arena in burning their face masks the way feminists (apocryphally) burned bras, and Vietnam War protesters actually burned draft cards.*

Milbank must not have studied the actual petri dish: the cruise ships. Weeks after the reopening, on May 19, 2020, Georgia's COVID-19 hospitalizations were down 34% for the month. Georgia ended up right at the U.S. average in COVID-19 deaths per capita, with most of the states in ahead of her issuing stricter lockdowns.

The *Atlantic*

The *Atlantic* is a left-leaning print and online publication that has been around since 1857. The online COVID Tracking Project was run by the *Atlantic* and provided excellent data on COVID-19 cases, hospitalizations and deaths. It became the single best resource to get state-by-state data, and much of the data cited here is from there. The CTP did some excellent work. It would be easy to cite anti-lockdown reporting by the *Hill* or the *Blaze*, but we're looking at what was impacting the thoughts of a wider group of Americans and politicians. The *Atlantic* did their share of reporting that supported lockdown mentality, but they also published some quality commentary on the damage of the lockdowns. If you're a centrist or right-leaning and can get past the often-political commentaries, the *Atlantic* often produces some thoughtful work.

The Bad

The *Atlantic* published pieces with high politicization, such as "How Trump Closed the Schools," suggesting the president's mishandling resulted in the pandemic getting out of control, thus rendering schools to be unsafe to reopen. It was a major hit piece blasting the president when so many countries did worse than the U.S. with huge societal damage. Another one was "Why Republicans are Ignoring the Coronavirus." Were they ignoring it or balancing risk and consequence policy? You can decide, but Republican-led states were less restricted, kept more kids in class, and did no worse than Democrat-led states. That's not as much fun to write about if you're left-leaning, though.

"Teachers Know Schools Aren't Safe to Reopen" came out in August 2020. Maybe teachers all over the rest of the world were clueless compared to American teachers, but they fared no worse than those staying at home. Oh, and then there was that CDC study from Wisconsin...

The Good

In August 2020, the dike broke and this strong opinion piece came out written by Chavi Karkowsky, a doctor and mom from New York, called "What We've Stolen From Our Kids. School provides so much more than an education."[322] It was a powerful and needed insight into the cost of closed schools. Seeing a major publication offer up a point of view like this felt like a real step forward. That same month the *Atlantic* published "We Flattened the Curve. Our Kids Belong in School." The curve was destined to spike up seasonally in the fall, but they were right on kids belonging in school.

Other similar articles were sprinkled in throughout the rest of 2020. In January 2021, they published "The Truth About Kids, School, and COVID-19."

Where the *Atlantic* gets some credit is that for being left-leaning, where for some reason liberals were mostly against reopening schools, the *Atlantic* not only demonstrated some actual journalism, they influenced other liberal media.

Emily Oster is an economist and professor at Brown University. She is also a writer and contributed several op-eds to the *Atlantic*. She wrote "Schools aren't Super-Spreaders: Fears from the summer appear to have been overblown," "Parents Can't Wait Around Forever, "The 'Just Stay Home' Message Will Backfire," and the big controversial one: "Yes, You Can Vacation With Your Unvaccinated Kids." Oster is not a conservative, embraced face masks, ran a school/COVID-19 database and is pretty darn level-headed. Check out some interviews with her on YouTube.

Her point was that unvaccinated kids are at about the same risk of getting sick or spreading COVID-19 as vaccinated adults, and that parents should get their kids out and normalize. She was right. Then she got blasted by people that knew a whole lot less than her about it the science and the data. Good for her for moving us forward and for the *Atlantic* for publishing good content in support of open schools that went against the liberal dogma.

The Great

Finally, the *Atlantic* published a very powerful piece that should be required reading for every person still embracing lockdowns and closed schools in 2021. Emma Green wrote "The Liberals Who Can't Quit Lockdown. Progressive communities have been home to some of the fiercest battles over COVID-19 policies, and some liberal policymakers have left scientific evidence behind."[323] This was one of the strongest analysis in the first half of 2021 because it came from a left-leaning publication. Opinions that deviate from a traditional ideology carry more weight. Highlights from Green's masterpiece:

- *For many progressives, extreme vigilance was in part about opposing Donald Trump. Some of this reaction was born of deeply felt frustration with how he handled the pandemic. It could also be knee-jerk. "If he said, 'Keep schools open,' then, well, we're going to do everything in our power to keep schools closed," Monica Gandhi, a professor of medicine at UC San Francisco, told me.*
- Even as scientific knowledge of COVID-19 has increased, some progressives have continued to embrace policies and behaviors that aren't supported by evidence, such as banning access to playgrounds, closing beaches, and refusing to reopen schools for in-person learning.
- *In Somerville [MA], a local leader appeared to describe parents who wanted a faster return to in-person instruction as "fucking white parents" in a virtual public meeting; a community member accused the group of mothers advocating for schools to reopen of being motivated by white supremacy.*

> *"I spent four years fighting Trump because he was so anti-science," Daniele Lantagne, a Somerville mom and engineering professor. "I spent the last year fighting people who I normally would agree with ... desperately trying to inject science into school reopening, and completely failed. [might be worth mentioning as a percentage, the kids of "fucking white parents" were less affected by closed schools than those of black or Hispanic kids]*

To support Green's observation, even after the CDC stopped recommending face masks for those vaccinated on May 13, 2021, A-list media figures could not let go. *MSNBC's* Morning Joe co-host Mika Brzezinski said, "If you want to follow the science," you should follow my lead and "still wear the mask" despite being vaccinated when you're around possibly unvaccinated people.[324] It's not clear to what science she was referencing.

Rachel Maddow is *MSNBC's* highest-rated anchor and was reluctant to embrace the CDC recommendation. Her initial comment to CDC Director Walensky was, "How sure are you because this was a really big change?"[325] No such comment came from Maddow when kids were prevented from going to school in 2020. Maddow then shared, "I feel like I'm going to have to rewire myself so that when I see someone out in the world who's not wearing a mask, I don't instantly think, 'You are a threat, or you are selfish, or you are a COVID denier and you definitely haven't been vaccinated. I mean, we're going to have to rewire the way that we look at each other."

The *View* host Whoopi Goldberg said on air, "What is it going to take, you think, for people to get comfortable following not just the science, but their [the CDC] own science, what is comfortable for them?"[326] *CNN's* chief political correspondent Dana Bash called the decision "very scary." *Time* magazine said it was a "baffling, whiplash-inducing decision." *Politico* called "a bitter disappointment to unions and other safety advocates." *Newsweek* warned of "deadly new variants" under the cover headline of "WINTER IS COMING." *CNN's* chief medical correspondent, Dr. Sanjay Gupta, criticized the recommendation as well, saying the CDC "made a critical error here in surprising basically everyone with a very significant change. [Masking] is so effective and it's not that hard to do in most situations — just to put a mask on."

The COVID-19 Media in Summary

Were many of the pieces above cherry-picked? Was there actual balanced coverage by the networks? Did I selectively choose to pick on the *Times*, *Post*, *Atlantic*, Twitter, and Facebook? And you may wonder why it matters that the press has the freedom to write whatever they choose. They do have that freedom, and that should always be supported. Most people lack critical thinking, either in natural ability or a laziness, preventing exploration of thought and ideas. The media knows this and catered to it. It's no different than advertising.

If you advertise something enough, you will reach critical mass awareness and eventually adoption.

Why the media so unanimously covered the pandemic like Dirty Laundry is still a mystery. Much of it was political, to keep viewers and readers addicted to [fear] porn, and because the media knew so little about what was actually happening, they reported what everyone else reported. In March 2020, Bruce Sacerdote, Ranjan Sehgal, and Molly Cook authored "Why Is All COVID-19 News Bad News?"[327] Sacerdote is an economics professor at Dartmouth College, and Sehgal (Dartmouth) and Cook (Brown University) are students. What a great experience for these two students to participate in such a groundbreaking study. They uncovered what we all knew anecdotally: media coverage in COVID-19 was heavily biased, promoting depression, fear, and polling that resulted in maintaining lockdown measures much longer than should have been.

At a time when the data showed kids were at practically no risk to COVID-19 and school reopenings were no riskier to kids and teachers than remote learning and circulating in their off time, 86% of the American media reported negative news on school reopening. 54% of the media in other English-speaking countries reported negatively on schools reopening. When looking at all COVID-19 stories since the pandemic broke, the fifteen major media players were 25% more likely than their international counterparts to disseminate negative information. This shows the majority of the media worldwide did not understand what was going on, or chose to ignore it, though much worse in the United States.

The researchers analyzed 43,000 articles associated with "vaccines, increases and decreases in case counts, and reopenings (of businesses, schools, parks, restaurants, government facilities, etc.)." Below are trends they uncovered:

- "Among the U.S. major media, 15,000 stories mention increases in caseloads while only 2,500 mention decreases, or a 6 to 1 ratio. During the period when caseloads were falling nationally (April 24-June 27, 2020), this ratio remained a relatively high 5.3 to 1." [the period of analysis for their study was 2020; anecdotally, their findings certainly continued through May 2021]
- No bias or negative-outlook correlation between traditional "conservative" or "liberal" media.
- U.S. media was 3-8 times more likely to promote social distancing or wearing face masks than their international counterparts.
- U.S. counties that relied less on national news were more likely to reopen schools in 2020. This follows some logic because higher in-person learning occurred in less urban communities.
- They concluded, "that there is little evidence that the negativity of the national news media causes a reduction in school reopenings." That

seems hard to believe logically. If the media were pounding on 1) the psychological impact and learning deficiency associated with remote learning, and 2) the data from what we've previously reviewed on kids and COVID-19 risk, polling would have driven more reopening support, politicians would've yielded to the polls, and teachers unions would've buckled.

- "The U.S. Federal Communication Commission eliminated its fairness doctrine regulation in 1987. This regulation required broadcasters to provide adequate coverage of public issues and to fairly represent opposing views. In contrast, the U.K. and Canada still maintain such regulations. On the surface, the fairness doctrine would appear most relevant to partisan bias as opposed to negativity. It may be that profit-maximizing U.S. news providers realized that they should provide not only partisan news to serve their consumers tastes but also negative news which is in high demand." That's probably true. It's definitely a sad state of journalism.

For context of the media serving Dirty Laundry, consider this. There were a total of 2.6 million articles scrubbed. Of those, look at the weighting of some of the reporting in the first seven months of 2020:

- 88,659 articles included a comment about "Trump and Masks," "Trump and Hydroxychloroquine," or "Hydroxychloroquine."
- 87,550 articles mentioned "Decreases" for the whole study period
- 33,000 articles mentioned "Decreases" between April 24 – June 27, 2020
- 325,550 articles mentioned "Increases" for the whole study period

More media articles chose to comment on President Trump and his COVID-19 comments versus the very positive news when COVID-19 cases/hospitalizations/deaths were decreasing. Four times more articles were written about COVID-19 activity increasing versus decreasing.

Within their study period, between March 15 and July 31, 2020, there were 138 days of measurable pandemic case and hospitalization data. Of those 138 days, 61 had decreasing hospitalization days. Four times more articles citing increases over decreases were published, while 44% of the days had a decrease. Case and death trend data was far too loose to include in this daily breakdown for two reasons. One, cases were in large part a product of testing, particularly with rapidly growing seroprevalence in the country. Two, deaths began to include probables and up to half of the deaths reported any given day were backdated. By the second quarter of 2021, well over half of the reported deaths were backdated as far as summer 2020.

The Polls

Politicians are driven by three things: their party, their ideology, polls. What people think is largely driven by their experiences, their beliefs, and the knowledge they acquire. It's not likely a plethora of articles for or against abortion will change a lot of minds; they're much more likely to reinforce beliefs. If there were 300,000 articles in a given year for gun control, it's still very unlikely gun owners and Second Amendment supporters would change their minds. The issues have been too ingrained for too long.

COVID-19 was very different. Everyone in the world started off on the same block in 2020. In this one instance, more than any other for anyone alive during the pandemic, the media had the power to shape thought. Before the pandemic, American's trust in the media was only 41%.[328] That was lower than President Trump's approval rating. In March 2020, this was the approval rating for several stakeholders during the pandemic:

	Approve	Disapprove
Your hospital	88%	10%
Your state government	82%	17%
Government Health Agencies	80%	17%
President Trump	60%	38%
Congress	59%	37%
The Media	44%	55%

In the summer of 2020, 1,000 citizens from several countries were polled on the pandemic.[329] Below is the mean percentage that the sampling showed people thought the COVID-19 death tallies were after three months of the pandemic:

	Population Percent that died from COVID-19	That Absolute Population Number	Actual Number of COVID-19 deaths at the time
United States	9%	29,700,000	132,000
United Kingdom	7%	4,830,000	48,000
Sweden	6%	600,000	6,000
France	5%	3,300,000	33,000
Denmark	3%	174,000	580

Now, do an online search with date parameters of July 20 – August 30, 2020, and see how many news articles featured this polling result. It's fewer than the number of your fingers. Mean percentages of respondents thought that 9% of Americans had died of COVID-19 in three months. That's equivalent to everyone in Texas. Isn't that alarming? Even if the polling result was 1%, that's over three million COVID-19 deaths, about the number of people that die in the

United States each year from all causes. That's also 50% more pandemic lives lost than the Spanish Flu caused, adjusted for population.

If we had a virus that killed 9% (or even ½ %) of the population in three months, the lockdowns would not be like we saw. Everyone would embrace quarantining we saw in *Outbreak* or *Contagion*. This type of general understanding of the pandemic, or lack of, is why we did not see protests throughout 2020 and 2021. One, liberals are more likely to protest than conservatives and liberals were generally much more supportive of lockdowns than conservatives. Two, most people, regardless of politics, just don't study data beyond headlines on Yahoo News and just didn't understand the context of the COVID-19 risk.

Franklin Templeton Poll

In July 2020, Franklin Templeton published polling that showed what a sad and disastrous perception Americans had of COVID-19 risk.[330] As you see the following charts, consider there was very little coverage in the media, from the CDC, and from state health agencies to level-set understanding of the pandemic. Ask yourself: if the media was doing a proper explanation of what was happening if the CDC communicated factually what was happening, how could results like this occur?

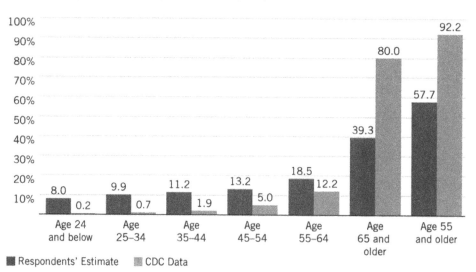

SHARE OF COVID-19 DEATHS BY AGE: BELIEFS VS. DATA

Estimates of the distribution of COVID-19 deaths reported by the Centers for Disease Control and Prevention (CDC)

Respondents clearly did not know the extent of how age-stratified COVID-19 deaths were skewed to the elderly. They surely would not have known that a third of all excess deaths were not caused by COVID-19 but rather the lockdowns.

FEAR OF HEALTH CONSEQUENCES FROM COVID-19 VS. ACTUAL MORTALITY DATA, BY AGE BRACKET

Share of respondents worried for serious health effects from coronavirus compared to deaths reported by the Centers for Disease Control and Prevention (CDC)

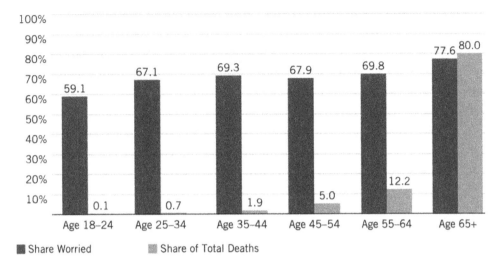

■ Share Worried   ■ Share of Total Deaths

This poll result closely connects to what we saw earlier: the highest stress was associated with younger age groups. They were about as stressed with ~0 risk as older Americans that were at very measurable risk. Franklin Templeton commented on their findings, calling it "stunning." Americans believed that people over 55 were about half the death victims, while it was actually 92%. They thought people under 45 years old were almost 30% of all deaths; they were less than 3%. They overestimated the risk to those under 24 by a factor of fifty.

It's not far off from the earlier poll where respondents on average thought 9% of Americans had died from COVID-19 after three months. Poll results like this should have driven Dr. Fauci, Dr. Birx, and Dr. Redfield, and the CDC to shout from the rooftops to educate Americans on what was happening. It should have caused responsible journalists to do special fact-based segments on COVID-19 risk and the data we had. What we heard was the sound of silence.

Gallup Polls

Gallup conducted weekly polls[331] on sentiment around the pandemic from the beginning in March 2020 well into 2021. Never fewer than 65% of respondents felt staying home was the appropriate thing to do from the beginning and for thirteen straight months.

	Better to Stay Home	Live Normal Life	What Was Happening
March 23-29, 2020	91%	9%	COVID-19 first hit, Imperial College projection of 2.2 million lives lost
June 1-7, 2020	65%	35%	Southern states were reopening, cases were decreasing
July 13-19, 2020	73%	27%	Sunbelt states were peaking in COVID-19 activity
September 14-27, 2020	64%	36%	Summer swell was over, low COVID-19 activity, most schools still closed
December 15, 2020 – January 3, 2021	69%	31%	Peak COVID-19 hospitalizations; vaccines were rolling out
April 19-25, 2021	55%	45%	COVID-19 cases/hospitalizations/deaths had all hit one-year lows; vaccine supply outpaced demand

A majority of Americans did not support returning to normal life at any time since the pandemic began in the spring of 2021. Polling after the CDC lifted indoor mask recommendations on May 14, 2021, for those vaccinated finally began to tilt the scale. COVID-19 hospitalizations began cratering in January 2021, and it was over by February, the pandemic by definition as we knew it. Between the vaccines and natural immunity from recovered infections, there was not a crisis like we saw in various parts of the country in 2020. Had the media reported that, Americans would have felt more comfortable getting back to normal. Even with the summer 2021 spike in the southern states and winter 2021 spike in the north, it was clear the mitigations so enthusiastically embraced had not worked and a combination of natural and vaccinated immunity was evolving the population. COVID-19 remained something to live with and remain cautious if one was at risk. As strict as Australia and New Zealand locked down, they too were seeing lockdowns did not work by October 2021 and were moving away from the impractical measures.

There was a potentially great segment on *MSNBC* in March 2021 where Chuck Todd was asking "experts" why Florida, with very few restrictions, had near-identical results to strictly locked down California. It was going great until they introduced an analysis by the *LA Times* that said had Florida locked down hard, they would have saved 3,000 lives, and had California relaxed its restrictions, they would have had 6,000 more deaths. The analysis was practically made up with no reasonable science and data behind it. Reporting like this was why America was not yet ready to move on.

On April 25, 2021, with the pandemic in retreat and hospitalizations a fraction what they were four months earlier, the respondents were asked, "How long do you think the level of disruption occurring to travel, school, work and public events in the U.S. will continue?" 95% answered with either "a few more months," "through 2021," or "longer than that." That did drop from 98% in February 2021. In April 2021, most remote workers and a plurality of the rest said their preference was to work remotely, not because of fear of COVID-19 but because of preference. Read: many loved lockdowns if they had a job.

MIT Student Studies

The Massachusetts Institute of Technology is one of the premier math, science, and engineering universities in the world. In 2021 they released two studies around social media and "COVID-19 Skeptics." Students from MIT and Wellesley College reported on many people I know and followed. How they viewed analytical points of view that condemned strict lockdowns was emblematic of how the media failed to report balanced context and why Americans were reluctant to return to normal life.

The first study was called "Viral Visualizations: How Coronavirus Skeptics Use Orthodox Data Practices to Promote Unorthodox Science Online."[332] (January 2021), and the second was "The Data Visualizations Behind COVID-19 Skepticism."[333] (March 1, 2021). The first study looked at a half-million Twitter tweets that used visualization of data to support removing nonpharmaceutical interventions governments around the world had instituted for over a year.

The study tone condemned Twitter users for interpreting the data that was not "healthcare consensus" and sharing conclusions visually to make it look like it was "science" and "credible." Early in the study, they made the comment, "As of this writing, Facebook has banned some of the groups we studied, who have since moved to more unregulated platforms (Parler and MeWe)." It's worth calling out that Facebook, YouTube, and Twitter are not regulated unless you consider self-regulated and censoring whomever they wish regulated.

The students enveloped people on Twitter that they perceived as viewing the pandemic as exaggerated and believed schools should be reopened (which the CDC maintained as far back as August 2020) as "anti-maskers." You should really check out the study from undoubtedly very bright students from one of the most elite universities in the world. The lack of impartial thought, the lack of a quest to learn and be open-minded, and mostly, the inability to analyze data without predisposition is disappointing. It's indicative of prevailing college thought all over the country, but this one hit home.

As the study classified those using charts to illustrate their cases, they broke out the following categories:

1. American politics and media
2. American politics and right-wing media
3. British news media
4. Anti-mask network of Twitter users
5. *New York Times* centric network
6. WHO and health-related news organizations

The two classes of media are "media" and "right-wing media." Does that mean there's "impartial journalistic media" and then "conspiratorial right-wing media?" The bias is that there is normal media and crazy right-wing media and then anti-maskers tweeting about the harm of lockdown interventions. This is how over 80% of the media, the CDC, and most state health agencies portrayed the environment, which made it an Everest-climb to reach an open debate.

The Twitter anti-mask network was led by Alex Berenson, the Ethical Skeptic, and Rational Ground founder Justin Hart. This is consistent with my premise that nearly all original thought condemning lockdowns as an unscientific approach were sourced on Twitter. They asserted that "anti-maskers value unmediated access to information and privilege personal research and direct reading over "expert" interpretations." Well, it's both reading "expert interpretations" and processing that based on critical thinking. Everyone should support unmediated access to information even if they disagree with "anti-maskers" on this one. You never know when you'll be on the other side (see Iraq War).

They grouped the anti-maskers as representing that COVID-19 was no worse than the flu. Knowing most of the high-profile Twitter users mentioned, that is flat out false. There is a gulf between thinking COVID-19 was no worse than the flu (it was much worse for those over 50 years old) and believing lockdowns didn't work and were unscientific. It may be students at elite universities and those in the elite media were too detached from middle to lower-class Americans and were out of touch with the consequences of the lockdowns. It may also be they saw it as a power grab. It may mean they just weren't that bright.

Critics of anti-maskers (this term is still nails-on-a-chalkboard; driving data to get schools open is a noble crusade) felt that processing data around excess deaths was conspiratorial. Many excess deaths were from the lockdowns. They then batched the anti-maskers as politically conservative. The face of lockdown criticism was Alex Berenson, and Berenson spent more of his life left-leaning than right-leaning. David Zweig, who wrote dozens of pieces supporting open schools, is no right-winger.

The students then wrote that "anti-maskers" argued there was an outsized emphasis on deaths rather than cases. It was quite the opposite. Everyone following this knew that the case data was fantastically overreported, that there were many times more cases, as well as hundreds of thousands of false positives and backdated dumping. In short, the margin of error of cases on any given day had a solid 50% margin of error, though it was directionally useful. Deaths, too, were unreliable for reasons discussed. The "anti-maskers" usually found COVID-19 hospitalizations as the best data point to measure what was happening, and that was the most reliable metric, not cases or deaths.

The Best Ad Campaign in History

The media represented so much negative news. I sat watching the Billboard

100 waiting for Don Henley's 1982 hit *Dirty Laundry* to climb back up the charts. The prolific critics of the lockdowns were apolitical before COVID-19. They were as critical of Republican leaders as Democrat leaders if they supported closed schools, closed restaurants, or masks outdoors (probably masks indoors too). You have to give it to the media, though. They ran the most effective advertising campaign in history. This wasn't creating critical mass for a pet rock. They accomplished something extraordinary and should be studied in every advertising class forever.

- The media was able to convince over 50% of the people under thirty that they were at serious risk of getting sick or dying from COVID-19.
- They were able to trigger more anxiety in young people than any other age group.
- They were able to convince people that putting face masks on two-year old's made sense.
- They convinced parents that keeping their kids out of school for a year and a half was a good thing.
- They convinced people they should wear a face mask when alone in their car, walking their dog or what we saw, hiking up a mountain.
- They convinced enough of the world they could control the spread of the virus like a dam.

If you're sick, you should listen to your doctor. If you climb a mountain you should listen to your guide. If you need defend your country, you listen to your generals. But if a policy is suggested that has a balance of risk and consequence, something that happens consequentially by following one direction, stop and give it thought and research.

It's healthy to question the media, politicians, healthcare experts or military experts. They are people like you and me, no smarter. In some cases, more informed on their specialty, but that breeds myopia. Sometimes they can get so close to something that they can't see it clearly. Sometimes they can see it but don't want to. Sometimes they have an agenda. History needs to remember the lockdowns as the most harmful, ineffective public policy America and the world ever saw. Study the data for yourself next time and reconcile any one opinion you hear about with another that gives an opposing view. And anytime we get passionate about a policy, we all need to be open-minded to consequences of a policy, as if it may be a zero-sum gain.

CHAPTER 19
Lockdown Hypocrites

Over the past few years my son and I took up rock climbing and mountaineering as our vacation hobbies. We've climbed some of the biggest objectives in Colorado, the Tetons, Yosemite National Park, and the Cascades. We've hired guides to lead us up each one over a class four (where a fall would be deadly). Why? Because it's dangerous. Many friends have been intrigued by our adventures and seek some adventure of their own. Our advice is always two things: get super fit and hire a guide. Why again? Because it's dangerous. We believe that. We know that. We practice that.

If you truly believe something is risky, you practice safety not because it's the law but because you don't want to get hurt or die. We would never hire a guide to do the 14ers we've done in Colorado because we don't view them as dangerous to our experience. We do hire guides to climb vertical walls and glaciated mountains because there is serious risk involved. Without a conscious effort, everyone practices that every day. On remote highways in Texas, you could easily drive over 100 mph. Few do. Why? Because they believe it's risky. We don't swim hundreds of yards offshore because it's dangerous. We brush our teeth daily because it's healthy. We seek protection during a tornado. We don't have pet rattlesnakes.

Leaders implemented very restrictive policies during the COVID-19 lockdowns. These included closing schools, wearing face masks, closing gyms, not eating indoors, not traveling for the holidays, and not getting together with people outside our households. These policies were enacted in the name of health. While the general population was required or encouraged to adhere to these policies, some broke the rules and did not abide. Who would do that? Surely not the people that set the policies, right? That was the case in dozens of situations during the lockdowns. You have to ask yourself if these leaders believed, truly believed their policies were critical to healthcare, why would they not follow the rules themselves? Below are a few dozen examples of activities leaders practiced during the lockdowns. There was not a single thing wrong with any of these activities. They simply should have been allowed for everyone.

Illinois was the second state to lockdown. All "non-essential" retailers closed. That included hair salons and barbers. Surely Illinois leaders must have believed it was dangerous and unhealthy to visit a barber or stylist to care for their hair. One did not. Chicago Mayor Lori Lightfoot visited her stylist in April 2020 for a little work. The stylist posted photos with the mayor on Facebook, writing she had the "pleasure of giving Mayor Lightfoot a hair trim."[334] Lightfoot defended the haircut, saying, "I'm the public face of this city. I'm on national media and I'm out in the public eye." Sometimes saying "I was wrong" works. Better yet, "It's okay to go get your hair cut too."

House Speaker Nancy Pelosi had her hair styled inside a San Francisco salon in September 2020 while there was a ban against such an unsafe activity.[335] The salon owner, Erica Kious, was angry that Pelosi broke the rules requiring similar treatments to be conducted outdoors and one at a time, compromising her business. Video footage showed the Speaker not social distancing nor wearing a mask when others were required.

LA County Supervisor Sheila Kuehl dined indoors at Il Forno Trattoria in Santa Monica just hours after she voted to ban all *outdoor* dining in November 2020.[336] Sheila Kuehl had earlier called outdoor dining the "most dangerous situation" because it puts servers at risk of getting infected with COVID-19 from unmasked patrons. Was she on a suicide mission? At the time of this writing, she is still alive, so that wasn't it. Could it be that she did not believe outdoor dining was all that unsafe?

Anthony Fauci advocated masks, then two masks, for everyone in 2020 and 2021. In July 2020, Fauci attended a Washington Nationals baseball game. In the stands, Fauci sat between two other fans with no social distancing and was talking. His explanation: "I had my mask around my chin. I had taken it down. I was totally dehydrated and I was drinking water, trying to rehydrate myself. And by the way, I was negative COVID literally the day before. So I guess people want to make a big event. I wear a mask all the time when I'm outside. To pull it down to take some sips of water and put it back up again, I guess if people want to make something about that, they can. But to me, I think that's just mischievous."[337] The pictures showed Fauci with his mask down without water in his hand, rather his phone. Fauci repeatedly dismissed negative COVID-19 tests, recovered infections, and vaccinations as justification for not wearing a mask.

New York was under a stay-at-home order in April 2020, and residents were told to stay home except for non-essential travel. New York City Mayor Bill de Blasio violated that rule to travel (with staff) eleven miles away to take a walk in the park with his wife.[338] Good for de Blasio and his wife. All New Yorkers should have been encouraged to take a walk in the woods.

Governor Andrew Cuomo was a big advocate for mask mandates. In the summer of 2020, he tweeted, "There should be a national mask mandate" and "Wearing a mask is about respect. We launched a national campaign to encourage every American to wear a mask. Stop the Spread. Save Lives."[339] Then, Cuomo was photographed in July without a mask while meeting closely with others in Georgia. In August, Cuomo was photographed walking his dog on a crowded street without a mask.

Pennsylvania Health Secretary Dr. Rachel Levine deserves a special shrine in COVID-19 hypocrisy. After implementing a policy requiring nursing homes to admit COVID-19 patients, she moved her 95-year-old mother out of a personal-care home and into a hotel.[340] While senators were under investigation for insider trading associated with the pandemic, this was perhaps the most egregious insider trading in history.

Professor Neil Ferguson was the author of the Imperial College model that triggered lockdowns in America and the U.K. He pushed for stay-at-home orders during the pandemic. Then, while positive with COVID-19 himself, he broke the order and had his married mistress visit his home on at least two occasions.[341] Ferguson then resigned his government role on the Scientific Advisory Group for Emergencies. You just can't make this stuff up.

Denver Mayor Michael Hancock shared Thanksgiving travel advice on Twitter, advising people to "Pass the potatoes, not Covid," by staying home to "avoid travel."[342] Within an hour of that tweet, Hancock ignored his own advice by getting on a plane to spend the holiday with his wife and daughter in Mississippi.

Illinois Governor J.B. Pritzker led the second lockdown in America, immediately following California. Illinois was one of the most rigid states during the lockdowns. In April 2020, Mrs. Pritzker, the billionaire wife of the governor, fled the stay-at-home order in Illinois to visit their $12 million home in Florida when Florida was reopening.[343] Pritzker canceled high school athletics as the 2020-2021 school year began, except for one high schooler. With activities canceled, Pritzker's daughter competed in equestrian in other states that were open.[344] Good for his daughter Teddi, bad for the millions of kids that didn't have the resources to skirt their state's lockdown orders.

Rhode Island was hit particularly hard by the pandemic. You can't say the governor didn't try; Rhode Island issued some of the stiffest lockdowns and even tried some things out of the box to mitigate COVID-19. Still, Rhode Island climbed to third in deaths per capita at one point in 2021, which shows you how well the lockdowns and mitigations worked. As activity was climbing in winter 2020, Governor Gina Raimondo tweeted this on December 7, 2020:

> *It's week two of our pause. I know it's been hard, but I want to thank every Rhode Islander who's following our guidance. Please, stay home except for essential activities & wear a mask anytime you're with people you don't live with. Together, we can turn our case numbers around.*

Four days later, the governor was photographed at a wine and paint party without a mask.[345]

Canadian Prime Minister Justin Trudeau encouraged Canadians to "stay home" and "Skype that big family dinner" at Easter in April 2020. Then Trudeau crossed the provincial border from Ottawa into Quebec to visit his wife and three children at Harrington Lake.[346] The lockdowns forced Canadians to abandon travel to see family, not visit their other homes, or vacation. At least Trudeau did not do this in Michigan; that was against the neighboring governor's state order. Ontario Premier Doug Ford visited his cottage on Easter Sunday as well after telling citizens not to visit their cottages.[347]

In November 2020, on separate nights, both San Francisco Mayor London Breed and California Governor Gavin Newsom had group dinners indoors without masks nor social distancing at the French Laundry restaurant in Napa Valley.[348] Newsom's dinner even included lobbyists and leaders in the healthcare industry. At this time, other restaurants in California were either closed, relegated to outdoor dining, or dealing with indoor capacity restrictions, none of which applied to the French Laundry.

In May 2020, Michigan had an order previously discussed that prevented homeowners from visiting their second home. The governor's husband leveraged his wife's position to get their boat out of the marina for Memorial Day, which backfired when it went public. He must have been itching to get out. He left the governor's mansion to visit their second home in northern Michigan.[349] It's lovely there, everyone should vacation in northern Michigan around the lakes sometime. As for the first husband, the governor explained, "My husband did go up to our place to rake some leaves and came home. He was there briefly for a night and came right back home after he raked our leaves!" That was surely an essential trip. Everyone knows how all the leaves fall in May.

New Mexico had one of the most rigid lockdowns in the country. At one point, the governor even ordered grocery providers to close to stop the spread, prompting havoc in some rural areas. During the initial lockdown in April 2020, "non-essential" retailers were ordered to close, even for curbside delivery. During this period, New Mexico Governor Michelle Lujan Grisham called in an order to a jewelry store and completed a purchase at a time when her residents were unable to do so.[350] It does make sense, though. A jewelry purchase during a pandemic lockdown was essential.

Sam Liccardo was the mayor of San Jose, California, when he played the Thanksgiving card. On November 25, 2020, the day before Thanksgiving, Liccardo tweeted this: "Cases are spiking, in part because we're letting our guard (and masks) down with family & friends. Let's cancel the big gatherings this year and focus on keeping each other safe." Why do politicians feel the need to govern by Twitter? Anyway, the day after this tweet, Liccardo attended a Thanksgiving gathering with eight family members from five households, clearly forbidden based on that area's guidelines at the time.[351] He apologized and promised to do better.

In June 2020, Kansas City Mayor Quinton Lucas issued a citywide face mask order for his town. Then, in July, he visited the restriction-free resort area of the Ozarks. I've done several interviews with radio host Christian Blood there, and he relished the freedom people there felt. The mayor went to the Ozarks and was photographed with a half dozen people all close together and unmasked.[352] Who would do that if they felt it was unsafe? Do you wonder if Lucas has any pet rattlesnakes? I don't. They aren't safe.

Massachusetts was one of the harder hit and more restrictive states during the pandemic. On May 21, 2020, Lieutenant Governor Karyn Polito tweeted this:

This week, @MassDPH issued an updated #SaferAtHome public health advisory.
High-risk individuals should stay home if possible
Only go out for essentials + reopened activities
Wear a face-covering if social distancing isn't possible

Again with Twitter. Sigh. Polito followed that up by hosting a large party at her home.[353] Her house party was surely essential.

Texas stories hit close to home since, well, Dallas is my home. Many of those instituting face masks and stay-at-home orders and distancing rules were caught violating them. Let's begin in Austin. Mayor Steve Adler was a big proponent of school closings, wearing masks, and staying at home. He was so adamant that when the governor lifted all restrictions in March 2021, he vowed to maintain the restrictions and was sued by the state. Around Thanksgiving 2020, Adler hosted a wedding of twenty for his daughter.[354] He admitted later not all guests wore masks. After the wedding, the mayor and a few guests hopped on a private jet to vacation in Cabo San Lucas. That sure sounded nice around then, when COVID-19 activity was ramping up in Texas.

While in Cabo, Adler said this to his constituents in a Facebook video: "We need to stay home if you can. This is not the time to relax. We are going to be looking really closely. We may have to close things down if we are not careful."[355] I imagine the beach was not in the background of his video address. Interim health director Dr. Mark Escott said that week to the residents of Austin: "If you're going out to a restaurant, go out with your family, the people who live in your household, not with family and friends outside your household and start to decrease those travels outside of your home that are not necessary." Do you think Adler went swimming with sharks while in Cabo? I doubt it. Why? Because it's not safe. Adler later apologized. Of course.

Dallas County Judge Clay Jenkins shut down Dallas in late March 2020 to the shock of North Texans. He maintained tighter restrictions throughout than neighboring Collier and Denton counties. At one time, I abandoned my LA Fitness in Dallas county for the one in Denton county because they were open and did not require masks. Go figure. In October 2020, Jenkins was photographed at a wedding without a mask and without social distancing.[356]

Tarrant County Judge Glen Whitley was another strict enforcer of the lockdown rules. He went so far as trying to fine people for not wearing masks. Whitley advised Tarrant County residents to avoid Thanksgiving gatherings. Can you see it coming? Whitley then hosted a Thanksgiving gathering at his home, a violation of the very order he gave.[357]

Indoor dining is a nice escape. We get served good food and it's the primary social vehicle for adults. If you're the mayor of a city that shut down indoor dining, what do you do? If it's in the middle of Montana, you probably suck it up. If you're the mayor of Philadelphia, you drive across the state line to Maryland and eat at a restaurant where it's allowed. That's exactly what Philadelphia Mayor Jim Kenney did in August 2020.[358]

When caught, he tweeted this (again with the tweets…) on August 31, 2020: "I know some are upset that I dined indoors at a restaurant in Maryland yesterday. I felt the risk was low because the county I visited has had fewer than 800 COVID-19 cases, compared to over 33,000 cases in Philadelphia. Regardless, I understand the frustration. Restaurant owners are among the hardest hit by the pandemic. I'm sorry if my decision hurt those who've worked to keep their businesses going under difficult circumstances. Looking forward to reopening indoor dining soon and visiting my favorite spots." Kenney did apologize. Of course.

Mask mandates indoors could have made sense if the SARS-CoV-2 aerosol particles were larger than pores in cloth masks. Mask mandates outside, particularly away from crowds of over fifty, never made scientific sense. There is no data in existence that supports wearing masks while you're walking your dog or hiking a trail. Still, governors and local leaders required them, demonstrating they had no idea what the actual science was; they just wanted to appear they were implementing the most aggressive rules possible. Zero-COVID-19 is all that mattered.

Oregon Governor Kate Brown violated her outdoor mask mandate while hiking a trail with her security team with no one wearing masks.[359] Good for them getting outdoors without wearing masks. Do you think they were seeking out mountain lions in Oregon? Probably not, that would have been unsafe.

Brown issued an advisory on November 13, 2020, urging Oregonians not to travel out of state. Meanwhile, local government leaders felt the need to get out of town and vacation on a beach. Washington County Commissioner Jerry Wiley thought it appropriate to go to Mexico, while Washington County Commissioner Dick Schouten went down to Hawaii. "This is the beginning of day three and we're having a great time!" Schouten said during a Zoom meeting. "The weather has been great. The sun has been warm."[360]

Multnomah County Commissioner Sharon Meieran worked remotely for two weeks in Hawaii as well. On November 13, Meieran tweeted, "At this point, we need to go back to staying home." She sent her tweet from Keauhou, Hawaii.[361] Leadership by Twitter. As retailers were closed and kids hadn't seen a day of face-to-face learning in months, these leaders thought it appropriate to send COVID-19 pointers from the beach.

At a time when California Governor Newsom was urging his state not to travel out of state as COVID-19 activity was ramping up in November 2020, ten California lawmakers thought it was a good idea to attend a conference in Hawaii. The conference at the Fairmont Kea Lani in Maui included lawmakers and lobbyists from four states discussing how to reopen the economy. "This event promotes intelligent public policy in our state," said Assemblyman Jordan Cunningham. "In fact, we are here discussing ways we can safely reopen our society and save our small businesses, workers, and kids."

Do you know how you open up the economy and schools? You open them.[362] Any readers out there that have attended island conferences know a boondoggle when they see it. While California leaders were tightening their grip on their residents, denying in-person schooling, and ruining thousands of businesses, these leaders thought a beachfront conference on taxpayer funds was appropriate. Think they went surfing on Maui's multi-story wave Jaws? No reports on that, probably because it would have been unsafe.

Paula Deacon is the superintendent of Leominster Public Schools in Massachusetts. Schools in Massachusetts were closed in the fall/winter of 2020 because it was deemed unsafe. Deacon announced in December schools would be closed and remote-only for the foreseeable future. Surely it was unsafe. Meanwhile, Deacon, likely a Tom Brady and football fan, flew down to Florida to see Brady's Buccaneers play the Atlanta Falcons.[363] Fans were not able to see the Patriots play, so why not go to one of the most open states in the country to catch a game? The school superintendent believed it was unsafe to open her own schools, but thought it was safe enough for her to travel to the state with the most open schools and no state mask mandate. Makes sense.

Gregory Hutchings is the superintendent of Alexandria City Public Schools in Virginia. His school district was all remote when he saw the effect it had on his kids: they weren't learning. He pulled his kids out of the public school and enrolled them in a hybrid-learning Catholic school.[364] If the private school was safe for his kids, why weren't the public schools safe for his and everyone's kids? Is this like a Coke employee drinking Pepsi, or a Ford executive driving a Lexus? No, because this was a real-world where kids were pawns in a game of the politics of not following the science.

For over a year, street reporters for television news wore masks while they reported. In the first quarter of 2021, *MSNBC* street reporters often wore two masks. Meanwhile, the indoor anchors did not. What data showed the outdoor reporters were at more risk than the indoor anchor? Hint: none. I was watching *MSNBC* real-time Memorial Day weekend 2020. A field crew was reporting on people in Wisconsin at Lake Geneva. In May 2020, it was refreshing to see people acting normal outdoors. The street reporter called out passersby for not wearing a face mask.

Then something happened live that was unforgettable. The masked reporter then turned his cameraman to shoot a man walking past, saying on air, "As you can see, no one is wearing them."

"Including the cameraman," the target shot back, adding, "half your crew's not wearing them."[365]

San Francisco reinstated an indoor face mask mandate in August 2021, regardless of vaccination status. People were required to wear them indoors unless actively eating or drinking. They were among the few places that required masks indoors, including Illinois, Oregon, the District of Columbia, Los Angeles County, and others. San Francisco Mayor London Breed decided it would be fun to go out with friends on September 16th to a nightclub called the Black Cat.[366]

Days later, a video surfaced showing Breed standing and dancing at the club without a face mask. She had no drink or food in her hand or anywhere near her. The images and story went viral. Breed responded, saying:

At the end of the day, everyone who comes in here has to show proof of vaccination. That gives me a lot of reassurance...It's sad that this is even a story. From my perspective, I was there, I was eating and I was drinking, and I was sitting with my friends and everyone who came in there was vaccinated. So the fact that we have turned this into a story about being maskless. No, I'm not going to sip and put my mask on, sip and put my mask on, sip and put mask on, eat and put my mask on. While I'm eating and I'm drinking I'm going to keep my mask off. And yes, while we're drinking, like everyone else there, we were all having a good time and again, all vaccinated. When I took a picture, as I do in any case or do an interview, yes I take my mask off when I take a picture. I'm vaccinated. I don't need to wear a mask to take a picture every single time. I don't want to.

When you enter these venues, people are going to drink, people have to be vaccinated ... like sip and drink, that's just not realistic. When you got to restaurants ... I was at a restaurant, same thing, I'm leaving my mask down while I'm enjoying my food. People are not doing that. So that's just not realistic, you all know it's not realistic.[367]

We don't need the fun police to come in and try to micromanage and tell us what we should or shouldn't be doing. We know what we need to do to protect ourselves. The message I want to get out is: Support our nightlife venues, support our restaurants, go out and enjoy yourself. Make sure you are vaccinated because of the requirements, but don't feel as though you have to be micro-managed about mask wearing. We don't need the fun police to come in and tell us what we should or shouldn't be doing. We know what we need to do to protect ourselves.

I'm being careful to not only protect myself and other people, but this is nitpicking, this is really unfortunate. And let me tell you, when the spirit moves you because you are watching history in the making, Bay Area royalty perform, I don't know about you but I'm not going to turn around and look for where my mask is or look to see if I'm picking up a drink. I'm just going to let the spirit move me.[368]

Breed is right. What she did was fine. What is not fine is that other San Franciscans could not legally do the same thing. Nor could a two-year-old at a daycare or on a plane be required to wear a mask take theirs off if they were "feeling the spirit."

On September 13, 2021, a large gala was held at the Metropolitan Museum of Art. Hundreds of celebrities and high-profile socialites attended. The COVID-19 rules for the event were stated as "All attendees at The Met Gala on September 13 must provide proof of full vaccination and will also be expected to wear masks indoors except when eating or drinking."[369] There were two glaring observations at the event: attendees were not wearing masks (though all were likely vaccinated), and the staff and servers were wearing masks. Surely the servers were vaccinated to work the event, so the question is, why were servers required to wear masks and not the attendees? Science.

The 2021 Emmy Awards were held on September 19, 2021. Like the Met Gala, servers were required to wear face masks in accordance with Los Angeles County's indoor face mask mandate. The celebrity attendees? They did not wear masks, one more example of lockdown hypocrisy. This was much like the fundraising event held in Napa Valley by Speaker Nancy Pelosi on August 22, 2021. Guests paid from $100 to $29,000 to attend. Attendees did not wear face masks, but the serving staff was required to wear them.[370]

We're in this together. Alone together. Together apart.

That's what we were told. Those slogans were delivered by governors and local leaders and repeated by the media for months. Leaders and those in the media condemned people that saw masks weren't working. They condemned spring breakers. They condemned vacationers when they went to the Ozarks on Memorial Day weekend 2020 (nothing happened). They condemned the people that went to South Dakota in August 2020 for the Sturgis bike rally (nothing happened). They condemned attendance at the Super Bowl and Alabama's national championship celebration. And yet, so many violated their own orders. There should be a special place in the world of resignations for those that violated their own restrictions just because they could.

While writing this, the sound of Dolores O'Riordan filled my ears, hearing her voice singing:

Another head hangs lowly
Child is slowly taken
Not for me
Not for my family
What's in your head, what's in your head,
Zombie, zombie, zombie-ie-ie

CHAPTER 20
Lockdown Deaths of Despair, Depression, and Domestic Abuse

There were five major collateral damage areas because of the lockdowns:
- education losses
- untreated/undiagnosed health conditions
- massive job loss and economic hardship
- increased deaths of despair
- increased domestic abuse

In 2020 about 2.6 billion people experienced lockdowns in one form or another. In the U.K., it was very strict. In Sweden, it was not very strict (counting Sweden because they did excuse high school students from class for a while, a lockdown measure). Japan was loose; New Zealand and Australia were militant. The world never saw a social lockdown like this. We know the impact the lockdowns had on the economy, but what about qualitative impacts? What effect did the lockdowns have on people's behavior, psychology, joy, or depression?

Quarantining, social distancing, and stay-at-home orders hit Americans much harder as a population than the coronavirus did. People are inherently social. People need to feel in control of their lives to feel freedom and peace. Sit for a minute on your couch. You could probably do that comfortably for the duration of a movie. Now, as you're sitting on your couch, imagine a glass enclosure boxing you around your couch with a few feet of space to move around, the same as you might readjust while you're watching that movie. Would you still feel at peace watching the movie, or would you become nervous knowing you did not have the freedom to move about? That anxiety was felt by millions of Americans during the COVID-19 lockdowns.

Child Abuse

Sadly, domestic violence seems to increase any time families spend more time together, like vacations and holidays. When my son came home from college to finish up at home in March 2020, we had a great few months. He started a podcast; I wrote *Lockdowns on Trial*. We played games to break up the monotony every day. We went climbing in July, which was in doubt for a while. We were supposed to climb in the Canadian Rockies, but the border was closed. Then we thought about California to climb, but California was locked down hard. That left us returning to the Tetons (thank you, Governor Gordon). Gyms were closed in Texas in April and most of May 2020, but fortunately, they opened in time to get ready.

Other families were less lucky. With more families contained than at any time in American history, domestic violence surged. Schools, coaches, youth activity leaders are all primary identifiers of child abuse. A child is abused at home and no one reports it. The parents or caregivers, if the abuser, don't of course. The child is afraid to report it. Someone at school notices it, or it gets conveyed through a friend, and they report it to the police or Child Protective Services. With kids isolated, few were available to report abuse. Fewer eyes were on our children. In many communities, we saw a contradiction of data: fewer cases reported and an increase in hospitalizations to treat child abuse.[371] Childcare vanished in most communities, protective eyes where a quarter of child abuse victims are younger than three years old. The Modoc Joint Unified School District in California saw a 30% decrease in child abuse reports from their CPS unit when schools went remote, according to Superintendent Tom O'Malley.[372]

The state of Texas reported in the spring of 2021 that child mortality due to abuse or neglect was up 10% during 2020, up 25 deaths.[373] When the lockdowns reached Texas, reports of child abuse plummeted.[374] That was bad news. It's equivalent to reduced cancer diagnoses. The problems don't go away, they go underground. Less reporting was scary news suggesting a back-end wave of incremental increases. Texas was one of the less restricted states. If you consider Texas is nine percent of the U.S. population, let's say there were an incremental 250 child abuse and neglect deaths in 2020 due to the lockdowns. That may not seem like much until you consider it's twice the number of COVID-19 deaths to children.

Child Sexual Exploitation

Sexual abuse of children went up sharply during the lockdowns, both in separate incidents and the frequency with the same children. If a child was abused once a week but was out and about living normally, that increased to multiple times per week in isolation. The National Center for Missing and Exploited Children identified that whereas there were just under a million reports of sexual exploitation in March 2019, that number soared to over two million reports in March 2020.

RAINN, the Rape, Abuse and Incest National Network, reported that in the spring of 2020, minors were half the visitors to their hotline for the first time ever.[375] Minors shared that 67% of their perpetrators were family members and 79% said that they were living with that perpetrator.

In addition to sexual abuse, sexual predation increased. Travel restrictions and the explosion in online usage triggered an increase in grooming online by predators. Thames Valley is a region in southwest England. Oxford is the center of that area, and that entire part of England was subject to some of the most stringent lockdown measures in the world. Side note: those stringent measures got them higher COVID-19 deaths per capita than the United States and top ten in the EU. The Thames Valley police reported a near doubling of sexual abuse cases in 2020.[376]

There are so many collateral disasters of the lockdowns around the world. As I sit here writing and researching this, it's a renewed triggering each day studying the data behind the human rights crimes against kids by hundreds of governments around the world that not just failed but ignored and doubled down against the science of COVID-19 and kids and population risk.

I visited with a social worker in Detroit that had foster kids visit her *triple-masked and wearing a face shield* because the foster parents were afraid based on media coverage. That and Governor Whitmer's mask order for two-year-olds when the WHO had clearly not recommended that and no other country in the world was doing so. Meanwhile, somehow she received a JFK Library Foundation award for courage. Whitmer changed her tune abruptly in September 2021 as her reelection polling was underwater, denying a statewide mask mandate going forward. Meanwhile, Kentucky Governor Andy Beshear required two-year-olds to be masked, as was California Governor Gavin Newsom following his recall election victory.

In a 2017 study by Dan Brown and Elisabetta De Cao called "The Impact of Unemployment on Child Abuse and Neglect in the United States," they identified a correlation between unemployment and partner and child abuse.[377] More prevalent in poor than wealthier families, a 1% increase in unemployment led to a 25% increase in neglect and a 12% increase in abuse. What would a 10% increase in unemployment do? Even with subsidized unemployment benefits, the results couldn't be good.

Tips to the National Center for Missing and Exploited Children nearly doubled from 6.3 million in the first half of 2019 to 12 million in the first half of 2020.[378] How do you even process a number like that? What we saw during the lockdowns is that teachers and counselors, daycare providers, and coaches that may observe and report on abuse are no longer potential watchdogs for abuse. In some areas, it's reported that numbers of child and adult abuse are down. Experts cited in many articles all said that it is a scary observation that those abused are prevented from reaching out for help or from being discovered. Lockdowns kill.

Child Depression

Youth mental health was one of the biggest casualties of the lockdowns. Considering the severity of it all, it was wildly underreported in 2020 and 2021. The media exhausted reporting on the need for people to wear masks and get vaccinated. Many reported competently on losses in education. Very few reported on how depressed millions of kids became over a year and a half and how quickly as soon as the March lockdowns hit. While some children suffered from abuse, many times more than that experienced depression. Suicidal depression.

During the lockdowns, mental health emergency department visits rose 24% for children ages 5-11 and 31% for those ages 12-17.[379] In March and April 2020, adolescent mental health insurance reimbursement claims doubled over the same months in 2019.[380]

A *Lancet* study in 2021 showed a 48% increase in probable mental health problems in 5–16-year-olds in 2020 in England.[381] Over a quarter of those ages 5-22 experienced disrupted sleep and one in ten often or always felt lonely. 18% felt fearful of leaving the house because of COVID-19. One of my friends had a 13-year-old during the lockdowns and that child suffered from anxiety attacks out of COVID-19 fear. His parents bear some of that burden; they weren't reading beneath the headlines and sharing that with their child.

The *JAMA Network* published "Caregiver Perceptions of Children's Psychological Well-being During the COVID-19 Pandemic" on April 29, 2021.[382] The research authors completed a survey of 32,217 caregivers of over 50,000 children on their observations of kids before and after the lockdowns. The children represented had a very even distribution of ages from kindergarten to twelfth grade. The percentages below represent affirmative responses to each behavioral characteristic.

Characteristic	Before Remote Learning	During Remote Learning
Agitated or angry	4.2%	23.9%
Anxious	12.6%	23.3%
Depressed or low mood	3.4%	14.0%
Lonely	3.6%	31.9%
Stressed	11.7%	24.4%
Self-harm, suicidal thoughts	.5%	.6%
Had positive social or peer relationships	66.1%	35.2%
Hopeful or positive	49.1%	29.4%
Interacted positively with siblings or family	60.4%	46.8%

| Relaxed | 52.4% | 36.9% |
| Talks about future plans | 44.3% | 30.9% |

In February 2021, *Reuters* conducted a survey of school districts representing over two million students, more than the number of students in Illinois or Pennsylvania.[383] The results should have been alarming to school leaders and politicians bickering over reopening when classes were full with near-normal protocols around the world and even in some schools in the United States.

Of the 74 districts that responded, 74% reported multiple indicators of increased mental health stresses among students. More than half reported rises in mental health referrals and counseling. According to the Reuters article, "Nearly 90% of responding districts cited higher rates of absenteeism or disengagement, metrics commonly used to gauge student emotional health. The lack of in-person education was a driver of these warning signs of trouble, more than half of districts said. The stresses didn't affect only students: 57% of responding districts reported an increase in teachers and support staff seeking assistance."[384]

Some students flat out disappeared from school, millions as previously discussed. Those students may have suffered depression in addition to those reported, which could have brought the total approaching ten million students. That's not an exaggeration. Depression inhibits motivation, and that was the single largest cause of suffering grades for college freshmen in the 2020-2021 school year. We can imagine that would be even greater for younger kids. Kids relegated to taking classes on their phones, sitting in front of a computer screen for hours, alone. It's depressing even looking back.

One in five students in the Somerset Independent School District outside San Antonio opted for remote learning even when in-person was available. That same school district saw "suicide assessments double during the 2020-2021 school year. Absenteeism and disengagement increased "exponentially" and mental health referrals doubled. These increases are concentrated among the students studying virtually, 75% of whom are failing."[385]

Youth shootings skyrocketed during the remote learning period as well. With kids able to do things other than study during the day, some were enveloped in violence. Philadelphia reported youth murders and shootings were up from 55 to 87 in 2020 over 2019, and nonfatal shootings were up 72%. That number may seem low, but consider two things: that is just Philadelphia with 32 increased deaths, and homicides were up all over the country in major cities. If you extrapolate that increase of 32 deaths to the other major cities, we see many times more deaths from shootings of kids not in class than from COVID-19.

A shortage of psychiatric beds for youths was far more exacerbated than hospital beds for COVID-19 during the lockdowns. The number of COVID-19 beds was higher, of course, but so was the capacity. Did you hear much about that during the lockdowns as the media reported on "overflowing" COVID-19 hospitalizations and the drama around reopening schools? I didn't either. ER visits and psychiatric beds were ruptured in many parts of the country. In Massachusetts, these ER visits quadrupled during the lockdowns.[386] The wait for a psyche bed was much longer than any wait for a COVID-19 bed.

Mental Health Minnesota reported the number of children under age 18 screened online for mental health problems soared last year to 7,882 screenings, up from 1,664 in 2019.[387] Process that number for a moment: that's a 500% increase. Is there any explanation possible than the lockdowns and isolation from school, friends, and activities?

At the 66-bed Clarity Child Guidance Center in San Antonio, CEO Jessica Knudsen saw a surge in patients with mental health issues. "Some nights, there have been five or six kids sleeping in an observation area waiting for beds," she said. Philadelphia saw similar increases in admissions and longer wait times to get in if the kids could at all.[388] The *Philadelphia Inquirer* reported this from Abington Hospital:

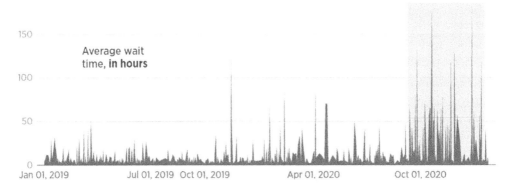

Chart: Staff Graphic • Source: Inquirer analysis of Abington Hospital data

Notice the increase during the lockdowns and during the fall of 2020 as schools remained remote: longer wait times and more frequent. In Miami, one of the better places to be during the pandemic, Banyan Health Systems saw a surge similar to that in Massachusetts, New York, and New Jersey. CEO Vincent Carrodeguas described "Every day is an emergency. I hate to say it, but our job right now is to normalize a crisis that has been going on for nine months. Calls to our centers are up 40 to 50% and our vulnerable behavioral health population has skyrocketed."[389]

Meanwhile, some treatment centers would not admit kids in need without a negative COVID-19 test, something that may not have been possible when you're on the clock. Nosocomial spread of COVID-19 is one thing, but hospitals went far overboard in suspending other admissions and visitation during the pandemic, a policy that worsened the crisis for those in need and created more depression. Virginia Governor Ralph Northam signed a temporary executive order in August 2020, halting admissions to psychiatric hospitals in an attempt to mitigate the spread of the virus. At that time, COVID-19 hospitalizations in Virginia were under 7% of capacity and never reached more than 17% during the pandemic.

Inpatient psych hospitals were stretched beyond capacity across Rhode Island, New York, and New Jersey. Kingston and Brooklyn, New York units were closed to accommodate potential capacity for COVID-19 patients.[390] Facilities were seeing patients that had not reported anxiety or depression in the past.

Pediatricians Marisa Censani, Jeffrey Dayton, and Cori Meredith Green wrote an opinion piece in the *New York Daily News* in April 2021 called "America's top priority: We urgently need a comprehensive plan to give kids their lives back."[391] In it, they shared observations from their practices:

Before the pandemic, one in five children had a mental health problem, and suicide was the second leading cause of death in children beginning at age 10. Now, youth with mental health concerns are pouring into our pediatric primary care offices. Some refuse to leave their homes because they are scared of the COVID-19 virus. Some are experiencing excessive grief due to losses they experienced, while others worry about whether their parents' unemployment threatens their housing or what they will eat.

Every week, more children screen positive for mental health concerns, and more children say they are having thoughts about suicide. School-aged children tell us they would rather die than live in a world with COVID-19. Social isolation is a risk factor for suicidal behaviors while feeling connected and engaged in school and activities are protective factors. Our youth are isolated right now with so much uncertainty about the future, making it harder to cultivate hope and resilience during these times.

There are so many stories in the media and likely within degrees of separation of people we know with kids adversely affected by the lockdowns. What have we done? So many children became so afraid of a virus that they would not leave their homes and would rather die than live in a world with something that didn't even harm them.

Child Obesity

Kristen Walsh is a pediatrician in New Jersey. I met Dr. Walsh through our shared cause of getting schools reopened and helping kids get back to normal. Kristen was the first person I encountered that identified a looming fallout from the lockdowns: child obesity. She directed me to several studies, beginning with one published in the *Journal of Sport and Health Science* called "Projecting the impact of the coronavirus disease-2019 pandemic on childhood obesity in the United States: A microsimulation model."[392]

Obesity is based on genetics, behavioral or environmental factors. The lockdowns challenged the latter two, and the *Journal of Sport and Health Science* summer 2020 study predicted an increase in child obesity if learning remained remote through the end of 2020. That remained in place into 2021 for tens of millions of kids. Below is their estimate based on several scenarios. Number four assumed schools would be remote through December. Considering tens of millions were still remote beyond that date, we were at something like a scenario six not on the chart.

Simulated trend in childhood obesity prevalence from April 2020 to March 2021 under the control (without COVID-19) and four alternative scenarios (with COVID-19)

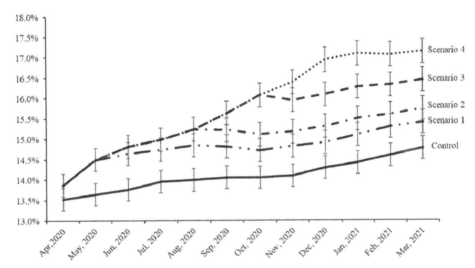

What this shows is based on the amount of remote learning and canceled sports and activities, childhood obesity prevalence hovered close to 20%. America overall is near 40%. Anecdotally we all saw decreased activity in kids during the lockdowns. This shows a nearly 50% increase in child obesity due to the lockdowns, an additional 1.5MM obese children. Closed schools resulted in decreased organized physical activity and increased sedentary lifestyle and screen time with the possibility of stress-induced indulgence in high calorie-dense and sugary foods, resulting in higher susceptibility to weight gain.[393]

When strict stay-at-home orders were issued all across America and much of the world in March 2020, think back to that period for a moment. Grocery shelves were emptied. Long shelf-life foods were gone. Chips, crackers, pasta, frozen meals, canned soups, cereal…all cleared out from stores in a panic-induced spree. Processed foods + staying at home + forbidden outdoor activities in many places + closed gyms or activity centers = weight gain.

This was particularly compromising in larger cities. If a child lived in a smaller community in Colorado, Georgia, or California, for example, they probably still got outdoors for some activity. The ones I know did. Smaller towns were much more relaxed about lockdown protocols than larger cities. However, if a child lived in Brooklyn, Somerville, Chicago, Baltimore, or any major city, it was very challenging to squeak out to play with friends outdoors or do something active. Screen time for kids went up an average of five hours per day. Not total, but above what it was before the lockdowns. There is an 85% correlation between increased screen time for kids and weight gain.[394] I saw this firsthand with kids I know. You probably did too.

McMaster's Children's Hospital saw a 90% increase in its Referrals for Eating Disorders Program in 2020 compared to 2019. Admissions for inpatient emergency treatment rose during the lockdowns, something one of their clinical managers called "unprecedented." Recovering from an eating disorder takes two to three years to resolve if it does.

Why is an increase in childhood obesity a big deal that should be sounding alarms? It's quite ironic. The lockdowns caused the number one health condition that makes young people a risk to serious illness if they contract COVID-19.

Increased Domestic Violence

The lockdowns may have slowed the spread of COVID-19. We can debate that. Isolation is certainly the only real mitigation that was effective. All the lockdown policies had associated risks and consequences. The consequence far outweighed the population risk. Do you want to avoid COVID-19? Stay home. But that should be your choice when only a sliver of the population was at risk and there was zero chance of the healthcare system being overloaded for the duration of the year and a half of interventions. Loss of income, housing instability, and nutritional stress were three primary causes of increased intimate partner violence.

25% of women and 10% of men are reported to be the victims of domestic violence in their life according to the CDC.[395] Stress related to social distancing, economic hardship, 24/7 parenting, and staying at home all contributed to increased relational conflict during the lockdowns. Domestic violence in China's Hubei province tripled during February 2020 year over year. In France, violence against women increased 30% after they initiated a March 17 lockdown; in Argentina, by 25%; and in Singapore, 33%.[396]

The National Commission on COVID-19 and Criminal Justice identified an increase of 8.7% in domestic violence incidents in 2020.[397] They qualified their findings by suggesting they were likely higher, but the stay-at-home and social distancing orders prevented watchful eyes that may have prompted more reporting. Their data was based on "crime reports, emergency hotline registries, hospital and other health records, and additional administrative documents." There were approximately 1,330 more domestic violence calls per day nationally during the lockdowns.

Below are some other data points from around the world and in the United States regarding domestic violence increases (and a couple of decreases) during the lockdowns:

- Phoenix and Salt Lake City had dramatic increases in domestic violence, Phoenix among highest in the country in one study[398]
- Louisville had an estimated 40% increase in assault crimes and a 28% decrease in non-residential crimes[399]
- Austin and Dallas were up 9% and 13%, respectively[400]
- Charlotte had 517 more calls in March 2020 than in March 2019, an 18% increase[401]
- Nashville and surrounding areas in Tennessee received a 55% increase in hotline calls since the lockdowns
- The Michigan Coalition to End Domestic and Sexual Violence reported calls increased to 393 in March and the first half of April in 2020, up from 189 at the same time last year. Michigan's Domestic and Sexual Violence Prevention and Treatment Board has also seen a jump in help requests, although data are not yet available. In my hometown area of Oakland County, a Detroit suburb, domestic violence charges jumped 47% in the first two weeks of April year-over-year.[402]
- In the UK, the abuse charity Refuge reported a "700% increase in calls to its helpline in a single day in April, while a separate helpline for perpetrators of domestic abuse seeking help to change their behavior received 25% more calls after the start of the COVID-19 lockdown."[403] In this report, they cited that three times the number of women were killed by men during the lockdowns in April, though the absolute number was 14.
- India saw a 131% increase year over year in domestic violence incidents and a 184% increase in cybercrimes (stalking, sexual harassment and trolling, and bullying).[404]
- Argentina experienced victim hotline call increases of 127%, where calls from others (police and non-victims) actually decreased 62%, supporting the absent-watchful-eye theory.[405] Mexico City was similar: hotline calls were up about 30% while police reports were down that much.[406]

The domestic violence spikes were highest in the initial eight weeks of the spring 2020 lockdowns. Restrictions eased in many states over the 2020 summer and then ratcheted back up. That domestic violence spikes were not so pronounced in the stricter late 2020 lockdowns suggests people were getting used to a "new normal," a term many grew to disdain as they longed for a return to actual normal.

Depression

Children weren't the only ones suffering from depression during the lockdowns. Young and older adults suffered the same. Over a hundred million people experienced depression and anxiety over both the fear of COVID-19 mortality and the lockdowns: stay-at-home orders, social distancing, closed schools, job insecurities, lack of activity, and isolation. The CDC did a study on this in the summer of 2020 and found marked increases in anxiety and depression.

Two prevailing data points jumped out from the initial survey and the ongoing Household Pulse Survey published by the CDC on anxiety and depression conducted weekly by state: young people who were at really no COVID-19 risk were the most depressed, and people in more restricted states were more depressed. Below are excerpts of the percent of people feeling depression and anxiety by age for all states, and then all ages from select states, the five least and five most restricted states:[407]

	May 5, 2020	October 26, 2020	December 21, 2021	February 1, 2021	March 29, 2021
Age 18-29	47%	52%	56%	57%	51%
Age 40-49	39%	40%	45%	41%	37%
Age 70-79	22%	23%	27%	26%	20%
Over 80	21%	19%	28%	23%	24%
U.S. Average	36%	38%	42%	42%	35%
California	37%	40%	45%	46%	39%
Illinois	37%	35%	40%	39%	36%
Michigan	39%	37%	46%	40%	35%
New Jersey	38%	36%	41%	42%	35%
New York	41%	39%	41%	36%	36%
Florida	37%	36%	42%	41%	35%
Nebraska	29%	33%	36%	34%	32%
North Dakota	28%	31%	34%	29%	27%
South Dakota	26%	29%	32%	29%	25%
Wyoming	31%	32%	39%	40%	36%

First, these are very high and alarming percentages of people stressed out over the pandemic and the lockdowns. To be sure, some of the first groupings of states listed above with tighter restrictions were hit harder by COVID-19 than the second grouping. This very likely caused some of the higher rates of depression and anxiety. Over time, as others were hit, it's reasonable that the message from each state's governor and local leaders had some effect on how people felt. A calming governor likely drove those numbers down, and a more panic-inducing-lockdown governor likely drove more anxiety and depression. Every one of the lesser stressed states was a majority traditional conservative voters. Conservative media did not support lockdown measures the way, and I hate that this is true, liberal/mainstream media rallied lockdowns.

Next, the younger you were, the more stressed you were. The older people at measurable risk were by far the least stressed. One reason may have been that they were retired and could stay at home without much disruption (my mom was in this category). Another may be they figured if it was their time, it was their time. And then there is perspective. Younger people tend to be more impulsive and reactive and more easily influenced by media, and social media, which largely drove panic and did not contextualize data. Or, maybe younger people felt stressed not because of COVID-19 but the lockdowns themselves, isolation, and career uncertainty. Dr. Meg Jay wrote in *The Defining Decade* that twentysomethings were already the most stressed-out age group before the pandemic.

The *JAMA Network* published survey results on September 2, 2020, that found "the prevalence of depression symptoms in the U.S. was more than 3-fold higher during COVID-19 compared with before the COVID-19 pandemic. Individuals with lower social resources, lower economic resources, and greater exposure to stressors (e.g., job loss) reported a greater burden of depression symptoms." [408] The skewing toward lower-income class Americans supports the depression was more from the lockdowns than the pandemic itself. Lower-income minorities were by percentage more affected by COVID-19 than those in higher income brackets. By far, lower-income Americans, and people worldwide, were far more adversely affected by the lockdowns than higher-income families.

Youth depression was at an all-time high in 2020. Considering the chart of 18-29-year-olds and their high anxiety levels, it's very believable. A quarter of college-age adults considered suicide in a June 2020 survey. Fortunately, it appears few acted on those thoughts, as data as of this writing shows that suicides did not rise in the year of lockdowns. Youth suicides were up in 2020, while all suicides were even to the previous year. However, all-cause deaths in the younger age group were the highest percent increase in excess deaths, and those were not COVID-19 deaths.

In California, over 100,000 above-usual gun purchases were made out of fear during the pandemic.[409] People weren't buying guns to prevent getting COVID-19 - that never made a CDC or WHO mitigation list. They were buying them out of lockdown fear. In addition, over 10% of Californians (over four million people) were concerned that someone they knew might harm themselves due to COVID-19 or lockdown-prompted fear. This was California. Imagine the response in moderate to higher gun-owning states. Gun sales in the U.S. set an all-time annual record by September 2020.[410]

The UC Davis researchers also estimated 47,000 new firearm owners. The respondents who bought firearms mainly did so for self-protection, citing worries about lawlessness (76%), prisoner releases (56%), and the government going too far (49%). With law enforcement loosening up in the wake of the George Floyd death in Minneapolis and millions upset over Floyd's death, crime soared in dozens of cities across America. Combine that with increased lockdown fear, unemployment, and depression, and the second half of 2020, well into 2021, was a mess in America in crime and depression.

Deaths of Despair

The Robert Graham Center for Policy Studies in Family Medicine and Primary Care conducted an analysis on the impact of the lockdowns, depression, job loss, and fear on suicide levels.[411] Their findings are below. "Three factors, already at work, are exacerbating deaths of despair: unprecedented economic failure paired with massive unemployment, mandated social isolation for months and possible residual isolation for years."

In 2018, there were 181,686 "deaths of despair" from alcohol, drugs, or suicide. They estimated that based on unemployment up and isolation growing, the lockdowns could result in 65,598 more deaths of despair annually for several years. Contextualize that with the pandemic – collateral deaths of despair and untreated/undiagnosed health conditions could far eclipse COVID-19 deaths. Measured in life-years lost, it won't be close worldwide. They based their data on actual results that occurred in the wake of the Great Recession twelve years before COVID-19 reached America. With unemployment up ten points in a month from the lockdowns, they predicted deaths that might eclipse actual COVID-19 fatalities.

The chart below represents possibilities based on 1-1.6% increases in unemployment. The incremental projections below are very small compared to the very high unemployment from the lockdowns. Projecting that may be off the charts. Unemployment did dip to single digits in 2021, and with robust unemployment benefits, let's hope time shows this does not materialize.

Table. Possible Additional Deaths of COVID-19 Recession on Deaths of Despair, Alternative Scenarios									
	Percent Change in Mortality with One Point Increase in Unemployment								
	1% increase			1.3% increase			1.6% increase		
	Slow	Medium	Fast	Slow	Medium	Fast	Slow	Medium	Fast
2020	9,859	9,333	8,343	12,817	12,133	10,846	15,774	14,932	13,349
2021	18,347	16,103	12,209	23,851	20,934	15,871	29,355	25,765	19,534
2022	15,879	11,840	5,832	20,642	15,392	7,581	25,406	18,944	9,331
2023	13,410	8,025	1,261	17,434	10,433	1,639	21,457	12,841	2,017
2024	10,394	3,973	-	13,512	5,164	-	16,630	6,356	-
2025	7,651	870	-	9,947	1,131	-	12,242	1,392	-
2026	7,103	316	-	9,234	411	-	11,365	506	-
2027	5,732	-	-	7,451	-	-	9,171	-	-
2028	4,086	-	-	5,312	-	-	6,538	-	-
2029	3,812	-	-	4,956	-	-	6,099	-	-
Total	96,273	50,460	27,644	125,155	65,598	35,937	154,037	80,735	44,230

Types of Recovery: Slow—Same as Great Recession; Medium—Twice as Fast; Fast—Four Times as fast.

Source: Well Being Trust & The Robert Graham Center Analysis: The COVID Pandemic Could Lead to 75,000 Additional Deaths from Alcohol and Drug Misuse and Suicide: https://wellbeingtrust.org/ areas-of-focus/policy-and-advocacy/reports/projected-deaths-of-despair-during-covid-19/

Casey Mulligan, an economics professor from the University of Chicago, authored a study suggesting deaths of despair rose 10-60% above normal during the lockdowns.[412] Yes, that is a large spread. With the study out at the end of 2020, the data was still coming in and would well into 2021. It can take months for suicides to be reported as a cause of death. Mulligan looked at overall mortality in 2020 and the excess compared to real COVID-19 deaths. Mulligan's analysis considered that 2020 mortality was greater than the combination of expected deaths plus COVID-19 deaths. He asserted that "Non-COVID excess mortality is the difference between excess deaths and COVID deaths, with a minor correction for COVID underreporting." As we look at these findings, consider the flaw that excess deaths are the simple difference between excess deaths and COVID-19 deaths. This is a flawed proposition for two reasons: COVID-19 deaths were inflated by about 30%, and roughly half the COVID-19 deaths were to those over life expectancy (meaning many would be "expected").

Still, Mulligan uncovered one data point we discussed in chapter eight: many people, mostly men, died in excess under 50 and without COVID-19. Below is a chart of his study in men, age 15-54, that are both COVID-19 and non-COVID-19 deaths. Now consider his COVID-19 line is inflated by about 30% because he used official CDC data, which means the spread is much wider between the two lines. More excess deaths in young to middle age males to causes other than COVID-19. Further, excess deaths from about July 2020 to December 2020 were evenly split between COVID-19 and non-COVID-19 causes.

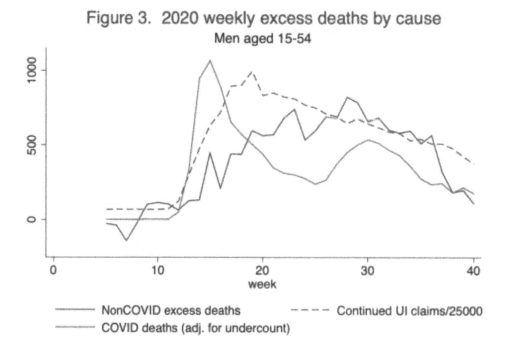

Figure 3. 2020 weekly excess deaths by cause
Men aged 15-54

NonCOVID excess deaths — — — Continued UI claims/25000
COVID deaths (adj. for undercount)

Suicides

On August 27, 2020, a close friend called me in tears. She's a liberal progressive living in San Francisco and was supportive of the lockdowns for months. "Why are you so upset?" She told me the son of one of her colleagues, a sixteen-year-old, committed suicide over the depression of the lockdown there and not being in school. Yes, he suffered from depression prior to the lockdown, but the isolation put him over the edge. He would have been in class at the time he took his life.

There was an expectation that suicides would skyrocket during the lockdowns worldwide. An Australian study predicted more suicide deaths than COVID-19 deaths. By the time the pandemic was over, we did not see suicides rise above average, both a surprise and good news. Perhaps depressed individuals saw light at the end of the tunnel, and perhaps they had help along the way. Perhaps the enhanced unemployment benefits made the difference. Whatever the reason, this was one expectation that did not develop, a sigh of relief to those fearing lockdowns might trigger these unnecessary deaths.

While the sum of suicides did not increase, youth suicides did. California teen suicides increased 24% year-over-year in 2020, while adult suicides dropped 11%. Overall, teen suicides went up 15% year-over-year nationally.[413]

When the financial crisis hit in 2007 and a recession ensued, suicides spiked by 10,000 over prior periods in America and Europe. Suicides are the tenth largest cause of death in America, claiming close to 50,000 lives a year. Mental health is an obvious reason why some choose to end their lives, but it's not the biggest reason. It's severe depression.

Large contributors to people committing suicide include job insecurity, losing a job, having a serious or chronic medical condition, being a victim of abuse, and a lack of helpful resources for those seeking help. All those depressive conditions would be magnified during the pandemic and lockdown. The highest age bracket for suicides is 45-54, followed by the elderly over 80. More than three-quarters of suicide victims are white compared to about half the population. Most commit suicide with a gun.

WILX in Lansing, MI, reported an opinion based on conversations with frontline healthcare workers in the Detroit area that they expect those under stress and depression would provide a 32% increase in suicides over the pandemic and lockdown. Dr. Lorna Breen was the highest-profile suicide during the pandemic. Breen was an ER doctor at New York-Presbyterian Allen Hospital in northern Manhattan. She was 49. She contracted the virus and recovered. If you've spent any time talking to physicians, they will tell you that working in the emergency room is the highest stress specialty in the field.

The longer one is quarantined, the more likely one is to suffer from mental health problems, post-traumatic stress, anger, and introversion. When SARS broke in 2003, there was an increase in elderly suicides. With the elderly the second highest segment of suicides and then facing greater lockdown isolation because they were the most vulnerable, they were forced to balance COVID-19 fear of death and depression because they were isolated from families in many cases.

Suicide hotlines experienced an 800% increase in calls when the lockdowns began. Former Congressman Patrick Kennedy said, "The tragedy of COVID is it exacerbates this already prevalent mental health and addiction crisis. No one doubts that mental health and addiction are real. Every single American has been faced with a mental health issue in this COVID crisis, themselves, not just a family member, but themselves."[414]

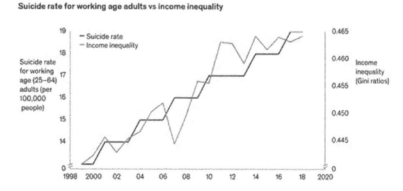

Association between income inequality and suicide rate in the United States

Suicide rate for working age adults vs income inequality

Source: CDC WISQARS, 2020; U.S. Census Bureau, Current Population Survey, 1968 to 2019 Annual Social and Economic Supplements (CPS ASEC)

McKinsey
& Company

The CDC analysis above draws direct lines between income inequality and suicides. With what grew to 40 million people out of work and many non-COVID-19 illnesses untreated for weeks, it seemed impossible not to see a suicide rise in America from 2020 to 2022. The data on suicides is very lagging. There was an expectation that suicides would markedly increase worldwide during the lockdowns, and into the middle of 2021, with the pandemic surges behind, that did not happen based on all reporting available.

In the U.S. Army, there has been "a roughly 30% jump in active-duty suicides this year, or 114 suicides this year compared to 88 at the same time last year. The first three months of 2020 actually saw a decrease in self-inflicted violent behavior and murders."

In May 2020 in California, medics at John Muir Medical Center in Walnut Creek near San Francisco witnessed a year's worth of suicide attempts in just a matter of weeks because of the strain of the lockdown. In Chicago, more African Americans in Cook County died by suicide through the first half of 2020 than during all of 2019.

More recently, Texas saw a huge uptick in suicide attempts. Cook Children's Hospital is in Dallas. I took my son there when he was just a few months old. Cook's admitted 29 children in August 2020 following attempted suicides, and over two hundred in 2020, more than double the amount admitted during the same time period previously. I spoke with nurses at hospitals in Detroit and Florida and was told by all they never saw as many suicide attempts and drug overdoses as they had in the first six months of the lockdowns.

Colorado hospitals were like so many overrun with adolescent suicide attempts. According to David Brumbaugh, MD, Children's Colorado chief medical officer, "I've been in practice for over 20 years in pediatrics, and I've never seen anything like the demand for mental health services we've seen at Children's Colorado in the past 15 months. There have been many weeks in 2021 that the No. 1 reason for presenting to our emergency department is a suicide attempt. Our kids have run out of resilience — their tanks are empty."[415]

There were many tragic stories of suicides triggered by the lockdowns, and even though the total was not higher than average, the situations are heartbreaking. Isolation drove many kids to end their lives, as well as adults and at all career levels. Nevada was even driven to reopen classes sooner than planned because there were so many indicators of youth suicides. You can find the stories. For my part, I don't see the need to spend paragraphs reopening those tragedies. It did show the need to give extra attention to those vulnerable, just like COVID-19 demanded that of those at measurable health risk.

Drug Use Accelerating During Lockdowns

While suicides did not jump during the lockdowns, drug and alcohol consumption went up. Alcohol sales jumped 34% year over year in the early months of the lockdowns.[416] This was not because bars and restaurants were closed and the same purchases shifted; non-alcoholic beverage sales only went up 17.7%, so there was definitely a net increase. In the very early weeks of the pandemic, some alcoholic beverage sales were up five to ten times the prior year, and online orders skyrocketed.[417] People drank more during the lockdowns.

Drug use skyrocketed during the lockdowns, which led to a very high increase in overdoses. Overdose-associated cardiac arrests increased 40% in 2020.[418] A higher concentration of these overdoses was found in minorities and in western states. The first chart below shows the percentage increase by state for overdose-associated cardiac arrests. States with higher rates overall (second chart) saw less increase than those with lower baselines. The increases were highly correlated to lower-income and minority communities. Lockdowns hurt marginalized communities disproportionately to higher-income communities.

A | Percent change in 2020

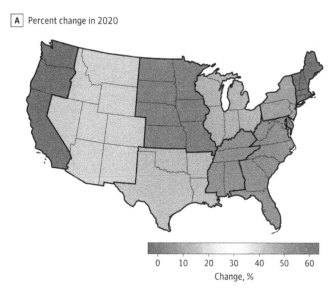

B | OCAs per 100000 in 2020

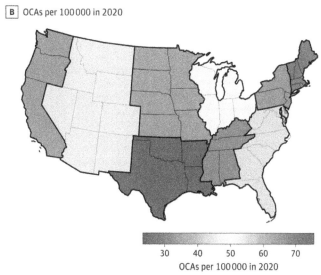

Increased drug use led to a significant increase in unintentional injury deaths in 2020 and 2021. Below is a chart of 2020 causes of death compared to previous years, compiled in a *JAMA Network* study.[419]

Table. Number of Deaths for Leading Causes of Death, US, 2015-2020[a]

Cause of death	No. of deaths by year					
	2015	2016	2017	2018	2019	2020
Total deaths	2712630	2744248	2813503	2839205	2854838	3358814
Heart disease	633842	635260	647457	655381	659041	690882
Cancer	595930	598038	599108	599274	599601	598932
COVID-19[b]						345323
Unintentional injuries	146571	161374	169936	167127	173040	192176
Stroke	140323	142142	146383	147810	150005	159050
Chronic lower respiratory diseases	155041	154596	160201	159486	156979	151637
Alzheimer disease	110561	116103	121404	122019	121499	133382
Diabetes	79535	80058	83564	84946	87647	101106
Influenza and pneumonia	57062	51537	55672	59120	49783	53495
Kidney disease	49959	50046	50633	51386	51565	52260
Suicide	44193	44965	47173	48344	47511	44834

[a] Leading causes are classified according to underlying cause and presented according to the number of deaths among US residents. For more information, see the article by Heron.[4] Source: National Center for Health Statistics. National Vital Statistics System: mortality statistics (http://www.cdc.gov/nchs/deaths.htm). Data for 2015-2019 are final; data for 2020 are provisional.

[b] Deaths with confirmed or presumed COVID-19, coded to *International Statistical Classification of Diseases and Related Health Problems, Tenth Revision* code U07.1 as the underlying cause of death.

Note the increase in diabetes and Alzheimer's deaths in 2020; these are likely collateral lockdown deaths from abandonment and untreated conditions. There's really no doubt the lockdowns caused increased dementia in 2020. Heart disease death increases were likely borne out of staying away from healthcare because they could not get in or were too afraid to get checked.

Unintentional injuries include accidents, homicides, and overdoses. Unintentional injuries are typically the third highest cause of death in America, after heart disease and cancer. With COVID-19 ranking third, this fell to fourth. Within unintentional injuries, overdoses and those resulting in death were well up during the lockdowns. One state saw a decrease in overdose deaths year-over-year September 2019-September 2020: South Dakota. Below are some examples of what and when we saw overdoses soar.

Louisiana

Louisiana had more overdose deaths during the pandemic than any other state, a 54% increase.[420] Only tightly locked Washington D.C. saw more. Dr. Shaden Murad worked at West Jefferson Hospital's emergency room in New Orleans. Recall that in the spring of 2020, only two areas were hard hit with COVID-19 outside the New York area: Detroit and New Orleans.

She said of the experience, "For a while, it was like you would have a COVID patient and an overdose patient, a COVID patient, an overdose patient. It was one for one, and definitely, I would say within the last year, we've seen a lot more overdoses and a lot more deaths because of overdoses."[421] It could have been isolation, fear, boredom, or another theory: the drug supply chain was interrupted and dealers were improvising their drugs with less safe mixtures. This was a prevalent theory across the country. In Maryland, there was a great story about an arrest.

The AP shared this insight into a Maryland entrepreneur. A Maryland man accused of operating a Darknet store selling prescription opioids boasted on his vendor page: "Even with Corona Virus, the shop is running at full speed." He told an undercover FBI agent that he was just waiting for a shipment because "this corona virus shit is fucking up inventory," according to court documents.[422] One more supply chain challenge that the country had to overcome.

Kentucky

Kentucky has long had overdose challenges, and in the same period reported as Louisiana above, had a 50% increase in overdose deaths.[423] Within a month of the state of emergency ordered, twenty counties saw an increase in deaths. At that time, Kentucky saw really no COVID-19 activity, and Governor Andy Beshear issued one of the stricter lockdowns. There was that moment when he banned drive-by Easter services in April 2020. Clearly, COVID-19 was a threat driving in your car to a church. Science, right?

Ohio

Overdose deaths in Ohio averaged about seventy per week from 2018 through the beginning of the pandemic. When the national emergency was announced in March 2020, the following week, overdose deaths reached 145 for the first time ever (chart below).[424] Overdose deaths continued above average

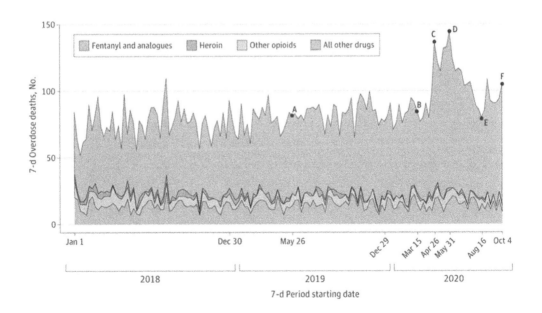

for three months and spiked again around scheduled school reopenings that did not happen in Ohio. This study concluded in October 2020 while trending up.

California

Northern California was largely untouched by COVID-19 in 2020-2021 compared to Los Angeles and southern California. Nearly half of all California COVID-19 deaths occurred in Los Angeles County. California locked down quick and hard in March and never let up. After fifteen months of COVID-19, San Francisco officially lost 550 people to the virus. In 2020, 700 people lost their lives to overdoses and were on track in 2021 to surpass that record.[425] There were many stories during the lockdowns of empty needles found on city streets. The city of San Francisco had created "safe injection sites" for drug users before the pandemic. That seems so foreign and unbelievable, and the topic of debate for a different book. Sites like this were closed during the lockdowns.

Sonoma County is in California's lovely wine country, one of the prettiest parts of the state with more natural beauty than perhaps any other. Sonoma and Napa are incredibly soothing places to visit, and just a few hours away are Lake Tahoe and Yosemite National Park. Sonoma County has a half-million residents. They had 318 official COVID-19 deaths compared to 135 overdose deaths in 2020 and a higher trend in 2021.[426] The overdoses were most prevalent among people in the 35-44 age range.

Further south, Los Angeles had a 48% increase in overdose deaths in the months that followed the March lockdown.[427] 78% of those deaths were to men. People ages 25-34 were the age group most susceptible, and the rate tripled with Asian Americans. There was about a 50% increase with other races. The absolute number was not close to COVID-19 deaths in LA County like it was in the bay area, but still a measurable increase.

Lockdowns Kill

One of the strictest coronavirus lockdowns was imposed by Michigan Governor Gretchen Whitmer. It was in Michigan where Steven Manzo, a 33-year-old bar employee in Mount Clemens who was recovering from heroin addiction, lost his job just before St. Patrick's Day. "Everything looks normal, but it doesn't feel normal," Manzo ominously told a *Washington Post* reporter on March 20.[428] "I live downtown with bars and restaurants and nobody is here. We have no idea how long it will be." Two weeks after making those comments, Manzo was found dead in his department of a drug overdose.

CHAPTER 21
COVID-19 and the Lockdowns
By The Numbers

712,958: total U.S. COVID-19 deaths according to the CDC on October 1, 2021

690,688: total U.S. COVID-19 deaths according to Worldometers on October 1, 2021

$16,000,000,000,000 (16 trillion): potential United States cost of COVID-19[429]

$27,000,000: cost per COVID-19 death by this estimate

$20 to $1,419: cost of a COVID-19 test[430]

$148: median cost of a COVID-19 test[431]

$10: cost to the federal government for a Johnson and Johnson COVID-19 vaccine[432]

$15: cost to the federal government for each dose of the Moderna vaccine[433]

$5,000,000: jackpot amount New York's vaccine lottery[434]

$1,000,000: amount five people could win weekly in Ohio's vaccine lottery[435]

$40,000: daily disbursement for Maryland's vaccine lottery, with a $400,000 jackpot in the summer of 2021[436]

$6,000,000,000,000 (6 trillion): total federal government bailout money through May 2021[437]

$41,870: amount spent per taxpayer by the federal government in COVID-19 relief[438]

$18,181: amount spent per American by the federal government in COVID-19 relief[439]

$76,000,000,000 (76 billion): federal COVID-19 relief for colleges and universities[440] (~ $38,000 per student)[441]

$193,000,000,000 (193 billion): federal COVID-19 relief bailout for K-12 schools[442]

$4,610: amount per K-12 student in federal COVID-19 relief granted for K-12 schools[443]

The huge relief allocated for schools was not to get schools ready to open. It was not for safety protocols. Most of the money was not required to be spent anytime in the vicinity of when schools were reopened. Below is the annual release and allocation of the education COVID-19 relief:[444]

2021: $ 6.4 billion
2022: $32 billion
2023: $25 billion
2024: $19 billion
2025: $ 9 billion
2026: $ 2.5 billion
2027: $ 1 billion

12%: amount of $13 billion 2020 federal granted Elementary and Secondary School Emergency Relief spent in 2020[445]

12 million: the number of kids that could attend school in-person full-time on September 3, 2020[446]

16 million: the number of kids that could attend school in-person full-time on December 3, 2020[447]

34 million: the number of kids that could attend school in-person full-time on May 3, 2021[448]

7,000: the number of daily tutoring sessions Tutor.com delivered in the fall of 2020, more than a 50% increase over 2019[449]

55,166 (up over 20%): applicants for law school for the 2021-2022 academic year[450]

$55 billion: federal bailout for the airline industry[451]

52 billion: number of face masks manufactured globally in 2020[452]

1.56 billion: estimated number of face masks that will end up in the oceans in 2021[453]

40.8 million: U.S. jobless claims during the spring 2020 lockdown[454]

2.28 million U.S. jobs saved (Q4 2020 vs. Q4 2019) due to the ability to work remotely[455]

672,316: hotel industry jobs lost in 2020[456]

478,245: expected hotel industry jobs lost in 2021[457]

5.2 million: additional people enrolled in Medicaid in 2020[458]

30%: increase in homicides in 2020 compared to 2019[459]

24%: decrease in residential burglary[460]

13%: increase in motor vehicle theft[461]

1 in 6: number of dry cleaners closed due to bankruptcy in 2020[462]

110,000: number of restaurants closed during the pandemic.[463] Less than half of those open in 2021 are expected to be open in the months or years to come.[464]

30%: percent of California's 76,000 restaurants permanently closed[465]

11,060: number of clothing retailers that permanently closed in 2020[466]

20,000: estimated number of clothing retailers that will permanently close in 2021[467]

8,900,000: the number of people that moved between March and December 2020[468]

2nd: Texas's rank in net migration in 2020[469]

3rd: Florida's rank in net migration in 2020[470]

49th: Illinois's rank in net migration in 2020[471]

50th: California's rank in net migration in 2020, last in the country[472]

$20.4 billion: lost health club revenue by the end of 2020

6,400: number of health clubs (17%) closed permanently[473]

41%: decrease in African American owned small businesses in 2020[474]

32%: decrease in Hispanic-owned small businesses in 2020[475]

26%: decrease in Asian-owned small businesses in 2020[476]

36%: decrease in immigrant-owned small businesses in 2020[477]

15.77 million (double what was expected): new Netflix paid subscribers in the first quarter of 2020[478]

339,917: fewer 2020 marriages compared to 2019[479]

3 billion: number of Tinder swipes on a single day in March 2020, a record[480]

70%: year-over-year increase in online dating Bumble video calls March through May 2020[481]

700%: year-over-year increase in OkCupid dates March through May 2020[482]

$1.45 billion: toilet paper sales in March 2020, an 845% increase over March 2019[483]

34%: the national incr
ease in pet adoptions in April 2020 compared to April 2019

1,500: increase in 2020 pet adoptions through the Lucky Dog Animal Rescue (Arlington, VA). There were 1,800 pet adoptions in 2019, an 83% increase[484]

40,000 fewer births (-4.3%) in the final forty-five days of 2020 compared to 2019 (many expected more births due to the lockdowns nine months earlier)[485]

6.4 hours: weekly decrease in sports activity (from 13.6 to 7.2 hours) for youths age 6-18 during lockdowns[486]

6.3%: increase in the Dow Jones Industrial Average from beginning to end in 2020[487]

72%: increase in Amazon stock price[488]

28%: increase in Google stock price[489]

50 million: new Amazon Prime subscribers during the pandemic, a 33% increase[490]

30%: increase in drive-through and app-ordered coffee[491]

40%: new coffees tried during the pandemic[492]

25%: increase in coffee makers sold[493]

23%: increase in coffee grocery sales in Italy during *the first week* of pandemic[494]

43%: year-over-year sales increase in 2020 for sleeping aid melatonin[495]

26% increase in fast food drive-thru visits in April, May, June 2020[496]

55 million fewer printed book sales globally by UK publishers in the first 6 months of 2020[497]

17% increase in ebook sales

42% increase in audiobook sales

35% increase in hardback fiction sales

10,000,000: Zoom peak daily usage in December 2019[498]

300,000,000: Zoom peak daily usage in April 2020[499]

$11.67 billion: 2019 global anti-depressant drug market[500]

$26.25 billion: 2020 global anti-depressant drug market[501]

-410,000,000,000: fewer U.S. vehicle miles driven in 2020 versus 2019 (-13.7%).[502] The northeast was down the most at -14.7% and western states the least at -10.2%.

-62%: decrease in U.S. domestic and international airline passengers in 2020 compared to 2019, down 655 million[503]

885: Number of people to summit Mount Everest in 2019[504]

8: Number of people to summit Mount Everest in 2020[505]

7,874,965,825: Number of people worldwide glad the pandemic was over

ENDNOTES

1   https://www.freep.com/story/news/local/michigan/2020/04/09/no-more-visiting-friends-and-neighbors-under-whitmers-expanded-coronavirus-order/5125426002/

2   https://www.ncbi.nlm.nih.gov/pmc/articles/PMC2130424/?page=1

3   https://bmcpublichealth.biomedcentral.com/articles/10.1186/1471-2458-8-61

4   https://www.nytimes.com/2020/04/22/us/politics/social-distancing-coronavirus.html

5   https://jamanetwork.com/journals/jama/fullarticle/208354

6   https://www.pnas.org/content/pnas/104/18/7582.full.pdf

7   https://www.kshs.org/kansapedia/flu-epidemic-of-1918/17805

8   https://www.nationalgeographic.com/news/2014/1/140123-spanish-flu-1918-china-origins-pandemic-science-health/

9   https://www.cdc.gov/flu/pandemic-resources/1918-pandemic-h1n1.html

10   US Department of Health, Education, and Welfare 1956.

11   https://www.ecohealthalliance.org/2018/05/outbreak-pandemic-strikes?gclid=Cj0KCQjw-Mr0BRDyARIsAKEFbeey1pvEww3GFeOyIVvhWFo9eAZd-p3OS1iDiJuGlXhSjySZp9cZwJxAaApdDEALw_wcB

12   https://employees.csbsju.edu/hjakubowski/classes/Chem%20and%20Society/Influenza/1918%20Pandemic.htm

13   https://www.history.com/news/spanish-flu-pandemic-response-cities

14   https://www.cdc.gov/flu/pandemic-resources/pdf/pandemic-influenza-implementation.pdf

15   https://assets.documentcloud.org/documents/6841076/2006-11-Disease-Mitigation-Measures-in-the.pdf

16   https://stacks.cdc.gov/view/cdc/11425

17   https://www.cdc.gov/mmwr/volumes/66/rr/rr6601a1.htm#T1_down

18   https://apps.who.int/iris/bitstream/handle/10665/329438/9789241516839-eng.pdf?ua=1

19   https://www.thelancet.com/journals/lanres/article/PIIS2213-2600(17)30229-1/fulltext

20   https://papers.ssrn.com/sol3/papers.cfm?abstract_id=3349234

21   https://academic.oup.com/cid/article/65/11/1934/4068747

22   https://bmjopen.bmj.com/content/bmjopen/5/4/e006577.full.pdf

23   https://www.cambridge.org/core/journals/epidemiology-and-infection/article/face-masks-to-prevent-transmission-of-influenza-virus-a-systematic-review/64D368496EBDE0AFCC6639CCC9D8BC05

24   https://www.sciencedaily.com/releases/2019/09/190903134732.htm

25   https://web.archive.org/web/20170512002228/https:/www.oralhealthgroup.com/features/face-masks-dont-work-revealing-review/

26   https://www.medscape.com/viewarticle/741245_print

27   https://multimedia.3m.com/mws/media/957730O/respirators-and-surgical-masks-contrast-technical-bulletin.pdf

28   https://www.cidrap.umn.edu/news-perspective/2014/05/commentary-protecting-health-workers-airborne-mers-cov-learning-sars

29   https://www.nursingtimes.net/clinical-archive/infection-control/the-effectiveness-of-surgical-face-masks-what-the-literature-shows-30-09-2003/

30   https://www.ccohs.ca/oshanswers/prevention/ppe/surgical_mask.html

31   https://www.thelancet.com/journals/lanres/article/PIIS2213-2600(20)30323-4/fulltext

32   https://www.politifact.com/factchecks/2020/sep/14/facebook-posts/face-masks-wild-fire-smoke-protection-and-covid-19-/

33   https://www.thelancet.com/journals/lanres/article/PIIS2213-2600(20)30323-4/fulltext

34   https://www.ncbi.nlm.nih.gov/pmc/articles/PMC6599448/

35   https://www.usatoday.com/story/news/health/2020/02/17/nih-disease-official-anthony-fauci-risk-of-coronavirus-in-u-s-is-minuscule-skip-mask-and-wash-hands/4787209002/

36   https://www.cbsnews.com/news/preventing-coronavirus-facemask-60-min-utes-2020-03-08/

37   https://www.cnn.com/2020/03/02/health/surgeon-general-coronavirus-masks-risk-trnd/index.html

38   https://www.cnn.com/2020/02/29/health/coronavirus-mask-hysteria-us-trnd/index.html

39   https://www.cbsnews.com/news/coronavirus-prevention-face-mask-not-helpful-wash-hands/

40   https://www.cnn.com/videos/health/2020/02/26/novel-coronavirus-questions-an-swered-sanjay-gupta-newday-vpx.cnn

41   https://barrie360.com/covid-19-face-masks-wont-prevent-illness-but-washing-your-hands-will-experts-say/

42   https://www.cidrap.umn.edu/news-perspective/2020/04/commentary-masks-all-covid-19-not-based-sound-data

43   https://www.teachthought.com/education/what-the-schools-arent-superspreaders-argument-misses-about-covid/

44   https://wallethub.com/edu/states-coronavirus-restrictions/73818

45   https://www.dailymail.co.uk/news/article-8624033/Wisconsin-government-agency-orders-employees-wear-masks-Zoom-calls-HOME.html

46   https://www.realclearpolitics.com/video/2021/08/03/nih_director_dr_francis_collins_parents_of_unvaccinated_kids_should_wear_masks_at_home.html

47   https://www.msn.com/en-us/health/wellness/experts-say-there-are-2-times-when-you-should-wear-a-mask-at-home/ar-BB19qHQc?ocid=msedgntp

48   https://www.webmd.com/lung/news/20200528/face-masks-at-home-reduce-covid-19-risk-study-says

49   https://www.cnn.com/2020/09/03/health/coronavirus-masks-sex-canada-trnd/index.html

50   https://www.usnews.com/news/health-news/articles/2020-09-16/cdcs-redfield-suggests-masks-may-offer-better-coronavirus-protection-than-a-vaccine

51   https://www.bmj.com/content/370/bmj.m3563#:~:text=Investigating%20close%20family%20members%20of,studies%20have%20reported%20similar%20results.

52   https://www.today.com/health/dr-fauci-shows-how-wear-2-masks-correctly-today-t208765

53   https://www.cdc.gov/mmwr/volumes/69/wr/mm6947e2.htm

54   https://www.medrxiv.org/content/10.1101/2020.10.21.20208728v2

55   https://www.acpjournals.org/doi/10.7326/m20-6817

56   https://www.nejm.org/doi/full/10.1056/NEJMoa2029717

57   https://phe.koha-ptfs.co.uk/cgi-bin/koha/opac-retrieve-file.pl?id=5f043ca658db1188ffae74827fa650d9

58   https://people.com/human-interest/man-wearing-n95-mask-passes-out-while-driving-car-crashing-into-pole/

59   http://scielo.isciii.es/pdf/neuro/v19n2/3.pdf

60   https://www.wkrg.com/health/coronavirus/dangers-of-wearing-masks-in-the-heat-and-humidity/

61   https://nypost.com/2020/05/06/two-boys-drop-dead-in-china-while-wearing-masks-during-gym-class/

62   https://pubmed.ncbi.nlm.nih.gov/30035033/

63   https://www.brusselstimes.com/news/belgium-all-news/health/130480/face-mask-obligation-in-school-major-threat-to-childrens-development-doctors-say/?fbclid=IwAR3n1hbqZYsxBfzw-TQKg05LytG_P3cu9ELJj6ATdKvQwFfQzf0hWw-BenVk

64   https://abc7.com/woman-arrested-for-not-wearing-mask-tased-because-she-wouldnt-put-on-a-face-logan-hocking-isd-alicia-kitts/6555132/

65   https://abc13.com/coroanvirus-news-southwest-kicks-off-woman-and-child-for-not-wearing-mask-chicago-mom-son-kicked-flight-covid-19/6422644/

66   https://www.nbcnewyork.com/news/coronavirus/nj-passenger-kicked-off-flight-en-route-to-super-bowl-for-wearing-specialty-mask/2871510/

67   https://www.nbclosangeles.com/news/coronavirus/southern-california-coronavirus/burroughs-high-varsity-baseball-team-suspended-coronavirus-masks-health-order-violation-burbank/2540482/

68   https://www.cdc.gov/mmwr/volumes/70/wr/mm7010e3.htm?s_cid=mm7010e3_w

69   https://www.nytimes.com/2021/03/05/health/coronavirus-restaurant-dining-masks.html?searchResultPosition=2

70   https://www.washingtonpost.com/opinions/2021/03/07/when-states-unmask-we-know-what-happens-next/

71   https://www.medrxiv.org/content/10.1101/2021.05.18.21257385v1.full.pdf

72   http://www.albasud.org/blog/en/1237/brote-de-covid-19-en-el-diamond-princess-qu-lecciones-podemos-aprender

73   https://cmmid.github.io/topics/covid19/diamond_cruise_cfr_estimates.html

74   https://www.bbc.com/news/world-asia-51568496

75   https://www.thelancet.com/journals/laninf/article/PIIS1473-3099(20)30244-9/fulltext)

76   https://www.theguardian.com/world/2020/mar/13/from-paradise-to-coronavirus-the-grand-princess-and-the-cruise-from-hell

77   https://www.cdc.gov/mmwr/volumes/69/wr/mm6912e3.htm

78   https://www.abc.net.au/news/2020-04-13/coronavirus-concerns-for-international-ruby-princess-passengers/12143544

79   https://www.bloomberg.com/news/features/2020-09-15/carnival-s-ruby-princess-cruise-ship-spread-coronavirus-around-the-world

80   https://www.nejm.org/doi/full/10.1056/NEJMoa2019375

81   https://www.cnbc.com/2020/04/13/navy-sailor-of-roosevelt-carrier-dies-from-corona-virus.html

82   https://www.nejm.org/doi/full/10.1056/NEJMc2034424

83   https://www.topuniversities.com/universities/imperial-college-london

84   https://www.usnews.com/education/best-global-universities/imperial-college-london-505571

85   https://pubmed.ncbi.nlm.nih.gov/19628172/

86   https://www.theguardian.com/world/2005/sep/30/birdflu.jamessturcke

87   https://www.theguardian.com/world/2005/sep/30/birdflu.jamessturcke

88   https://www.theguardian.com/education/2002/jan/09/research.highereducation

89   https://www.imperial.ac.uk/news/196234/covid-19-imperial-researchers-model-likely-impact/

90   https://www.imperial.ac.uk/media/imperial-college/medicine/sph/ide/gida-fellowships/Imperial-College-COVID19-NPI-modelling-16-03-2020.pdf

91   https://www.telegraph.co.uk/news/2020/04/04/science-clash-imperial-vs-oxford-sex-smear-created-rival-covid/

92   https://www.usnews.com/news/health-news/articles/2020-03-30/odds-of-hospitalization-death-with-covid-19-rise-steadily-with-age-study

93   https://www.telegraph.co.uk/news/2020/06/02/prof-lockdown-neil-ferguson-admits-sweden-used-science-uk-has/

94   https://www.telegraph.co.uk/news/2020/04/04/science-clash-imperial-vs-oxford-sex-smear-created-rival-covid/

95   https://www.newscientist.com/article/2238578-uk-has-enough-intensive-care-units-for-coronavirus-expert-predicts/

96   https://www.washingtonexaminer.com/news/is-the-coronavirus-as-deadly-as-they-say-professors-claim-more-data-needed-to-know-mortality-rate

97   https://www.washingtonpost.com/health/2020/04/06/americas-most-influential-coronavirus-model-just-revised-its-estimates-downward-not-every-model-agrees/

98   https://www.medrxiv.org/content/10.1101/2020.03.27.20043752v1.full.pdf

99   https://www.rochesterfirst.com/news/state-news/watch-live-gov-cuomos-daily-briefing-amid-covid-19-outbreak-in-new-york-state-4/

100   https://www.nytimes.com/2020/04/01/us/la-county-coronavirus-hospitals.html

101   https://covidtracking.com/data/national

102   http://www.healthdata.org/special-analysis/estimation-excess-mortality-due-covid-19-and-scalars-reported-covid-19-deaths

103   https://www.nytimes.com/2020/02/03/nyregion/nyc-coronavirus-what-we-know.html

104   https://www.rnz.co.nz/news/national/408675/nz-to-close-doors-on-foreign-travellers-from-china

105   https://thehill.com/homenews/campaign/481028-biden-slams-trump-for-cutting-health-programs-before-coronavirus-outbreak

106   https://www.bls.gov/opub/ted/2020/unemployment-rate-2-percent-for-college-grads-3-8-percent-for-high-school-grads-in-january-2020.htm

107   https://www.denverpost.com/2020/01/24/colorado-unemployment-rate-historic-low/

108   https://www.sltrib.com/news/politics/2020/01/24/utahs-unemployment-rate/

109   https://www.cnbc.com/2020/01/23/weekly-jobless-claims.html

110   https://www.orlandoweekly.com/Blogs/archives/2020/01/24/floridas-unemployment-rate-hits-record-low-but-how-does-orlando-rank

111   https://www.marketwatch.com/story/new-jobless-claims-fall-5th-straight-week-to-204000-in-sign-of-strong-us-labor-market-2020-01-16

112   https://mynorthwest.com/1680642/washington-unemployment-rate-2019/

113   https://www.crainsdetroit.com/economy/michigan-unemployment-down-payroll-jobs-advanced-throughout-2019

114   https://www.edd.ca.gov/newsroom/unemployment-january-2020.htm

115   https://www.fox10phoenix.com/news/dow-closes-above-29000-for-the-first-time

116   https://www.canyon-news.com/paddleboarder-arrested-for-violating-stay-at-home-order/107042

117   https://kesq.com/news/2020/04/10/riverside-county-unveils-app-to-report-coronavirus-violations/

118   https://www.bridgemi.com/michigan-government/gop-led-legislature-sues-michigan-gov-whitmer-over-emergency-powers

119   https://www.washingtonpost.com/outlook/florida-beach-coronavirus-desantis/2020/04/22/9a45c782-8429-11ea-ae26-989cfce1c7c7_story.html

120   https://www.propublica.org/article/he-faced-a-criminal-charge-for-not-self-isolating-when-he-had-covid-19-symptoms-prosecutors-just-dropped-the-case

121   https://www.nbcnews.com/news/us-news/kentucky-gov-announces-mandatory-quar-antine-anyone-who-attends-easter-services-n1181716

122   https://www.fox10phoenix.com/news/judge-city-cannot-prevent-drive-in-easter-service

123   https://www.washingtonpost.com/outlook/2020/03/25/hydroxychloroquine-false-hope-trump/

124   https://www.michigan.gov/documents/lara/Reminder_of_Appropriate_Prescribing_and_Dispensing_3-24-2020_684869_7.pdf

125   https://www.nytimes.com/2020/04/01/health/hydroxychloroquine-coronavirus-malaria.html

126   https://nypost.com/2020/04/02/hydroxychloroquine-most-effective-coronavirus-treatment-poll/

127   https://www.metrotimes.com/news-hits/archives/2020/04/02/gov-whitmer-says-she-sees-great-potential-with-coronovirus-drug-hydroxychloroquine-detroit-is-now-leading-nations-first-large-scale-study

128   https://www.foxnews.com/media/karen-whitsett-trump-hydroxychloroquine-saved-my-life

129   https://www.nationalreview.com/news/detroit-dems-to-censure-state-lawmaker-who-thanked-trump-for-touting-chloroquine/

130   https://www.detroitnews.com/story/news/local/detroit-city/2020/04/25/detroit-democrats-unanimously-censure-lawmaker-karen-whitsett-who-credited-trump-covid-19-recovery/3025907001/

131   https://www.theguardian.com/us-news/2020/may/26/gretchen-whitmer-husband-marc-mallory-boat-lockdown

132   https://www.texastribune.org/2020/12/19/coronavirus-south-texas-enforcement/

133   https://www.texastribune.org/2020/12/19/coronavirus-south-texas-enforcement/

134   https://pjmedia.com/culture/megan-fox/2020/04/29/new-normal-wisconsin-cops-caught-on-camera-threatening-mom-for-letting-child-play-with-neighbor-n386692

135   https://www.kare11.com/article/news/health/coronavirus/ten-people-statewide-cited-for-violating-stay-at-home-order/89-4c564349-c518-4cfe-9ecc-c7ea99334af0

136   https://www.wfmynews2.com/article/news/crime/protestors-arrested-violating-stay-home-order-greensboro-guilford-county-abortion-clinic-a-womans-choice-violation/83-d161d8f9-ee9f-4f6a-b30d-52d97ab80de7

137   https://www.nytimes.com/2021/05/11/briefing/outdoor-covid-transmission-cdc-number.html

138   https://www.cdc.gov/nchs/data/nvss/coronavirus/Alert-2-New-ICD-code-introduced-for-COVID-19-deaths.pdf?utm_source=rss&utm_medium=rss&utm_campaign=new-icd-code-introduced-for-covid-19-deaths

139   https://wwwn.cdc.gov/nndss/conditions/coronavirus-disease-2019-covid-19/case-definition/2020/

140   https://www.cdc.gov/nchs/nvss/vsrr/covid_weekly/index.htm

141   https://www.cidrap.umn.edu/news-perspective/2021/03/intellectual-disability-obesity-tied-covid-19-hospitalization-death

142   https://www.nytimes.com/2020/04/14/nyregion/new-york-coronavirus-deaths.html

143   https://www.foxnews.com/media/physician-blasts-cdc-coronavirus-death-count-guidelines

144   https://revcycleintelligence.com/news/hospitals-to-lose-1k-per-covid-19-case-despite-medicare-rate-bump

145   https://www.foxnews.com/us/pa-removes-200-deaths-official-coronavirus-count-questions-mount-reporting-process-data-accuracy

146   https://denver.cbslocal.com/2020/04/30/coronavirus-nursing-home-deaths-colorado-public-health/

147   https://durangoherald.com/articles/324539-montezuma-county-disputes-states-coronavirus-death-count

148   https://www.wisn.com/article/milwaukee-county-medical-examiner-says-states-coronavirus-death-count-too-high/34226894#

149   https://www.medrxiv.org/content/10.1101/2020.04.28.20083147v1.full.pdf

150   https://www.cdc.gov/mmwr/volumes/70/wr/mm7014e1.htm

151   https://www.cdc.gov/nchs/covid19/mortality-overview.htm

152   https://www.cdc.gov/mmwr/volumes/70/wr/mm7014e2.htm?s_cid=mm7014e2_x

153   https://www.reuters.com/article/us-health-coronavirus-new-orleans/why-is-new-orleans-coronavirus-death-rate-twice-new-yorks-obesity-is-a-factor-idUSKBN21K1B0

154   https://www.cnbc.com/2021/03/08/covid-cdc-study-finds-roughly-78percent-of-people-hospitalized-were-overweight-or-obese.html

155   https://www.sciencenews.org/article/coronavirus-covid19-obesity-risk-factor

156   https://www.washingtonpost.com/health/2020/04/24/strokes-coronavirus-young-patients/

157   https://www.cdc.gov/nchs/data/nvsr/nvsr68/nvsr68_09_tables-508.pdf

158   https://www.washingtonpost.com/health/patients-with-heart-attacks-strokes-and-even-appendicitis-vanish-from-hospitals/2020/04/19/9ca3ef24-7eb4-11ea-9040-68981f488eed_story.html

159   https://www.sfchronicle.com/local/article/STD-cases-have-plunged-during-COVID-but-not-16148656.php

160   https://jamanetwork.com/journals/jamanetworkopen/fullarticle/2768946

161   https://jamanetwork.com/journals/jamaoncology/fullarticle/2778916?guestAccessKey=b5850253-e8b7-4c31-9f10-6d43993a563a&utm_source=silverchair&utm_medium=email&utm_campaign=article_alert-jamaoncology&utm_content=olf&utm_term=042921

162   https://www.thelancet.com/journals/lanonc/article/PIIS1470-2045(20)30388-0/fulltext

163   https://www.theguardian.com/society/2020/oct/01/nhs-covid-disruption-could-cause-tens-of-thousands-of-deaths-mps-warn

164   https://bmjopen.bmj.com/content/10/11/e043828

165 https://wkow.com/2021/03/05/studies-show-many-cancers-are-going-undiagnosed-during-the-pandemic/

166 https://www.healthleadersmedia.com/clinical-care/missed-cancer-screening-during-coronavirus-pandemic-raises-alarm

167 https://jamanetwork.com/journals/jamaoncology/fullarticle/2774867

168 https://ehrn.org/articles/dclayed-cancer-screenings-a-second-look

169 https://www.thelancet.com/journals/lanonc/article/PIIS1470-2045(21)00067-X/fulltext#:~:text=Aoife%20Regan%2C%20head%20of%20clinical,of%20cancer%20trials%20were%20halted

170 https://jamanetwork.com/journals/jama/fullarticle/2771761

171 https://www.eurekalert.org/pub_releases/2020-09/uol-toe092820.php

172 https://qz.com/1918541/more-adults-have-died-from-dementia-during-the-covid-19-pandemic/

173 https://www.cidrap.umn.edu/news-perspective/2021/03/intellectual-disability-obesity-tied-covid-19-hospitalization-death

174 https://www.alz.org/media/Documents/alzheimers-facts-and-figures.pdf

175 https://www.cdc.gov/mmwr/volumes/69/wr/mm6942e2.htm#F1_down

176 https://www.businessinsider.com/half-europes-covid-19-deaths-in-long-term-care-facilities-2020-4

177 https://www.nytimes.com/2020/03/04/health/coronavirus-nursing-homes.html

178 https://www.dispatch.com/news/20200521/70-of-ohio-coronavirus-deaths-have-occurred-in-long-term-care-facilities

179 https://www.nytimes.com/interactive/2020/05/09/us/coronavirus-cases-nursing-homes-us.html

180 https://www.sfchronicle.com/bayarea/article/Nearly-half-of-California-s-COVID-19-deaths-are-15258337.php

181 https://chicago.suntimes.com/coronavirus/2020/5/8/21252728/nursing-homes-coronavirus-deaths-illinois-48-percent-covid-19

182 www.kansascity.com›news›local›article242262076

183 https://www.wbur.org/commonhealth/2020/04/24/seniors-coronavirus-nursing-homes-testing

184 https://www.indystar.com/story/news/investigations/2020/04/27/nursing-homes-now-account-one-third-indiana-coronavirus-deaths/3034770001/

185 https://coloradosun.com/2020/04/22/colorado-nursing-home-deaths-rise-coronavirus-covid19/

186 https://www.walb.com/2020/04/24/reports-georgias-covid-deaths-were-residents-long-term-care-facilities/

187 https://www.iberianet.com/news/coronavirus/nursing-home-resident-covid-19- deaths-continue-to-rise/article_88577500-7f44-11ea-8748-1fc173c19f04.html

188 https://www.washingtonpost.com/world/europe/nursing-homes-coronavirus-deaths-europe/2020/04/23/d635619c-8561-11ea-81a3-9690c9881111_story.html

189 https://wwmt.com/news/local/state-of-michigan-reports-more-than-2000-nursing-home-patients-have-covid-19

190 https://www.fox13news.com/news/outlook-for-covid-19-in-floridas-long-term-care-facilities-worsens-as-new-data-emerges

191 https://www.thecentersquare.com/virginia/nearly-60-percent-of-virginia-s- coronavirus-deaths-are-in-nursing-homes-other-long-term/article_3c9d1152-94a6-11ea-b37b-bb1588c0d0bf.html

192 https://www.expressnews.com/news/local/article/40-percent-of-coronavirus-deaths-in-Texas-linked-15238887.php

193 https://www.mcall.com/coronavirus/mc-nws-pa-transparency-virus-wolf-20200506-dqmz7wbhtnalhhj7rne2r5cmru-story.html

194 https://www.startribune.com/minn-nursing-homes-already-site-of-81-of-covid-19-deaths-still-taking-in-infected-patients/570601282/

195 https://www.newsweek.com/deaths-coronavirus-are-devastating-nursing-homes-united-states-1502408

196 https://www.washingtonpost.com/world/the_americas/coronavirus-canada-long- term-care-nursing-homes/2020/05/18/01494ad4-947f-11ea-87a3-22d324235636_ story.html

197 https://abcnews.go.com/Health/wireStory/nursing-home-protections-limit-families-sue-75808005

198 https://www.clickondetroit.com/news/local/2021/03/11/how-many-covid-related-deaths-occurred-in-michigan-nursing-homes-lawmakers-families-want-answers/

199 https://www.clickondetroit.com/business/2021/03/15/nessel-declines-gop-request-to-probe-michigan-covid-nursing-home-deaths/

200 https://www.npr.org/2021/01/04/953314476/december-proved-to-be-deadliest-month-for-residents-in-long-term-care

201 https://www.jdsupra.com/legalnews/in-nursing-homes-covid-19-deaths-and-5566566/

202 https://www.cdc.gov/mmwr/volumes/69/wr/mm6937a5.htm

203 https://www.finance.senate.gov/hearings/a-national-tragedy-covid-19-in-the-nations-nursing-homes

204 https://www.nbcnews.com/business/corporations/ceos-public-u-s-firms-earn-320-times-much-workers-n1263195

205   https://wallethub.com/edu/states-coronavirus-restrictions/73818

206   https://www.worldometers.info/coronavirus/#countries

207   https://www.healio.com/news/infectious-disease/20170210/cdc-reports-pneumonia-influenza-mortality-rate-hits-epidemic-threshold

208   https://nymag.com/intelligencer/2021/05/study-number-of-kids-hospitalized-for-covid-is-overcounted.html

209   https://www.cdc.gov/mmwr/volumes/70/wr/mm7014e2.htm?s_cid=mm7014e2_x

210   https://www.jpeds.com/article/S0022-3476(20)31023-4/fulltext

211   https://www.kff.org/coronavirus-covid-19/issue-brief/millions-of-seniors-live-in-house-holds-with-school-age-children/

212   https://www.cdc.gov/mmwr/volumes/70/wr/mm7004e3.htm?s_cid=mm7004e3_w

213   https://www.cdc.gov/mmwr/volumes/69/wr/mm6937e3.htm?s_cid=mm6937e3_w

214   https://www.theblaze.com/op-ed/horowitz-risk-low-among-children

215   https://docs.google.com/spreadsheets/d/1e4RGnqt5j7dOqn2uo7lsf97g-8UP0-Z-fLTSngBwvRs/edit#gid=1949603537

216   https://www.cdc.gov/mmwr/volumes/69/wr/mm6931e1.htm

217   https://www.cnn.com/2020/07/31/health/georgia-camp-coronavirus-outbreak-cdc-trnd/index.html

218   https://adc.bmj.com/content/archdischild/105/7/618.full.pdf

219   https://www.ijidonline.com/article/S1201-9712(20)30598-1/fulltext

220   https://www.bmj.com/content/372/bmj.n521

221   https://www.medrxiv.org/content/10.1101/2020.11.01.20222315v1?ijkey=abb437dc4410a6ba47227c5be08480f01441f8c1&keytype2=tf_ipsecsha

222   https://jamanetwork.com/journals/jamanetworkopen/fullarticle/2777976?utm_source=silverchair&utm_medium=email&utm_campaign=article_alert-jamanetworkopen&utm_content=wklyforyou&utm_term=033121

223   https://www.eurosurveillance.org/content/10.2807/1560-7917.ES.2020.26.1.2002011

224   https://www.nejm.org/doi/full/10.1056/NEJMc2026670?query=TOC

225   https://www.standard.co.uk/news/londoners-diary/the-londoner-let-children-be-ex-posed-to-viruses-says-professor-gupta-a4538386.html

226   https://www.nytimes.com/2020/03/10/opinion/coronavirus-school-closing.html

227   https://nypost.com/2020/04/30/study-explores-how-american-parents-are- enduring-covid-19-lockdown-with-their-children/

228   https://www.nytimes.com/interactive/2020/08/14/opinion/politics/covid-school-re-opening-guidelines.html

229   https://globalepidemics.org/wp-content/uploads/2020/07/pandemic_resilient_schools_briefing_72020.pdf

230   https://www.wired.com/story/44-square-feet-a-school-reopening-detective-story/

231   https://web.archive.org/web/20200820110408/https://www.edweek.org/ew/section/mul-timedia/school-buildings-and-social-distancing-downloadable-guide.html

232   https://www.propublica.org/article/the-students-left-behind-by-remotelearning

233   https://www.clickondetroit.com/features/2020/09/14/school-report-this-is-furthering-the-divide-between-the-haves-and-have-nots/

234   https://abc13.com/houston-isd-back-to-school-ted-oberg-investigates-virtual-learn-ing/6419355/

235   https://ktxs.com/news/local/failure-rate-just-under-50-percent-for-abilene-isd-remote-learners-in-first-six-weeks

236   https://www.dallasnews.com/news/education/2020/11/06/huge-learning-losses-during-covid-19-disruptions-may-have-disd-lowering-its-academic-goals/

237   https://www.texastribune.org/2020/10/23/texas-students-remote-learning-failing-schools/

238   https://www.texastribune.org/2021/03/03/texas-schools-missing-students/

239   https://assets.documentcloud.org/documents/7223216/Chart-Pack-EdSource-Educa-tion-Issues-Poll.pdf

240   https://www.washingtonpost.com/education/2020/12/01/california-school-lawsuit/

241   https://www.nydailynews.com/new-york/education/ny-nyc-covid-high-school-failing-20210120-nngoaq2mrzbmfmw2m3zlykptfa-story.html

242   https://patch.com/new-york/new-york-city/no-failing-grades-nyc-students-amid-coro-navirus

243   https://rmbodenheimer.medium.com/a-progressive-parents-rant-about-the-politics-surrounding-school-reopening-a816cae963fd

244   https://nypost.com/2021/05/01/teachers-union-collaborated-with-cdc-on-school-reopening-emails/amp/?utm_source=twitter_sitebuttons&utm_medium=site%20buttons&utm_campaign=site%20buttons&__twitter_impression=true

245   https://www.illinoispolicy.org/chicago-teachers-refusing-to-return-to-school-face-disci-pline-up-to-firing/

246   https://laist.com/2020/09/24/lausd_lawsuit_distance_learning_parents.php

247   https://www.dailywire.com/news/audio-los-angeles-county-health-director-says-she-expects-schools-to-reopen-after-the-election

248 https://www.utla.net/news/utla-statement-ab-sb86-vaccines-and-member-vote

249 https://wgntv.com/news/ctu-silent-as-vice-president-vacations-while-arguing-in-person-learning-is-unsafe/

250 https://www.politico.com/news/2021/04/04/california-teachers-childcare-coronavirus-478972

251 https://www.foxbusiness.com/politics/biden-spending-education-covid-relief

252 https://www.youtube.com/watch?v=pw66KxaZkBw

253 https://en.unesco.org/covid19/educationresponse

254 https://thriveglobal.com/stories/covid-19-thousands-of-deaths-expected-at-u-s-colleges-this-fall/

255 https://www.washingtontimes.com/news/2020/sep/29/colleges-covid-19-quarantines-and-the-chaos-they-c/

256 https://www.nytimes.com/interactive/2021/us/college-covid-tracker.html

257 https://www.tandfonline.com/doi/full/10.1080/10255842.2020.1869221

258 https://www.insidehighered.com/quicktakes/2021/01/05/survey-pandemic-negatively-affected-grades-fall

259 https://www.chronicle.com/article/good-grades-stressed-students?bc_nonce=0d90ljntci mrr1w9bwg9y6&cid=reg_wall_signup

260 https://www.clickondetroit.com/all-about-ann-arbor/2020/09/14/student-video-criticizing-university-of-michigans-quarantine-housing-goes-viral/

261 https://sdsucollegian.com/20600/news/behind-the-closed-doors-of-quarantine-and-isolation-housing/

262 https://housing.virginia.edu/return-2020

263 https://www.nytimes.com/2020/09/05/world/coronavirus-covid.html

264 https://www.insidehighered.com/news/2020/09/21/covid-19-roundup-colleges-quarantine-students-cancel-football-games

265 https://www.insidehighered.com/news/2020/09/21/covid-19-roundup-colleges-quarantine-students-cancel-football-games

266 https://madison.com/ct/news/local/education/uw-announces-two-weeks-of-online-courses-two-dorms-quarantined/article_e2898c5d-c92f-5137-af4f-13138dd615a8.html#tracking-source=home-breaking

267 https://www.insidehighered.com/news/2020/09/21/covid-19-roundup-colleges-quarantine-students-cancel-football-games

268 https://www.sunjournal.com/2021/04/01/bates-college-imposes-temporary-quarantine-to-slow-covid-19-outbreak/

269   https://www.foxnews.com/us/umass-students-suspended-maskless-photo-complete-overkill

270   https://www.cbsnews.com/news/columbia-tuition-strike-students/?ftag=CNM-00-10aab7e&linkId=110262141

271   https://www.theguardian.com/us-news/2020/may/26/andrew-cuomo-nursing-home-execs-immunity

272   https://www.politico.com/states/california/story/2020/10/30/newsom-sends-his-children-back-to-school-classrooms-in-california-1332811

273   https://www.nytimes.com/2020/11/25/opinion/gavin-newsom-french-laundry-california.html

274   https://www.zerohedge.com/covid-19/michigan-gov-whitmer-comes-clean-after-photograph-showed-her-breaking-her-own-rules

275   https://www.newsweek.com/uk-covid-variant-houston-texas-mask-mandate-lifted-too-soon-1574766

276   https://www.washingtonpost.com/nation/2021/03/02/coronavirus-covid-live-updates-us/

277   https://abcnews.go.com/Health/recipe-disaster-health-care-workers-react-dropped-mask/story?id=76340313

278   https://www.newsweek.com/maskless-spring-break-visitors-descend-texas-beaches-covid-curbs-lifted-1575995

279   https://www.usatoday.com/story/news/health/2020/12/29/covid-vaccine-floridas-roll-out-seniors-gets-off-rocky-start/4067324001/

280   https://www.aarp.org/caregiving/health/info-2020/nursing-homes-deadliest-covid-month.html

281   https://www.rollingstone.com/politics/politics-features/south-dakota-kristi-noem-covid-1142068/

282   https://www.theguardian.com/world/2020/nov/23/south-dakota-gripped-by-pandemic-amid-kristi-noem-no-mask-approach

283   https://www.msnbc.com/rachel-maddow-show/south-dakota-s-noem-scrambles-defend-pandemic-failures-n1250905

284   https://www.washingtonpost.com/politics/2020/12/08/kristi-noem-hails-south-dakota-coronavirus-success-story-using-badly-cherry-picked-numbers/

285   https://www.washingtonpost.com/politics/2021/02/05/south-dakotas-covid-19-numbers-have-been-terrible-governor-says-thats-wrong-metric/

286   https://www.marketwatch.com/story/pennsylvania-becomes-1st-in-nation-to-curb-governors-emergency-powers-01621451442

287   https://www.washingtontimes.com/news/2020/mar/26/widespread-isolation-and-stopping-all-human-intera/

288   https://www.cnn.com/2020/08/12/politics/scott-atlas-donald-trump-coronavirus/index.html

289   https://www.washingtonpost.com/nation/2020/09/17/scott-atlas-youtube/

290   https://gbdeclaration.org/

291   https://nypost.com/2020/06/30/rand-paul-rips-anthony-fauci-says-schools-should-be-reopened/

292   https://www.washingtonpost.com/nation/2020/11/13/rand-paul-covid-immune-masks/

293   https://www.bmj.com/content/372/bmj.n99

294   https://www.courier-journal.com/story/news/politics/2021/03/18/rand-paul-vs-fauci-u-s-sen-doctor-clash-over-covid-vaccine-masks/4752513001/

295   https://www.washingtonpost.com/archive/lifestyle/wellness/1987/03/31/safe-sex-in-the-era-of-aids/c7b9c225-9345-4382-9675-5d2f94430c8a/

296   https://www.mynews13.com/fl/orlando/news/2020/02/15/disease-expert--flu-a-bigger-risk-in-the-us-than-coronavirus

297   https://www.documentcloud.org/documents/20793561-leopold-nih-foia-anthony-fauci-emails

298   https://www.breitbart.com/clips/2021/03/22/fauci-i-dont-think-u-s-made-mistakes-with-lockdowns/#

299   https://www.washingtonpost.com/politics/as-deaths-mount-trump-tries-to-convince-americans-its-safe-to-inch-back-to-normal/2020/05/09/bf024fe6-9149-11ea-a9c0-73b93422d691_story.html

300   https://www.pbs.org/newshour/show/an-infectious-disease-expert-on-the-dangers-of-trumps-non-scientific-claims

301   https://www.nytimes.com/2020/08/07/opinion/coronavirus-lockdown-unemployment-death.html

302   https://www.cnn.com/world/live-news/coronavirus-pandemic-vaccine-updates-02-04-21/h_79d5e7007e41fe4ba91371423128f4c2

303   830 WCCO, a News/Talk station based in Minneapolis discussion on March 19, 2021

304   https://coronavirus.medium.com/covid-19-march-14-update-281599207ba8

305   https://coronavirus.medium.com/to-open-the-us-economy-we-need-a-contact-tracing-workforce-of-180-000-82ebad460a2a

306   https://coronavirus.medium.com/7-pandemic-differences-between-the-u-s-and-europe-626c697d0171

307   https://www.msnbc.com/stephanie-ruhle/watch/-it-s-going-to-require-more-patience-from-the-public-than-people-may-want-andy-slavitt-on-covid-cases-falling-101167685981

308   Tom Woods

309   https://www.statista.com/statistics/381569/leading-news-and-media-sites-usa-by-share-of-visits/

310   https://www.nbcnews.com/news/us-news/youtube-pulls-florida-governor-s-video-says-his-panel-spread-n1263635

311   https://help.twitter.com/en/rules-and-policies/medical-misinformation-policy

312   https://www.nytimes.com/2020/04/18/opinion/trump-coronavirus-testing.html?searchResultPosition=5

313   https://www.nytimes.com/article/coronavirus-facts-history.html

314   https://www.nytimes.com/2020/07/18/health/coronavirus-children-schools.html

315   https://www.baltimoresun.com/coronavirus/ct-nw-nyt-coronavirus-children-lurie-childrens-hospital-study-20200731-enq5fjcjxzbtvceqombbuekfka-story.html

316   https://www.nytimes.com/2020/07/24/health/cdc-schools-coronavirus.html

317   https://www.nytimes.com/2020/09/01/health/coronavirus-parents-schools.html

318   https://www.chicagotribune.com/coronavirus/sns-nyt-coronavirus-spares-children-not-teens-20200929-ck54td7g7ncarknnxnqweahj4e-story.html

319   https://www.nytimes.com/2020/10/23/health/covid-deaths.html

320   Jeffrey Tucker, Liberty or Lockdown, AEIR, page 111

321   https://www.washingtonpost.com/opinions/2020/04/21/georgia-leads-race-become-americas-no-1-death-destination/

322   https://medium.com/the-atlantic/what-weve-stolen-from-our-kids-40a52d6ffa75

323   https://www.theatlantic.com/politics/archive/2021/05/liberals-covid-19-science-denial-lockdown/618780/

324   https://www.foxnews.com/media/glenn-greenwald-rips-liberals-scientific-training-mask-advice

325   https://www.foxnews.com/media/rachel-maddow-cdc-unmasked-people-threat

326   https://www.foxnews.com/opinion/covid-follow-the-science-media-cdc-dan-gainor

327   https://cpb-us-e1.wpmucdn.com/sites.dartmouth.edu/dist/4/2318/files/2021/03/Why-Is-All-Covid-News-Bad-News-3_22_21.pdf

328   https://news.gallup.com/poll/267047/americans-trust-mass-media-edges-down.aspx

329   https://www.kekstcnc.com/media/2793/kekstcnc_research_covid-19_opinion_track-er_wave-4.pdf?fbclid=IwAR3HgPih2KPCdE8RUWogxBrn_yEMrNqDXdG16GYQP-Tj73Vkh23Jtb-tLH8U

330   https://www.franklintempletonnordic.com/investor/article?contentPath=html/ftthinks/common/cio-views/on-my-mind-they-blinded-us-from-science.html

331   https://news.gallup.com/poll/308222/coronavirus-pandemic.aspx

332   https://arxiv.org/pdf/2101.07993.pdf

333   http://vis.mit.edu/covid-story/

334   https://www.nbcnews.com/news/nbcblk/chicago-mayor-defends-hairstylist-visit-amid-coronavirus-outbreak-n1181546

335   https://edition.cnn.com/2020/09/02/politics/nancy-pelosi-hair-salon/index.html

336   https://www.thegatewaypundit.com/2020/11/la-county-supervisor-caught-dining-res-taurant-just-hours-voting-ban-outdoor-dining-covid-19-concerns/

337   https://nypost.com/2020/07/24/anthony-fauci-denies-hypocrisy-after-watching-game-without-mask/

338   https://www.thesun.co.uk/news/11494700/mayor-bill-de-blasio-confronted-walking-in-prospect-park/

339   https://www.breitbart.com/politics/2020/09/01/new-york-gov-andrew-cuomo-spotted-without-mask/

340   https://nypost.com/2020/05/13/pennsylvania-health-official-moved-mother-from-nurs-ing-home/

341   https://www.breitbart.com/europe/2020/05/05/professor-lockdown-quits-after-break-ing-own-rules-to-meet-lover/

342   https://www.theguardian.com/us-news/2020/nov/26/michael-hancock-denver-mayor-apology-thanksgiving

343   https://www.breitbart.com/politics/2020/04/29/illinois-gov-pritzkers-billionaire-wife-reportedly-skips-out-states-lockdown-orders/

344   https://prairiestatewire.com/stories/555396046-pritzker-s-illinois-prep-sports-ban-excepts-his-equestrian-daughter-teddi

345   https://www.foxnews.com/politics/democratic-governor-photographed-wine-paint-night-inessential-activities

346   https://globalnews.ca/news/6815936/coronavirus-justin-trudeau-andrew-scheer-easter-travel/

347   https://toronto.ctvnews.ca/ontario-premier-explains-why-he-visited-his-cottage-de-spite-telling-people-to-stay-home-1.4930589

348   https://www.foxnews.com/politics/san-francisco-london-breed-french-laundry-party-gavin-newsom

349   https://hannity.com/media-room/just-raking-leaves-michigan-gov-admits-husband-traveled-to-second-home-to-rake-leaves-during-pandemic/

350   https://www.washingtonexaminer.com/news/new-mexico-governor-disputes-report-that-she-had-a-store-reopen-during-shutdown-to-buy-jewelry

351   https://www.foxnews.com/politics/san-jose-mayor-apologizes-thanksgiving-family-dinner

352   https://www.kansascity.com/news/politics-government/article244347487.html

353   https://turtleboysports.com/karyn-polito-has-huge-party-at-shrewsbury-mansion-while-telling-the-commoners-to-socially-distance-and-avoid-groups-during-memorial-day-weekend/

354   https://www.statesman.com/story/news/coronavirus/2020/12/02/austin-mayor-stressed-residents-lsquoneed-to-stay-homersquo-he-was-vacationing-in-cabo-at-time/115087704/

355   https://www.statesman.com/story/news/coronavirus/2020/12/02/austin-mayor-stressed-residents-lsquoneed-to-stay-homersquo-he-was-vacationing-in-cabo-at-time/115087704/

356   https://thefederalist.com/2020/12/01/texas-county-judges-caught-red-handed-violating-their-own-covid-rules/

357   https://thefederalist.com/2020/12/01/texas-county-judges-caught-red-handed-violating-their-own-covid-rules/

358   https://news.yahoo.com/philadelphia-mayor-apologizes-dining-indoors-180332493.html?guccounter=1

359   https://www.lawenforcementtoday.com/oregon-governor-violates-own-mask-mandate-refuses-to-honor-heroic-actions-of-state-trooper/

360   https://www.kgw.com/article/news/investigations/elected-officials-in-oregon-face-backlash-after-vacationing-in-hawaii-and-mexico-as-covid-cases-surged/283-9fa0c0bb-d186-4dd8-bde2-3e2be06dcf8f

361   https://www.kgw.com/article/news/investigations/elected-officials-in-oregon-face-backlash-after-vacationing-in-hawaii-and-mexico-as-covid-cases-surged/283-9fa0c0bb-d186-4dd8-bde2-3e2be06dcf8f

362   Jennifer Cabrera from Rational Ground

363   https://www.nbcboston.com/news/coronavirus/leominster-superintendents-trip-to-florida-as-students-learn-remotely-draws-criticism/2272708/

364   https://reason.com/2020/10/07/alexandria-public-schools-superintendent-gregory-hutchings/

365   https://nypost.com/2020/05/27/msnbc-reporter-cal-perry-humiliated-on-air-after-mask-shaming-backfires/

366   https://www.sfgate.com/bay-area-politics/article/London-Breed-San-Francisco-mask-mandate-COVID-19-16472998.php

367   https://www.sfgate.com/bay-area-politics/article/London-Breed-San-Francisco-mask-mandate-COVID-19-16472998.php

368   https://www.businessinsider.com/san-francisco-mayor-london-breed-mask-mandate-tony-toni-tone-2021-9

369   https://www.goodmorningamerica.com/style/story/met-gala-require-attendees-covid-19-vaccines-wear-79264271

370   https://californiaglobe.com/fr/speaker-pelosi-has-french-laundry-moment-at-large-napa-valley-fundraiser/

371   https://www.usatoday.com/story/news/nation/2020/05/13/hospitals-seeing-more-severe-child-abuse-injuries-during-coronavirus/3116395001/

372   https://www.reuters.com/investigates/special-report/health-coronavirus-students/

373   https://www.dfps.state.tx.us/About_DFPS/Reports_and_Presentations/PEI/documents/2021/2021-03-01_FY2020_Child_Fatality_and_Near_Fatality_Annual_Report.pdf

374   https://www.statesman.com/story/news/local/2021/02/15/child-abuse-reports-texas-dropped-when-school-went-online-amid-covid/4260653001/

375   https://www.rainn.org/news/first-time-ever-minors-make-half-visitors-national-sexual-assault-hotline

376   https://www.bbc.com/news/uk-england-oxfordshire-56575811

377   http://conference.iza.org/conference_files/Gender_2017/de_cao_e6099.pdf

378   https://www.usatoday.com/story/news/nation/2020/10/22/coronavirus-child-abuse-nj-online-child-exploitation-reports-increase/6004205002/

379   https://www.childrenshospitals.org/-/media/Files/CHA/Main/Quality_and_Performance/behavioral_health/bh_focus_children_mental_health.pdf?la=en&hash=09D2BBC2068B7DA410D589F15C43BF40C4872BED

380   https://www.nytimes.com/2021/05/13/magazine/high-school-students-coronavirus-pandemic.html

381   https://www.thelancet.com/journals/lanpsy/article/PIIS2215-0366(20)30570-8/fulltext

382   https://jamanetwork.com/journals/jamanetworkopen/fullarticle/2779300?utm_source=silverchair&utm_medium=email&utm_campaign=article_alert-jamanetworkopen&utm_content=mthlyforyou&utm_term=050921

383   https://www.reuters.com/investigates/special-report/health-coronavirus-students/

384   https://www.reuters.com/investigates/special-report/health-coronavirus-students/

385   https://www.reuters.com/investigates/special-report/health-coronavirus-students/

386 https://apnews.com/article/anxiety-mental-health-boston-coronavirus-pandemic-massachusetts-004adb5ee0ef17ff4b5e2e294e36ff3d

387 https://news.yahoo.com/news/news/no-place-child-kids-languish-231300830.html

388 https://www.inquirer.com/health/coronavirus/philadelphia-area-mental-health-crisis-centers-hospitals-grapple-with-shortage-inpatient-beds-20210315.html

389 https://www.statnews.com/2020/12/23/mental-health-covid19-psychiatric-beds/

390 https://dailynurse.com/covid-related-closures-bed-shortages-are-driving-in-patient-psych-hospitals-to-acrisis-point/

391 https://www.nydailynews.com/opinion/ny-oped-americas-top-priority-20210412-n7772tcyhffjdaaouk42ks6kaa-story.html

392 https://www.sciencedirect.com/science/article/pii/S209525462030065X

393 https://www.ncbi.nlm.nih.gov/pmc/articles/PMC7644278/

394 https://link.springer.com/article/10.1007/s10389-019-01043-x

395 https://journals.sagepub.com/doi/10.1177/0002764221992826

396 https://journals.sagepub.com/doi/10.1177/0002764221992826

397 https://covid19.counciloncj.org/2021/02/23/impact-report-covid-19-and-domestic-violence-trends/

398 https://jnix.netlify.app/publication/39-ppr-covid-dv/

399 https://crimesciencejournal.biomedcentral.com/articles/10.1186/s40163-020-00117-6

400 https://link.springer.com/content/pdf/10.1186/s40163-020-00117-6.pdf

401 https://www.nbcnews.com/news/us-news/police-see-rise-domestic-violence-calls-amid-coronavirus-lockdown-n1176151

402 https://www.bridgemi.com/children-families/stay-home-dont-stay-safe-domestic-violence-calls-amid-michigan-lockdown

403 https://phys.org/news/2020-06-lockdown-crimes-home-authorities.html

404 https://www.nber.org/system/files/working_papers/w27562/revisions/w27562.rev1.pdf

405 https://www.santiagoperezvincent.com/research

406 https://papers.ssrn.com/sol3/papers.cfm?abstract_id=3688384

407 https://www.cdc.gov/nchs/covid19/pulse/mental-health.htm

408 https://jamanetwork.com/journals/jamanetworkopen/fullarticle/2770146

409 https://health.ucdavis.edu/health-news/newsroom/concerns-about-violence-increase-in-california-amid-covid-19-pandemic--/2020/10

410   https://www.theguardian.com/us-news/2020/oct/29/coronavirus-pandemic-americans-gun-sales

411   https://www.graham-center.org/content/dam/rgc/documents/publications-reports/reports/Projected-Deaths-Despair-COVID-19.pdf

412   https://www.marketwatch.com/story/deaths-of-despair-during-covid-19-rose-by-up-to-60-in-2020-new-research-says-2021-01-04

413   https://data.cdc.gov/NCHS/AH-Deaths-by-Age-Sex-and-Week-2018-2020/w56u-89fn

414   https://fox17.com/news/local/feeling-the-pressures-of-the-pandemic-suicide-hotlines-see-800-percent-spike-in-calls

415   https://www.beckershospitalreview.com/patient-flow/overrun-with-kids-attempting-suicide-children-s-colorado-declares-state-of-emergency.html?utm_medium=email&utm_content=newsletter

416   https://www.acpjournals.org/doi/10.7326/M20-7271

417   https://www.newsweek.com/how-alcohol-sales-have-shifted-during-covid-19-1564524

418   https://jamanetwork.com/journals/jamapsychiatry/fullarticle/2780427?guestAccessKey=21b8606b-dd63-46f2-9451-8a4b0f48516c&utm_source=silverchair&utm_medium=email&utm_campaign=article_alert-jamapsychiatry&utm_content=olf&utm_term=052621

419   https://jamanetwork.com/journals/jama/fullarticle/2778234

420   https://www.wwltv.com/article/news/local/americas-top-state-for-overdose-death-increase-during-covid/289-d2b509b5-b0df-447b-8ff9-06e368852516

421   https://www.wwltv.com/article/news/local/americas-top-state-for-overdose-death-increase-during-covid/289-d2b509b5-b0df-447b-8ff9-06e368852516

422   https://mynbc15.com/news/nation-world/crime-drops-around-the-world-as-covid-19-keeps-people-inside-04-11-2020-152408165

423   https://www.courier-journal.com/story/news/local/2021/04/19/kentucky-overdose-deaths-spike-during-covid-19-pandemic-data-shows/7250937002/

424   https://jamanetwork.com/journals/jamanetworkopen/fullarticle/2778560

425   https://www.sfchronicle.com/politics/article/Overdoses-keep-piling-up-in-S-F-putting-city-in-16048227.php

426   https://www.sfchronicle.com/local/article/Overdose-deaths-spiked-in-Sonoma-County-during-16051544.php

427   http://publichealth.lacounty.gov/sapc/MDU/SpecialReport/AccidentalDrugOverdoseReport.pdf

428   https://www.washingtonexaminer.com/news/data-shows-drug-overdoses-soaring-following-virus-lockdowns-up-18-in-march-29-in-april-42-in-may

429   https://news.harvard.edu/gazette/story/2020/11/what-might-covid-cost-the-u-s-experts-eye-16-trillion/

430   https://www.healthsystemtracker.org/brief/covid-19-test-prices-and-payment-policy/

431   https://www.healthsystemtracker.org/brief/covid-19-test-prices-and-payment-policy/

432   https://www.managedhealthcareexecutive.com/view/the-price-tags-on-the-covid-19-vaccines

433   https://www.managedhealthcareexecutive.com/view/the-price-tags-on-the-covid-19-vaccines

434   https://www.nbcnews.com/news/us-news/states-are-introducing-vaccine-lotteries-some-multimillion-dollar-prizes-combat-n1268048

435   https://www.nbcnews.com/news/us-news/states-are-introducing-vaccine-lotteries-some-multimillion-dollar-prizes-combat-n1268048

436   https://www.nbcnews.com/news/us-news/states-are-introducing-vaccine-lotteries-some-multimillion-dollar-prizes-combat-n1268048

437   https://fee.org/articles/federal-covid-spending-will-cost-41-870-per-taxpayer-did-you-see-that-much-in-benefit/

438   https://fee.org/articles/federal-covid-spending-will-cost-41-870-per-taxpayer-did-you-see-that-much-in-benefit/

439   https://fee.org/articles/federal-covid-spending-will-cost-41-870-per-taxpayer-did-you-see-that-much-in-benefit/

440   https://www.future-ed.org/what-congressional-covid-funding-means-for-k-12-schools/

441   https://www.future-ed.org/what-congressional-covid-funding-means-for-k-12-schools/

442   https://www.future-ed.org/what-congressional-covid-funding-means-for-k-12-schools/

443   https://www.future-ed.org/what-congressional-covid-funding-means-for-k-12-schools/

444   https://www.crfb.org/

445   https://thejournal.com/articles/2020/12/03/new-department-of-ed-portal-gives-snapshot-of-cares-act-ed-funding.aspx

446   Burbio

447   Burbio

448   Burbio

449   https://marketscale.com/industries/education-technology/tutor-com-has/

450   https://www.law.com/2021/03/04/a-year-like-no-other-top-law-schools-are-inundated-with-strong-applicants/

451 https://www.travelpulse.com/news/airlines/draft-of-coronavirus-relief-package-gives-more-money-to-airlines.html

452 https://www.thedenverchannel.com/news/national/more-than-1-5-billion-masks-be-lieved-to-have-entered-oceans-in-2020

453 https://www.thedenverchannel.com/news/national/more-than-1-5-billion-masks-be-lieved-to-have-entered-oceans-in-2020

454 https://www.washingtonpost.com/business/2020/05/28/unemployment-claims-corona-virus/

455 https://blog.zoom.us/findings-from-the-impact-of-video-communications-during-covid-19-report/

456 https://www.ahla.com/covid-19s-impact-hotel-industry

457 https://restaurant.org/news/pressroom/press-releases/restaurant-industry-in-free-fall-10000-close-in

458 https://jamanetwork.com/journals/jamanetworkopen/fullarticle/2779458?utm_source=silverchair&utm_medium=email&utm_campaign=article_alert-jamanetworkopen&utm_content=wklyforyou&utm_term=050521

459 https://covid19.counciloncj.org/2021/01/31/impact-report-covid-19-and-crime-3/

460 https://covid19.counciloncj.org/2021/01/31/impact-report-covid-19-and-crime-3/

461 https://covid19.counciloncj.org/2021/01/31/impact-report-covid-19-and-crime-3/

462 https://www.nbcnews.com/business/business-news/one-year-later-many-dry-cleaners-are-still-hanging-thread-n1259642

463 https://fortune.com/2021/01/26/restaurants-bars-closed-2020-jobs-lost-how-many-have-closed-us-covid-pandemic-stimulus-unemployment/

464 https://www.travelpulse.com/news/hotels-and-resorts/new-data-shows-covid-19s-impact-on-hotel-industry.html

465 https://apnews.com/article/california-lifestyle-coronavirus-pandemic-business-health-d4deaa45439a906fcdfac2f0e12b1880

466 https://sourcingjournal.com/topics/retail/store-closings-bankruptcy-2020-cov-id-19-250100/

467 https://sourcingjournal.com/topics/retail/store-closings-bankruptcy-2020-cov-id-19-250100/

468 https://www.mercurynews.com/2021/02/01/lots-of-people-moved-out-of-california-and-new-york-in-2020-heres-where-they-went/

469 https://www.ktvu.com/news/study-confirms-california-exodus-with-more-people-leav-ing-the-state-despite-the-pandemic

470 https://www.ktvu.com/news/study-confirms-california-exodus-with-more-people-leav-ing-the-state-despite-the-pandemic

471   https://www.ktvu.com/news/study-confirms-california-exodus-with-more-people-leaving-the-state-despite-the-pandemic

472   https://www.ktvu.com/news/study-confirms-california-exodus-with-more-people-leaving-the-state-despite-the-pandemic

473   https://www.wsj.com/articles/the-gym-is-open-but-everythings-different-11615887001

474   https://onlinelibrary.wiley.com/doi/10.1111/jems.12400

475   https://onlinelibrary.wiley.com/doi/10.1111/jems.12400

476   https://onlinelibrary.wiley.com/doi/10.1111/jems.12400

477   https://onlinelibrary.wiley.com/doi/10.1111/jems.12400

478   https://www.marketwatch.com/story/netflix-in-the-age-of-covid-19-streaming-pioneer-may-have-new-edge-on-competition-2020-04-07

479   https://www.bloomberg.com/news/articles/2021-01-05/divorces-and-marriages-tumbled-in-u-s-during-covid-study-shows

480   https://fortune.com/2021/02/12/covid-pandemic-online-dating-apps-usage-tinder-okcupid-bumble-meet-group/

481   https://fortune.com/2021/02/12/covid-pandemic-online-dating-apps-usage-tinder-okcupid-bumble-meet-group/

482   https://fortune.com/2021/02/12/covid-pandemic-online-dating-apps-usage-tinder-okcupid-bumble-meet-group/

483   https://www.businessinsider.com/why-toilet-paper-demand-spiked-845-how-companies-kept-up-2020-5

484   https://www.washingtonpost.com/dc-md-va/2021/01/06/animal-shelters-coronavirus-pandemic/

485   https://www.brookings.edu/blog/up-front/2021/05/05/the-coming-covid-19-baby-bust-is-here/

486   https://www.aspenprojectplay.org/state-of-play-2020/pandemic-trends

487   https://www.statista.com/statistics/1104278/weekly-performance-of-djia-index/

488   https://www.yahoo.com/now/stock-market-news-dec-31-143102262.html#:~:text=The%20Dow%20Jones%20Industrial%20Average,finished%20the%20day%20in%20red.

489   https://seekingalpha.com/symbol/AMZN/historical-price-quotes

490   https://www.theverge.com/2021/4/15/22385370/amazon-prime-subscription-jeff-bezos-2020-shareholders-letter

491   https://www.prnewswire.com/news-releases/covid-19-drives-record-at-home-coffee-drinking-on-the-go-ordering-2021-national-coffee-data-trends-report-301260248.html

492 https://www.prnewswire.com/news-releases/covid-19-drives-record-at-home-coffee-drinking-on-the-go-ordering-2021-national-coffee-data-trends-report-301260248.html

493 https://www.prnewswire.com/news-releases/covid-19-drives-record-at-home-coffee-drinking-on-the-go-ordering-2021-national-coffee-data-trends-report-301260248.html

494 https://www.bbc.com/future/bespoke/made-on-earth/how-the-coffee-trade-survived-Covid-19.html?fbclid=IwAR1CwlOxqkshOZy6knMQpBlXodbf4MYpMY0bsC8g-WGmBhwJLltyrIpL4EA

495 https://www.chicagotribune.com/suburbs/post-tribune/opinion/ct-pt-davich-sleep-deprivation-during-pandemic-covid-somnia-st-0129-20210128-5faw3knt7nhi3lhb-cimeqz5n3i-story.html

496 https://www.cnbc.com/2020/10/01/drive-thru-times-slow-by-nearly-30-seconds-as-demand-soars-study.html

497 https://www.theguardian.com/books/2020/nov/14/pandemic-drives-ebook-and-audio-book-sales-by-uk-publishers-to-all-time-high-covid

498 https://www.businessofapps.com/data/zoom-statistics/

499 https://www.businessofapps.com/data/zoom-statistics/

500 https://www.fortunebusinessinsights.com/antidepressants-market-105017

501 https://finance.yahoo.com/news/antidepressants-global-market-report-2021-104500347.html

502 https://www.fhwa.dot.gov/policyinformation/travel_monitoring/20novtvt/

503 https://www.bts.dot.gov/newsroom/passengers-all-2020-us-based-flights-down-62-2019

504 https://phys.org/news/2019-06-everest-summits-deadly-bottlenecks.html

505 https://www.outsideonline.com/2414317/chinese-team-summits-everest-may-2020